About the Author

Susie Murphy is an Irish historical fiction author. She loves historical fiction so much that she often wishes she had been born two hundred years ago. Still, she remains grateful for many aspects of the modern age, including women's suffrage, electric showers and pizza. A Class Coveted is her fourth published novel.

CW00552274

ISBN-13: 978-1-915770-04-2

www.susiemurphywrites.com

Join the Susie Murphy Readers' Club
for updates and free stories:

https://bit.ly/susie-murphy-readers-club

A Class Coveted

A Matter of Class, Book Four

Susie Murphy

Also by Susie Murphy

A Class Apart
A Class Entwined
A Class Forsaken
A Class Reunited

For my sister, Deirdre, who is only ever a heartbeat away, even when we're continents apart.
And for John, who is her pillar of strength just as much as she is his.

CHAPTER 1

Bridget winced as she struggled along the street, her boots pinching her swollen ankles and sweat gathering in various crevices of her body in a most unladylike manner. The sun glared down between the buildings and the air was so muggy that it felt like she was wading through soup.

Boston in August was stiflingly hot.

She rubbed a soothing palm over the curve of her belly and promised the baby they would rest soon. Cormac walked just ahead of her, his hand wrapped around Emily's. Their daughter had to take two skipping steps to match his longer stride, each skip becoming decidedly less jaunty than the last. Her doll, Mabel, drooped from her hand as though limp with sunstroke.

'Christ, I think I'm going to melt right into the ground,' came a mutter behind Bridget.

Glancing over her shoulder, she saw Tess flapping her fingers in front of her face in a failed attempt to conjure a puff of air; strands of her vivid red hair clung to her temples in damp streaks. Next to her, Cormac's sister Orlaith blew out her cheeks and wiped the back of her wrist across her forehead. She nodded at her friend's words but didn't seem to have the energy to agree out loud.

Bridget recalled everyone's recent relief as they disembarked at the port after spending weeks crossing the Atlantic Ocean. It had been tedious aboard the ship with little to do apart from tend to Emily when she was seasick, but what Bridget wouldn't give right now for a refreshing sea breeze.

Feeling quite short of breath, she sent up a silent prayer of thanks when Cormac suddenly halted in front of her. He scanned the facade of the building next to them.

'This is it,' he said and Emily let out a rather wilted whoop.

A port agent had given Cormac the name of a boarding house often frequented by newcomers to the city and Bridget was very glad his directions had proved to be sound – she couldn't wait to take the weight off her feet. The fellow had also facilitated the exchange of their pounds for foreign American dollars; Cormac surreptitiously patted his pocket where he had stowed the money and beckoned them all towards the door of the boarding house.

The building's cool interior was a welcome respite from the suffocating heat. Orlaith and Tess emitted identical sighs of relief and laughed. They stayed near the door with Emily and everyone's baggage while Cormac and Bridget crossed the small lobby to approach a trim-looking man standing behind a high counter. He offered them a friendly smile.

'May I help you?' he said in a broad accent as unfamiliar as the money.

'Yes, we're looking for accommodation,' Cormac answered. 'Two rooms, if you have them.'

'Of course,' said the man and pulled an open register towards him. 'How long will you be staying?'

'A week or so at least, I think,' said Cormac.

Bobbing his head, the man started writing in his register. 'New to Boston?'

'Yes, we've just arrived.'

'Well then, welcome to the finest city in New England,' the man said, his tone warm with pride. 'Where have you travelled from?'

'Ireland,' said Cormac, just as proudly, and Bridget felt a pang of longing for the home they had left behind.

But the man's expression had changed.

'I'm afraid we have no rooms available,' he said, his voice several degrees cooler than before.

Cormac's fair eyebrows shot up. 'Pardon me?'

'We're full,' the man said shortly and rang a little bell on his counter. A young porter materialised from a back room and stood to attention.

Confused, Bridget pointed to the register. 'But you said you had two rooms.'

The man drew a definitive line through what he had written. 'I was unfortunately mistaken. We can assist you to the door with your baggage if needs be.'

This was equally perplexing, given that their baggage was minimal and already at the door by Orlaith and Tess's ankles. The young porter balanced on the balls of his feet; Bridget couldn't tell if his hovering stance conveyed helpfulness or hostility. Beside her, Cormac's jaw tightened but then he shrugged.

'That's disappointing. Thank you for your time.'

He took Bridget's elbow and guided her back to the door. Orlaith opened her mouth but Cormac shook his head and indicated that they should all pick up their baggage and leave. As they exited the lobby, Bridget heard the man behind the counter grumble to the porter, 'They might speak better than the typical sort but they're still no-good Irish. Good riddance to them.'

The blast of heat when they emerged outside felt as much a slap in the face as the rebuff they had just received within. Bridget squinted in the brightness and shifted her valise from one hand to the other as Orlaith and Tess looked at Cormac, the question plain in both of their expressions.

His cheeks were red with anger but he kept his voice level as he said, 'It seems the Irish do not have a favourable reputation in this city, or at least not in this particular establishment.'

Tess clicked her tongue. 'The lousy sod,' she said, glowering at the door of the boarding house.

Bridget made a mental note to have a word with Tess later about the choice language she used around Emily.

'What will we do now?' Orlaith asked.

'We'll find somewhere else,' said Cormac. 'Come on.'

He started off down the street again, a rigid determination in the set of his shoulders. This time Bridget took Emily's hand and, together with Orlaith and Tess, they followed Cormac like a group of ducklings. A carriage rattled by them at a reckless speed; Bridget pulled Emily closer to her side and turned her face away from the cloud of dust that swirled in its wake. She swallowed but her throat felt as arid as a desert. Glancing at other pedestrians passing by, she noticed that no one else appeared quite so bothered by the heat and she wondered if the locals were simply accustomed to it or if the city's temperature was in fact unexceptional and only seemed amplified to immigrants who hailed from a soggy country not known for its hot weather.

Cormac led them onwards, his gaze raking the building fronts on either side. A couple of streets further on he stopped again.

'Let's try here,' he said. A sign in the window proclaimed the availability of 'Comfortable Rooms, Pleasant Service'. 'We'll see about that,' he muttered and led the way inside.

This lobby was a little shabbier than the previous one and it contained a desk rather than a counter, but the proprietor sitting behind it wore the same welcoming smile. Bridget wondered how long that would last.

All five of the travellers approached the desk, which was positioned at the foot of a narrow flight of stairs. Orlaith and Tess looked ready to throw punches if they were turned away. Emily rubbed one of her eyes and yawned.

'Good day,' said Cormac to the man behind the desk. 'Would you have two rooms available? We're looking to stay for at least a week.'

The man's smile grew wider. 'Certainly, let me check for you.' He made a show of turning the pages of his register to consult the entries for the coming days. Casually, he added, 'And where are you from?'

Bridget bit the tip of her tongue and glanced at Cormac.

'England,' he said through gritted teeth.

Beaming, the proprietor said, 'Excellent. I believe we can accommodate you for the full seven nights. If you think you'll need to extend your stay beyond that, don't hesitate to inform me.'

He took Cormac's name along with enough money to cover the cost of the first two nights. Bridget thought of their finite supply of dollars and tried not to worry as the proprietor twisted towards an open door behind him and barked, 'Walter!'

An elderly fellow tottered out, straightening his threadbare jacket and peering at them through rheumy eyes.

The proprietor handed a ring of keys to his porter and said to Cormac, 'Your rooms are the first two on the second floor. Walter will bring your baggage upstairs.'

Even in her tired and pregnant state, Bridget felt she was in better shape to be carrying their baggage than this old man.

Cormac must have thought the same because he kept a firm hold on his own valise and said, 'Thank you, Walter. We would be grateful if you could direct us to our rooms.'

He waved his arm to indicate that Walter should go ahead of them and the fellow wobbled towards the stairs. They followed

5

him up just one flight before turning onto a corridor and Bridget realised that 'second floor' had a different meaning in America. She wanted to embrace all the idiosyncrasies of this new country but right now she just felt too fatigued to care.

Walter unlocked the doors to the two rooms. Cormac gestured towards the second room and said to Orlaith and Tess, 'You take that one and get some rest. We'll be right next door. Just knock if you need anything.'

They disappeared inside the room with a weary grunt of farewell, and Bridget, Cormac and Emily entered the other. Emily immediately climbed up onto the bed and lay spread-eagled upon it, her golden curls fanning out around her head like a halo and Mabel sprawled across her chest. Walter pointed to the washstand, mumbled something about mealtimes, and backed out of the room. Bridget and Cormac set down their valises and Cormac shut the door behind the old man.

'I didn't know whether this proprietor would have the same attitude as the first,' he said, 'but I thought it was better to be on the safe side.' His mouth compressed into a thin line and he rested his back against the door as though he could no longer stand upright without its support.

Bridget untied the ribbons of her bonnet and took it off, glad to be free of its sweaty confines. As she placed it on top of her valise, she remembered Agnes McLoughlin, who wanted to eject them from her boarding house in Cove on account of their adultery, and the Irish tenants at Oakleigh, who spurned Bridget because of her English breeding, and her friend Madeleine, who cast aside their longstanding friendship as soon as she learned that Bridget had violated the conventions of upper class society by leaving her husband to run away with a man of no social rank.

'Will we ever fit in anywhere?' she said with a sad sigh.

Cormac put out his hand and, when she took it, he pulled her into his embrace. They leaned against the door, sticky and despondent.

'I won't lie to you,' he said softly into her chestnut hair, 'because the reality is that we might never find a place where we're truly accepted.' She felt his head turn towards Emily, already dozing on the bed. 'None of us.'

She put her hand around his neck to coax his gaze back to her and saw the anxious question in his eyes.

'I don't regret my choice,' she said, pressing her fingers hard against his skin to convey the weight of her words. 'You are worth everything. To both of us.'

He bowed his head. Their lips met with a contact as gentle as two feathers brushing together. His touch and his taste were so familiar to her now and yet she still could not get enough. She eased their mouths open and offered him her tongue. He grazed it with his own, languorously, like he was sampling a very rare wine. But they could not maintain such restraint for long, and soon they were kissing with a passion that had been well-nigh impossible these past weeks on the ship with so many other passengers in the vicinity.

They knew it would not lead anywhere, not with Emily occupying the bed and the exhaustion of their travels heavy in their limbs. Gradually, the pace of the kiss slowed until it was feather-light again, his lips skimming hers one last time before their mouths separated with a soft sound of satisfaction.

Feeling more peaceful than she had a few minutes earlier, Bridget took a step back to look around the room.

'I'll be glad to get some rest without the sensation of a moving ship below me,' she said. 'Although my legs feel rather unsteady, like I'm still standing on deck.'

'Mine do as well,' said Cormac. 'It'll wear off in a day or so.'

He moved away from the door, shrugged out of his coat, and draped it over Emily's snoozing, spread-eagled form.

'Bless her,' he said, 'she does have a talent for taking up the whole space.' He reached down to pull out the narrow truckle bed. 'Made for one,' he said regretfully. 'We'll have to disturb our sleeping beauty after all.'

As he manoeuvred Emily and his coat onto the truckle bed, drawing a faint, drowsy protest from the little girl, Bridget sat on the edge of the main bed with the intention of removing her ankle boots. Instead, she fell back onto the bedcovers and blinked groggily at the ceiling.

'I don't recall the time Walter mentioned for the evening meal,' she said, 'but I feel like I could sleep from now until next week.'

Cormac chuckled and sat next to her. 'That seems perfectly acceptable. We've reserved the rooms for that duration.'

With an effort, she dragged herself back up into a sitting position. 'And what will happen after that?'

He pressed his palms onto his knees, tapping his fingers as he deliberated. 'We'll stick to the course of action we formulated on the ship, though it may prove more challenging if our presence is so unwelcome.' His shoulders drooped a little but then he straightened up. 'I'll aim to secure some form of employment and we'll seek out our own accommodation. We can't continue to pay for us all to stay in a boarding house, not when we don't know how long it might take to find Bronagh in a city that's totally unfamiliar.' He turned to her with a shy smile. 'And you'll need to be in a settled place to deliver the baby.'

Her heart glowed at the unmistakable adoration in his expression. She wrapped her arms around him, kissed his cheek, and gently pulled him down towards the bedcovers and blessed slumber.

CHAPTER 2

Cormac marched along Boston's waterfront, refreshed after a restful night's sleep at the boarding house and in full possession of his land legs once more. He kept an observant eye on the other pedestrians around him as he strode along – the odds were minuscule that he might simply bump into Bronagh on the street but he did not intend to pass up any opportunity that could potentially lead to locating his long-lost sister.

Realistically, his mission to find one young woman among thousands of people was going to be a gargantuan task and one not likely to be quickly resolved, given that he didn't even know where to start. Good fortune had played a large part in discovering the whereabouts of his family so swiftly back in Dublin and he didn't dare hope they might be that lucky again. They needed the means to survive in this new country for an indeterminate length of time and although Bridget's uncle, Lord Walcott, had given them a sum of money for their travels and initial accommodation costs, it would not be sufficient to support them beyond the immediate future. So Cormac's most pressing goal at this juncture was to obtain some form of paid work.

He didn't have any illusions about his prospects. He could lay claim to a gentleman's education and had resided in the home of an earl for almost five years, albeit under false pretences, but he had arrived into this city as an immigrant without a character reference. His only recourse for employment would be with the working classes.

This did not trouble him. After all, he had been a stable hand for several years and he knew very well what it was like to earn his living by straightforward, physical work. He had no airs and graces that would make him believe such work was now beneath him just because he had studied mathematics and philosophy.

However, he did worry about the inauspicious sentiments of the first boarding house's proprietor the previous day. If Irish people were deemed an objectionable race here, might he be obliged to pretend he was otherwise simply to make a living? The very idea of returning to a duplicitous existence filled him with dismay. It would not be as extreme as when he took on the persona of Oliver Davenport, masquerading as the nephew of Lord and Lady Bewley, but it would still be a measure of deceit which he had hoped he had left behind him for good.

Grimacing at the thought, he continued along the waterfront which was a hive of bustle and noise. Men hurried in and out of warehouses and swarmed around the docks, loading and unloading cargo from ships, shouting commands or exchanging lively banter. A wooden crane held a large crate suspended in the air and dockworkers gathered beneath it to guide it down onto the wharf. Cormac sidestepped as an enormous fellow crossed his path carrying a barrel across his shoulders as easily as he might carry a child. Then came a bellow louder than all the rest.

'Watch out!'

Cormac whirled back to see the crate dangling precariously – one of the ropes holding it had snapped. The men below scurried out of the way as the remaining ropes split apart under the increased strain and the crate went crashing to the ground. One man slipped in his haste to retreat and the corner of the crate struck him on his hip before it hit the wharf and smashed into pieces. A jagged chunk flew through the air and landed almost at Cormac's feet.

More shouts went up.

'Jaysus, who was meant to be minding the ropes?'

'You goddamn fool, weren't you paying attention?'

'It wasn't my fault!'

'Check on Higgins. Is he hurt?'

Between the accusations and expressions of concern, Cormac noted something very interesting – they were speaking with Irish accents. He moved closer to the commotion as the men clustered around the dockworker sprawled on the ground.

'I'm grand,' he said. Though his voice was shaky, he appeared to be unharmed. 'It was only a light knock.'

One of his workmates laughed and pulled him to his feet. 'Better to be born lucky than rich!'

'Higgins!' The bark came from beyond the group and the dockworkers parted hurriedly to allow another man to approach. Bulky and round-shouldered, he glowered around at them all before fixing his gaze on the now-upright Higgins.

'Are you injured?' he demanded. He had an American accent and, judging by the other men's deference, Cormac guessed he was their foreman.

'No, sir. Lucky escape, thank God.'

The foreman surveyed the broken mess of the crate. 'We'll have to assess the damage to the contents, and the cost will be subtracted from the wages for this job. Who is responsible?'

The dockworkers glanced from the ruined crate to each other. No obvious communication passed between them but then one fellow piped up, 'We all are, sir.'

'Very well,' said the foreman. 'An equal amount will be forfeited by each of you.'

As he turned away, Cormac thought he glimpsed a fleeting expression of approval on the man's face.

The dockworkers exchanged resigned looks and returned to their labours, while the foreman strode off towards a warehouse across from the wharf. Cormac chewed the inside of his cheek for a few moments before following.

It was dim inside the warehouse, and it smelled of dust and sweat. The centre of the space was vacant but an assortment of barrels, casks, crates and chests huddled against the sides in a haphazard fashion. In one corner, a walled enclosure with a gap for a door marked the foreman's office. Through the gap, Cormac could see that the man had squeezed his bulky form behind a desk and was perusing a document of some kind.

Cormac went up to the enclosure. A sign nailed to its wall read 'D. Walker, Foreman' and, below that, 'Robert Smith & Co.'. He knocked on the wall and stuck his head around the doorframe.

'Excuse me, Mr Walker. Could I have a word?'

The foreman looked up and frowned. 'Who are you?'

Cormac took a step into the office. 'My name is Cormac McGovern. I was wondering if I could speak with you about whether Robert Smith & Company is in a position to hire at present?' He pointed back in the direction of the sign.

Mr Walker put down the document and scrutinised Cormac. 'As a dockworker?'

'Yes, sir.'

'Have you worked on the docks before?'

'I haven't, sir.' Though he had tried to seek employment at the docklands when he had been destitute in Dublin, the competition for jobs had been fierce and the local men had always prevailed over uninvited outsiders. 'But I was once a stable hand and am well used to hard work.'

Mr Walker continued to study him. 'Where are you from?'

Cormac took a chance. 'County Carlow in Ireland.'

The foreman didn't flinch. 'Well, in that respect you'd certainly fit in. Catholic too, I suppose?'

'Yes, sir. Do you have the capacity to take anyone new on?'

'The port is growing busier every day so there's always a need for more men. Especially when the ones we have are careless. Only for a margin of mere inches today, I might have been looking to replace one of my workers on the spot.' Mr Walker folded his arms behind the desk, his round shoulders giving him a hunched posture. 'But I don't know if you're right for the job.'

Disappointed, Cormac said, 'I unfortunately can't provide a character but—'

'That doesn't matter. I have two eyes and two ears. You're able to read, your hands look as soft as a baby's arse and you sure as hell don't talk like a stable hand.' Mr Walker unfolded one arm to level a reproving finger at Cormac. 'You're too educated for a place like this. Why are you really here?'

Cormac resisted the urge to hide his hands behind his back. 'I'm simply looking for honest work to help me support my family. We've just arrived in this country, my wife is expecting our second child, and I need to be able to provide for them. I swear that's the truth.'

The foreman said nothing. Cormac waited and wondered whether, if refused employment here, he ought to lower the standard of his vocabulary in the next place.

'The workers here are a close-knit bunch,' Mr Walker said at last. 'They have each other's backs and they won't suffer a scoundrel among them. If you turned out to be a deceitful sort, they'd report it to me on the double.'

'They would have nothing to report, sir,' said Cormac. 'However, I understand that you don't have anything to go on but my word and I regret once again that I have no impartial testimonial to support it.' He made a move to leave.

'Wait.'

Cormac paused.

Mr Walker sat back in his chair, rubbing his hand over his jaw. 'A testimonial is only a piece of paper. I'll be best able to judge your character by your actions.'

Cormac kept his expression neutral while privately thinking that his character was blacker than the foreman might ever suspect. After all, he was a murderer.

This stark fact was impossible to forget. Every now and then on the ship, when his joints had stiffened after long periods of inactivity, he had experienced a faint ache in his arm where the ball from Cunningham's pistol had torn through his flesh. But he did not need that pain to remind him of what had happened in the alleyway back in Dublin; the memory of it constantly preyed on his thoughts.

Despite the beating he had taken from Cunningham's men, he could still recall the details with startling clarity. The smug grin on the money lender's face. The stink of his lackey Munroe as he knelt over Cormac on the dirty ground, preparing to cut out his eyeballs or his tongue. Their ensuing tussle and the weight of Munroe's dagger in Cormac's palm, fitting his grip with horrible familiarity. The graceful arc of the dagger as it soared through the air and lodged in the money lender's stomach.

Cormac's intention had been to kill Cunningham; he couldn't hide from that truth. The man had terrorised his family and for that Cormac had wanted to eradicate him from this earth. And although he had fled from the alley without witnessing Cunningham's last breath, the rumours that had circulated around the Dublin streets afterwards indicated that the money lender was gone for good. Which made Cormac a murderer.

It wasn't the first time he had found blood on his hands. At the very beginning of his career as the money lender's henchman, he had coerced the borrower Doyle into giving up all the money he possessed to repay what he owed to Cunningham, even though it had left him desperately short of funds to cover the costs of his sick daughter's medicine. Cormac had been the cause of her death too, he was sure of it.

Sometimes, self-loathing threatened to overwhelm him. He had no right to take another human being's life, no matter the circumstances. He was not God. His past was filled with mistakes, but those two wicked deeds marked the blackest parts of his soul and they could never be erased.

However, he drew consolation from the journey he and his family had just made to America. Their main purpose was to try to find Bronagh, but he also viewed it as a fresh slate for himself. In this new country, he could finally be the honourable man that Bridget and his children needed him to be, liberated from the sins he had committed in the past.

With that thought foremost in his mind, he said to Mr Walker, 'I would appreciate the opportunity to prove myself, sir. All I seek is decent employment that will enable me to take care of my family. I promise I won't give you or the other men any grounds to mistrust me.'

The foreman rolled back his shoulders in what looked like a conscious gesture to improve his posture. 'I don't dislike what I see so far,' he said, 'therefore I'm willing to give you a chance. You can start next week.' He pointed at Cormac once more. 'It's up to you to show us you're trustworthy.'

Relief flooded through Cormac. 'Thank you, sir, I will.'

The foreman grunted. 'We'll see. You might have a hard time settling in—the men will be able to tell there's something different about you. Hmm, maybe it would be best to pair you up with the other odd one out,' he added, almost as an aside to himself.

When he didn't elaborate any further on this, Cormac asked, 'Are most of the workers here Irishmen then?'

'In this company? The majority of them, yes.'

Cormac hesitated before continuing, 'Yesterday, I encountered a distinctly cool attitude towards me and my family when the individual learned that we were from Ireland. Is this a commonly held sentiment in Boston?'

This time, the foreman's grunt was closer to a grumble. 'There's a certain set who have contempt for the Irish. According to them, you're nothing but papists, layabouts and drunkards whose immigrant presence grows more and more undesirable as greater numbers of you arrive into the city.'

Cormac made a conscious effort not to clench his fists. 'And what is your opinion, Mr Walker?'

The foreman picked up the document he had been reading earlier and folded it in two before tucking it into a drawer in his desk. 'I think those people forget that Irish women make their beds and empty their pisspots, and Irish men build their houses and unload their goods at port. There are wasters among them, but it's not fair to tar them all with the same brush.' For the first time, Mr Walker cracked a smile. 'Although I'd have no personal desire to brawl with an Irishman who's got drink in him.'

Cormac couldn't disagree with him on that. 'I imagine there might be some neighbourhoods in the city which are more welcoming to Irish newcomers than others? My family and I are seeking a place to live and I would prefer to make our home in reasonably hospitable surroundings.'

Mr Walker lifted one round shoulder in a shrug. 'I can't claim to know a lot about the Irish districts in the city, but I've heard there's a decent-sized Irish community around Broad Street.

Some of the men in this company live in that area. I don't know if it's worth checking out.'

'It sounds like a good place to start,' said Cormac, concealing his uplifted spirits behind a courteous bow of his head. 'Thank you very much for your help, sir.'

The accidental snapping of a rope had led to a great deal of good fortune for him today. It was indeed better to be born lucky than rich.

CHAPTER 3

Emily skipped up the steps of the cathedral, her mama and papa in front of her and her two aunties close behind. She hopped as she ascended: one foot, two feet, one foot, two feet. The shadow of the great spire darkened a portion of the steps and, as she jumped within its boundaries, she imagined that she was entering the lair of a fearsome beast. The beast itself loomed ahead, its mouth gaping wide.

'I'll save you, Mama,' she whispered as her unsuspecting mama stepped inside those cavernous jaws.

Emily ran forwards and flung her arms around Mama's waist, protecting her from the beast and bracing for its teeth to sink into her own flesh instead.

Mama looked down at her with a kind smile. 'We must be very calm in here, Emily,' she said. 'Let's be on our best behaviour, shall we?'

Emily remembered that Papa had said something similar before they left the boarding house – he had been so serious that she had even left Mabel behind. She took Mama's hand and walked steadily onwards with no skipping or running. As it turned out, the beast wasn't a dangerous creature after all – it let them enter unharmed and it purred contentedly as Auntie Orlaith and Auntie Tess followed after them.

It was cool and quiet inside the cathedral. Emily stared up in awe at the soaring ceiling, storing it away in her mind for her next painting, while Mama and Papa talked in low voices next to her.

'Are you entirely certain we should do this?' Papa asked. 'Catholics are not too popular here.'

'That won't change my mind,' Mama replied and, even without looking, Emily could tell she was wearing her happy face. 'Though I can't have it for myself, I want this for our children, born and not yet born.'

A man in a robe came towards them. Papa greeted him as 'Father' so Emily knew he must be a priest because Papa's own papa was no longer alive. She had never met him but Papa once said to her on the ship that Jack McGovern would have loved the bones of her body. She looked down at herself and, not for the first time, wondered how her grandpapa would have loved her bones if he could not see them.

Auntie Orlaith and Auntie Tess stood on either side of Emily while Mama and Papa went to speak with the priest. Auntie Tess muttered, 'Given my long list of sins, I'm surprised I didn't burst into flames when I crossed the threshold,' and Auntie Orlaith giggled quietly with her hand over her mouth.

Emily was going to tell Auntie Tess that she needn't worry because the beast was actually a friendly creature, but then Mama and Papa came back over to them. The priest had moved to a tall stone basin where he was setting a book down on its smooth edge.

Mama bent so she was at Emily's eye level and said, 'This is an important day for you, gooseberry. Can you tell me why?'

Emily drew herself up – she knew it was one of the most important days in her whole seven and a quarter years. 'Today I'm making a promise to God that I will be a good person.'

'That's right. And how will you do that?'

'By saying my prayers and following his commandments.'

'Good girl. Do you remember learning those when we were on the ship?'

Emily nodded. There were ten commandments but she nearly always forgot one when she was reciting them.

'Let's go meet the priest now, *a stór*,' said Papa, using the special name he reserved just for her. 'His name is Father Whitty and he's going to bless you.'

Papa wrapped his warm, reassuring hand around Emily's and everyone approached the stone basin. The priest picked up his book which Emily recognised as a Bible by the cross embossed on the front. He talked for a little while and she did her very best to listen but he was speaking in Latin which she didn't understand.

Auntie Tess looked bored. She picked at one of her nails and craned her neck away from the group to hide a yawn.

At last, Father Whitty dipped his fingers into the stone basin and said, 'The Catholic Church acknowledges that your infant baptism in the Church of England denomination was validly administered. To complete your conversion to the Catholic faith, I invite you to attend today's Mass where you will receive your first Holy Communion.' He made the sign of the cross on Emily's forehead with his wet thumb. 'We welcome you, Emily McGovern.'

***

As a steady current of worshippers streamed into the cathedral before the Mass began, Bridget observed that the class divide still existed even in this country and even in the presence of God – the wealthier members of the flock filled the pews in the nave, while the poorer souls occupied the pews in the adjacent aisles.

Men and women were segregated to a degree too, but Father Whitty had informed Bridget and Cormac that it was acceptable for families to sit together, so they led Emily, Orlaith and Tess to a pew in a side aisle and knelt for the celebration of Mass.

Cormac took Emily up to the altar during the Communion rite, the little girl's palms pressed solemnly together in front of her. Orlaith and Tess followed them but Bridget remained in the pew, despite several suspicious frowns cast in her direction. She and Cormac had made Father Whitty aware that she had been raised in the Church of Ireland faith but she wondered if she ought to hang a sign around her neck for the benefit of the other churchgoers.

When it was Emily's turn to receive Communion, she knelt at the cloth-covered altar rail and put her hands beneath the white cloth. Father Whitty held up the host before her and said, '*Corpus Christi*.'

'Amen!' she said so loudly that Bridget was positive they had heard her back in Ireland. Some of the other members of the congregation exchanged benevolent smiles. Father Whitty placed the host on Emily's outstretched tongue. As she turned from the altar rail, she sought out Bridget and waved, beaming as brightly as she could with her mouth firmly closed.

Bridget was full of happiness for her daughter on this momentous day, but she couldn't help experiencing a certain despondency on her own account. She had intended to convert too but had come to realise that this was, quite simply, an impossibility. Even though she knew deep in her soul that her religious beliefs had grown to be Catholic in nature, she could not profess her faith in any formal way due to one insurmountable impediment: she was still married to Garrett while cohabiting with Cormac, an unforgivable transgression in the eyes of the church. Even in the unlikely event that Garrett legally divorced her, she would never be permitted to convert.

Shame bore down upon her as she acknowledged that she and Cormac had freely broken two of the commandments they had been teaching their daughter: she had committed adultery and he had coveted another man's wife. Though their sins were great, they were also irreparable – neither she nor Cormac could ever desire to reverse their actions, not when they had discovered the sheer wonder of pure, wholly reciprocal love. But the church would not view such notions with any kind of tolerance.

To compound their misdeeds, Father Whitty believed that she and Cormac were lawfully married, albeit in a mixed-religion union, and they had not disabused him of that assumption. They meant to allow everyone they met in America to take it for granted that they were husband and wife. God knew this was not the truth but Bridget believed he could also see the good intentions in their hearts. They would always strive to be decent people, despite their irrevocable faults. And she would practise the Catholic faith as truly as any other churchgoer, even if she could not receive Communion.

Cormac, Emily, Orlaith and Tess returned to the pew. Kneeling between Bridget and Cormac, Emily whispered her prayers fervently with her forehead furrowed in concentration. Cormac, too, looked like he was praying with great intensity. He had already confided in Bridget that he would find this part of Mass deeply troubling – Holy Communion was meant to be received in a state of grace but he did not repent the mortal sin he had committed. He had vowed to her that he would pray the Act of Contrition over and over in the hope that God would forgive his unclean soul.

They were both sinners; there was no denying it. And yet, as Cormac knelt with his elbows propped on the pew in front and his brow resting on his clasped hands, Bridget gazed at him and, try as she might, she could not perceive his wickedness. She had witnessed this man risk his life to protect his family.

She had observed the joyful bond he had established with their daughter and knew he would be just as wonderful a father to their next child. Above all, in his passionate willingness to build his life with Bridget, he had utterly transformed her. He offered her love, respect and a sense of value which had been so starkly absent in her life before he came back into it. She felt like a different person – a human being of worth and not a piece of property to be used or spurned at will. And when he offered her his body, and venerated hers with such devotion, all she wanted was to pull him closer until they were inseparable, all she yearned for was the exultation of that deep, penetrating union...

'*Oremus*,' said Father Whitty and, cheeks flaming, Bridget returned her gaze to her own clasped hands.

CHAPTER 4

By the time they left the Cathedral of the Holy Cross after the end of Mass, the spire's shadow had all but disappeared. Cormac led them down the front steps but, instead of heading back in the direction of the boarding house, he turned the opposite way.

'Where are you going?' Bridget asked, puzzled.

He grinned. 'I'm taking us to our new home.'

Her eyes widened. Next to her, Orlaith said eagerly, 'You found a place?' Emily jumped up and down and even Tess struggled to look unaffected by the news.

'I did indeed. Follow me.'

A swell of excitement rippled through the group as they made their way down the street. It was another hot day and Cormac began to perspire almost at once. A pair of figures came walking against them: a mother and daughter holding identical cream parasols. The girl, not much older than Emily, clutched hers at a jaunty angle and laughed beneath its shade. Cormac caught Emily's manifest gaze of envy as the pair passed by; she peeked back over her shoulder several times to continue goggling at the girl's parasol. Guilt pricked at him and some of his enthusiasm about their destination leaked away – they were not heading to a place where pretty parasols would be a common sight.

This conviction was borne out as soon as they reached Broad Street where the first person to cross their path was a barefoot child in shabby clothes who emitted a wheezy cough and demanded of Cormac, 'Spare a penny, sir?'

The child was so dirty that he couldn't even tell if it was a boy or girl. He dug in his pocket for a coin and handed it to the urchin, who ran off without saying thanks. Carrying on, Cormac led the others along Broad Street until they came to a building with a peeling door. He pushed it open and they entered a hallway with a door off either side and a tall stairs right in front of them. Two young, brown-haired girls sat on the bottom step – they were not as ragged as the first child and they looked up at the newcomers with powerful curiosity.

'Are ye moving in upstairs?' one asked boldly.

'We are,' said Cormac with a smile.

They didn't say anything further but quickly hopped off the step. As Cormac guided his family up the stairs, he glanced back and saw the two girls clinging to the banisters at the foot, their inquisitive, eager gazes focused particularly on Emily.

The next floor was a duplicate of the first with a door to the left, another to the right, and a flight of stairs leading upwards again. Cormac halted at the left door.

'This is it,' he said, his nerves mounting. He really didn't want to disappoint Bridget but there was only so far his earnings would stretch once he began working at the docks.

He opened the door and they all trooped inside. Emily barged forwards, running about the space on an initial exploratory mission. Bridget, Orlaith and Tess took it in more slowly, looking around with guarded expressions.

A window set in the opposite wall admitted enough murky light to reveal their surroundings. They stood in a general sort of living area which contained a stained table, flanked by a bench and a stool, and a tattered sofa with a low base squatting in front of a well-used fireplace. A single cupboard was wedged beneath the window sill and the view through the window itself showed the grubby wall of the adjacent building.

Much like the hallway, there were two doors facing each other on either side of the room. Cormac gestured towards the one on the left and Bridget skirted around the sofa to peer through it, just as Emily came barrelling out of the one on the right.

'A bedroom!' she announced. 'Just one big bed and nothing else, I think. It's really dark in there.'

Having inspected the accommodation thoroughly when he first came to view it, Cormac knew that Emily's report also applied to the room Bridget was appraising, save for one difference: the front bedroom boasted a narrow window which looked down onto Broad Street, while the back bedroom had no window at all.

It was downright meagre in comparison to Wyndham House in London, where Bridget and Emily had lived with Garrett, or the imposing Oakleigh Manor in Carlow, before it had tragically burned down mere months ago. And yet, the landlord who owned this building had informed Cormac that eleven people had previously occupied this set of rooms prior to departing west for perceived better opportunities in Chicago. Sharing three rooms between just five people would be an absolute extravagance in this neighbourhood.

Bridget turned back to the living area but it was Tess who delivered the first judgement.

'It's a palace,' she said, her eyes bright with excitement. 'An actual fireplace! I can't believe it.'

Orlaith grinned. 'And look, no broken glass in the window. We'll be proper cosy come winter.'

Cormac eyed Bridget for her reaction. She stepped around the sofa again to reach his side and linked her arm through his.

'Our first home together,' she breathed, squeezing against him. 'That's enough to make it the finest dwelling in the whole city.'

He would have kissed her soundly had they been alone.

Emily darted into the front bedroom and they heard a muffled thump as she jumped up onto the bed.

'Who gets which room?' she called. 'I like this one with the window!'

'You mustn't be greedy—' Bridget started to remonstrate, but Orlaith cut her off.

'No, it makes sense,' she said. 'We're only two people and yous are three, soon to be four. Yous will need a decent room more than us.'

Tess looked a bit put out but she didn't demur.

'Thank you,' said Cormac, envisioning the challenge of wedging two adults, a growing girl and a baby into one bedroom. 'We appreciate it.'

A scuffle out on the landing drew their attention back to the door they had entered through, beyond which came loud whispers.

'I'll tell them—'

'No, *I'll* do it—'

'Ma said I could.'

'She did not.'

'She *did*.'

Cormac pulled the door wide to reveal the two young girls they had met at the bottom of the stairs, their heads close together as they argued. They froze momentarily but the taller of the two recovered first.

'Ma said she's coming up now,' she declared quickly, throwing a triumphant glance at the smaller girl who looked ready to burst into tears. Any further squabbling evaporated as footsteps sounded on the stairs and the girls scurried backwards to let a lean woman reach the doorway. She had vivid green eyes and she balanced a small, wriggling boy on her hip.

'Well, here ye are now, and welcome!' she said. 'I knew this place wouldn't be empty for long. Derval Carey's my name. We live downstairs right below ye. Are ye all the one family?'

'You could say that,' said Cormac, as Emily came galloping out of the bedroom to meet all the visitors. 'I'm Cormac McGovern and this is my wife, Bridget, our daughter, Emily, and my sister, Orlaith.' He gestured towards Tess. 'And this is Tess O'Leary, a close friend and as good as a sister.'

He had assumed Tess would be pleased to be identified as a member of the family, but instead he glimpsed a faint grimace on her face before she turned to Derval Carey with a raised eyebrow.

'Are these all yours?' she asked, motioning to the boy and the two girls.

Derval laughed. 'For my sins,' she said with a wink. 'There's another one skulking about somewhere too. Rory!' she called.

They heard the shuffling of feet and a boy appeared in the doorway. A little older than his siblings, he had his mother's green eyes, his sisters' brown hair, and a pair of prominent ears that were entirely his own.

'Come here to me, lad,' his mother said and, when he reached her side, she passed the youngest child into his arms; the little boy writhed this way and that in a vain bid for freedom. She jerked her chin at the two girls hovering behind and they joined them as well. Then she tapped each one on the crown of the head, saying, 'Rory, Una, Sorcha and little Brian. Ten, six, four and two. Don't worry if ye forget—I do all the time.' She touched an affectionate knuckle to the younger girl's cheek.

'They are lovely names,' said Bridget. 'Are many of the families on this street Irish, Mrs Carey?'

'Derval,' the woman corrected. 'The only missus around here is old Mrs Kane three doors down who'll swing a broom at you if you're in her way. Isn't that right, Rory?'

Rory shifted the weight of his brother from one hip to the other. 'Yes,' he muttered, a world of resentment contained within that single syllable.

Grinning, Derval went on, 'Plenty of Irish folk around here. We're all Irish in this building apart from the fella on the top floor. With a name like Lorenzo, he'd have to have a bit of foreign blood, wouldn't he? We don't hold it against him, although my husband does draw the line at kissing cheeks.' She winked again. 'Himself is away at sea at the moment. A deckhand on the *Integrity*.'

Una piped up, 'Da said he's going to be home for Christmas!'

Sorcha bobbed excitedly on her toes. 'He promised!'

Their mother's cheery expression faded just a fraction but she said, 'He sure did, girls. And Da always keeps his promises.' She looked around at the McGoverns. 'So, what brings ye here? Are ye new to Boston or just new to Broad Street?'

'New to Boston,' said Cormac. 'We sailed recently from Ireland. We're searching for my sister, Bronagh, who we believe made the same journey a couple of years ago. Although we don't know for certain, we hope we'll be able to find her in this city.'

Derval nodded. 'Ye'll be wanting to use *The Boston Pilot* so.'

'What's that?' asked Orlaith.

'A newspaper. They print notices for immigrants looking for their family members. There's a new issue every Saturday.' Derval stuck her thumb over her shoulder. ''Tis how old Mrs Kane's nephew Donie found a whole host of their Limerick cousins up in the North End.'

Cormac felt a spark of elation flare inside him. It couldn't possibly be that easy, could it? Orlaith's face lifted with hope too, but Tess took a bleaker view.

'Bronagh can't read,' she said. 'Why would she even bother to look at a newspaper?'

Derval hoisted the squirming Brian out of Rory's arms and set him on his feet, holding onto his wrists to keep him in place. 'Arrah, there are no scholars in the North End either, I can tell you. Lots of folk can't read but the paper still gets shared around. Some can recognise the letters of their own name or they might get another person to read it for them.'

She shrugged and, in the process, Brian managed to slip from her grasp. He took off at once, running towards the open door onto the landing. Una caught him around his middle and brought him flailing back to their mother.

'Don't be a bold boy now,' Derval admonished him. As she clutched his wrists again, she added in conclusion to the others, 'If people think their family's looking for them, they'll find some way to check *The Pilot*.'

Cormac deflated at that; Bronagh had no inkling that they had followed her to America, if indeed it had even been her who had been listed in the passenger records of the Cork Harbour Commissioners. But he said, 'It's certainly worth a shot. Thanks very much for the advice, Mrs—Derval.'

'Not at all. And if ye need anything else, just holler. What about some sheets for them beds? Ye won't want much in this heat and that'll give ye time to get your own before the cold weather comes.'

'We would be very grateful for that,' said Bridget. 'Thank you, you're too kind.'

Derval waved the thanks away while Sorcha, who had been scrutinising Bridget with palpable interest, suddenly chirped, 'Are you going to have a baby?'

Bridget smiled and rested a hand on her pregnant bump. 'I am, but not for a few months yet. How clever of you.'

Una looked annoyed. 'I noticed too. I just didn't say it.' She pointed at her mother. 'Ma helps other mas have their babies.'

'Good gracious, do you really?' said Bridget to Derval, her eyes wide with eagerness.

'I do, for sure,' Derval replied. 'If you think you'll need me when the time comes, I'd be more than happy to help.'

'Oh, yes!' said Bridget. 'Thank you, that would ease my mind a great deal.'

Cormac shared her relief – having a midwife living right below them would be ideal should any complications arise during the birth.

As soon as he had that thought, he pushed it away.

'My first bit of advice to you,' Derval said, swinging Brian up into her arms again, 'is take the weight off your feet. You've been out walking for long enough in that heat, I can tell.'

'I will later,' Bridget assured her, 'but next we must go back to the boarding house to collect our things.'

'No, you should stay here,' said Cormac, keen to prove to the midwife that he was taking appropriate care of the expectant mother. 'I can go back for them.'

'I'll go with you,' said Tess.

'Me too,' said Orlaith. 'There isn't much. We'll manage between us.'

'Shall I go too, Papa?' Emily asked half-heartedly.

'You stay behind and look after your mama, *a stór*. That's the most important responsibility of all. Can you do it?'

Her face broke into a grin. 'I can!'

She made a show of towing Bridget over to the tattered sofa and persuading her to sit down, although her gaze casually roved over to Una and Sorcha as she did so. They returned her attention with equal interest. Emily took a seat demurely next to her mother but, all of a sudden, she gasped, leapt up and came dashing back to Cormac.

'Papa!' she said urgently, pulling on his arm. 'Don't forget Mabel!'

'I wouldn't dream of it,' he said with deepest sincerity.

He still had to promise four more times that he would remember to fetch Mabel before Emily would permit him, Orlaith and Tess to leave.

When they emerged onto the street, the long walk in the heat seemed more bearable to Cormac with the knowledge that they would shortly be returning to a place they could now call home. Their nomadic lifestyle was finally at an end and he was unspeakably thankful for it.

At the boarding house, he packed his, Bridget's and Emily's belongings into their two valises. Emily had left Mabel tucked into the truckle bed – as per his daughter's instructions, he made certain the doll was sitting comfortably inside the valise before he closed it.

He met Orlaith and Tess back down in the lobby. Walter lingered near them, ready to carry their baggage the ten steps to the door if need be. Cormac approached the proprietor at his desk.

'I'd like to pay the balance owed on the two rooms under the name McGovern,' he said.

'Very good,' the proprietor said genially. While he checked his register and made some calculations, he asked, 'And you were satisfied with the accommodation, I trust?'

'Yes, thank you,' said Cormac, the polite response tripping automatically off his tongue. But as he dug into his pocket for the dollars to pay the remaining amount for their stay, he reconsidered his words. Had they been satisfied with their experience here?

The proprietor confirmed the final figure and held out his hand expectantly. Cormac made no move to give him the money and the other man's forehead creased.

'I'd like to ask you a question,' said Cormac. 'Were you happy with us as guests?'

Looking bemused, the proprietor said, 'Yes, indeed.'

'We didn't cause an ounce of trouble?'

'No, of course not! Your behaviour was exemplary.'

Cormac leaned closer over the desk. 'Then I'd like to inform you that we are in fact Irish, not English.'

The proprietor's face fell comically.

Cormac placed the money into the man's still-outstretched hand. 'Please remember that the next time Irish people come looking for accommodation at your establishment.'

He headed for the door with his two valises, Orlaith and Tess close on his heels. Walter stared after them, his wizened mouth opening and closing like a fish.

CHAPTER 5

No matter how hard Bridget scrubbed, the stains on the table were there to stay. Sighing, she dropped her cloth on the tabletop in defeat as Orlaith's and Tess's sleep-clogged voices drifted from their bedroom. Their door was ajar to let in enough light to see what they were doing while maintaining their privacy – they wouldn't be so wasteful as to light a candle for the few minutes it took to get dressed for the day.

'Y'know,' mumbled Orlaith, 'I've been thinking about what we should do.'

'What we should do about what?' asked Tess, her last couple of words distorted in a loud yawn.

'About earning a living.'

Silence followed this statement and, as Bridget picked up her cloth and started scouring the table again in an effort to avoid eavesdropping, she imagined Tess's expression. Would she be dubious? Enthusiastic? Derisive?

When Tess spoke, her tone was neutral. 'Go on.'

'I know what it's like to live in poverty, and I know what it's like to live under someone else's thumb, and I never want to go through either of those again. We've got my brother looking out for us now but that's not good enough for me.' Orlaith's voice became muffled; it sounded like she was pulling a garment

34

down over her head. 'I need to be independent. If there's more hardship ahead, I want to be able to rely on me and no one else.'

Bridget rubbed at the table so vigorously that she scraped a fingernail against its rough surface. She winced as she stopped to examine the broken tip.

'But...you're only thirteen.'

'So?' Orlaith challenged. Bridget thought she was entitled to her defiant attitude; forced to grow up too quickly in Dublin, she was no longer a child but a young woman and, although Tess had to be eight or nine years older, Orlaith often seemed the more mature of the pair.

'So maybe it'd be nice to let your brother take care of you for a little while,' said Tess.

There were two thuds, like a pair of boots being laid out on the floor. 'I know he means well. But he's as blind as the rest of us in this strange city.' Orlaith clicked her tongue. 'What about you? Are *you* happy to depend on a man for your survival?'

Bridget gave up trying to distract herself; the conversation in the bedroom had her full attention. She strained to hear Tess's answer.

'If I had to depend on one man, it'd be him.' There was a creak as she sat on the bed. 'But I've survived by myself before. I know I can do it again if I have to.'

'I don't mean *that*,' said Orlaith sharply. 'That's still depending on men.' She paused. 'I want to become a nurse, or a midwife. Stand on my own two feet and help others along the way.'

Tess's response was lost in a racket of running footsteps out on the landing as Emily, Una and Sorcha went tearing from one flight of stairs up the next, chattering and giggling. The two Carey girls had shown Emily where to fetch water from the public well first thing that morning and they were now supposed to be explaining to her how the children in the building were responsible for keeping the stairs and hallways swept daily, although Bridget suspected that the objective of the lesson had gone astray in the delight of new friendship.

'...start with Derval Carey.' Orlaith's declaration was full of determination. 'She seems like a decent woman. I'll ask her to teach me how to be a midwife and then see where I can go from there. What do you think?'

Bridget crossed over to the cupboard beneath the window and plunged her cloth into the basin of water sitting on top. She had filled it from the pail Emily had brought back from the well and it was already murky from her morning's labours. She had risen early to commence a proper clean of their new home, but Orlaith and Tess had slept quite a bit later than everyone else – Bridget hoped that wouldn't become a regular occurrence as she would need their help with the upkeep of the place the further her pregnancy advanced.

Tess's voice grew louder; she was opening the bedroom door wide. 'I think you're right. Count me in.'

As they came into the living area, Bridget decided not to let on that she had overheard their discussion. Orlaith's lack of faith in Cormac was regrettable but understandable – past errors committed by him and Bridget both had unintentionally led to a great deal of suffering on Orlaith's part. She was justified in her desire to strive for her own autonomy. In any case, it would be advantageous to have more than one person earning money in the family. Bridget had designs on contributing in that regard too once they were settled, although perhaps not until after the baby was born.

Emily and Una came sprinting in from the landing, followed belatedly by Sorcha on her shorter legs.

'Papa's back!' Emily exclaimed. 'He's coming up the street. We saw him from Mr Lorenzo's window.'

'What were you doing up there?' Bridget said in exasperation.

'Why d'you call him *Papa*?' demanded Una.

'Where's he coming back from?' asked Orlaith.

In the midst of the subsequent tumult, Cormac walked in with a narrow mattress slung over his shoulder.

Emily let out a cry of exultation. 'My new bed!'

For their first night in Broad Street, she had shared the bed in the front bedroom with her parents, snuggled comfortably between them. However, by dawn Bridget and Cormac had both found themselves forced out to the edges of the bed while their daughter reclined with arms and legs extended like a starfish. They had swiftly agreed that Cormac's primary task of the day would be to organise more suitable sleeping arrangements.

As the children crowded around Cormac, Bridget said to Orlaith, 'Derval said she would lend us another sheet. Would you mind going downstairs for it?'

Orlaith's eyes gleamed. 'For sure. It'd be nice to chat and get to know her a little better too.'

'I'll go as well,' Tess chimed in.

They vanished out the door while Cormac carried the mattress into the front bedroom, Emily bounding after him. In lieu of a truckle bed, the mattress would be hidden away beneath the big bed during the day and pulled out nightly at bedtime. As Cormac set it on the floor, Bridget heard Emily say happily, 'Now there are three things in the whole world that are mine: Mabel, my watercolour box, and my bed!'

When they re-emerged, the three girls ran off again, Emily's voice drifting back as she said to Una, 'He used to be Mr Davenport but really he's Cormac McGovern but I call him Papa because he's my real papa...'

Bridget cringed and hoped Una wouldn't repeat that back to her mother. Although what Emily had said made no apparent sense, it might raise suspicion in their kind new neighbour and that was the sort of sentiment that Bridget wished to leave far behind them. She had no desire to deceive but neither did she want to be judged. She touched the two rings on her left hand: the circle of threads twisted together, which represented the lifelong promise she and Cormac had made to each other, and the gold ring wrought in the shape of a pair of hands holding a crowned heart, which was society's accepted proof of marriage. They had the belief and the evidence, just not the legal union.

Cormac broke her out of her distracted thoughts by fishing in his pocket and presenting a small object between his thumb and forefinger. 'As my lady requested.'

'Oh, terrific!' she exclaimed, almost as thrilled as Emily had been about her new bed. While she still possessed paper and a pen, she had run out of ink long ago on the ship. She took the ink pot from Cormac and went into their bedroom to rummage in the half-unpacked valise for her unfinished letters and her pen. She extracted them and returned to the other room, where she sat on the bench at the table and spread out the pages.

'I hadn't realised they were so pressing,' said Cormac as he produced his last purchase – a small block of cheese – and placed it on top of the cupboard next to the basin. 'I got this at Quincy Market. Honestly, Derval Carey is a godsend. She knew where I should go for everything.'

'She truly is a blessing,' Bridget agreed. 'The letters aren't pressing exactly, but I would still like to send them sooner rather than later.'

She had begun them on the ship as a way to pass the time but they could not be posted until one crucial element was ready to be included – an address to which replies could be sent. As she picked up a page, Cormac slid onto the bench next to her.

'This one is to Ellen,' she told him, thinking fondly of the former lady's maid who had become a dear confidante to her over the years. Ellen had married Liam Kirwan, Cormac's friend and fellow stable hand at Oakleigh, and they now lived with their two sons in the cottage that had once been home to Cormac's family. 'She will have already given birth by the time my letter arrives so I'm writing to ask whether she had a boy or a girl. And, of course, to impart the news of our own impending arrival too. Our babies will be born only a few months apart.'

Cormac dipped his head over Bridget's rounded belly. 'Do you hear that, *a leanbh*? A piece of paper is going to travel all the way across the ocean to tell our friends you're coming.'

"'*A leanbh*"?' said Bridget. 'Not "*a stór*"?'

Cormac's eyes twinkled. 'My instinct informs me that Emily might take umbrage if I addressed anyone else as my "treasure". I think "child" is less proprietary.'

'Hmm, a wise decision.' Bridget set down the page and scanned another one on the tabletop. 'I shall let my uncle know too. No doubt he will count back the months and make some bawdy remark about how the child must have been conceived under his roof and how he'll never live with the shame of it.'

'Lord Walcott does have a black sense of humour, *a leanbh*,' said Cormac, resting a hand on Bridget's bump. 'But I saw him slip an iced cake to Emily when he thought your mother and I weren't looking, so stay on his good side and you'll do well.'

With Cormac hindering her view, Bridget was having difficulty reading the next letter which she had addressed to Laurence Enright and John Corbett, the two stewards she had appointed to oversee the management of the Oakleigh Estate. She couldn't even reach the ink pot. 'Cormac—' she started to complain.

He looked up at her with a shining face. 'When will I be able to feel the baby kick?'

Her annoyance melted away and she put her own hand over his. 'It's a bit soon yet,' she said. 'But maybe in the next few weeks.'

'Can *you* feel anything?'

'A little now and then.' Anticipating his next question, she said, 'It's a tiny movement, like butterfly wings. Sometimes it's so light that I wonder if I imagined it.'

Fascinated, he leaned down close again to her belly. 'God, I can't wait to meet you, *a leanbh*.'

Bridget had forgotten that, even though this was her third time with child, it was Cormac's first time to witness it. Garrett had been there for her previous two pregnancies and, despite the incontrovertible chasm between the two men's characters, Cormac's absorption was in fact quite similar to Garrett's. Garrett had never talked to her bump or caressed it, but he had been just as enthralled by it. She used to catch him eyeing her stomach, peering covertly around the side of his newspaper at the breakfast table or casting furtive, sidelong glances as they passed each other on the stairs. She had never called attention to it, allowing him those lingering moments of paternal expectation which he evidently preferred to experience alone. For all his failings, he had really wanted to be a father. And he had been, for the bitterly short time they had cherished with James. And he still was, to a boy he had refused to acknowledge as his own.

Bridget's gaze landed on the last letter in her pile.

'Cormac?' she said.

'Hmm?'

She put her finger under his chin to encourage him to sit upright. He left his palm curved over the top of her belly.

'I have a letter for Garrett too.'

The joy in his expression diminished but he gave a grudging nod.

'Needless to say, I won't be relating our address to him. I'll advise him that he may write to Oakleigh if he wishes and they can redirect his correspondence to us. But I was wondering...'

She hesitated; they had skirted this delicate topic a few times but had never discussed it outright. She nipped the tip of her tongue and carried on, 'Ought we to tell him that we know where Patrick is?'

Cormac tensed. He took his hand back and turned from her to rest both of his forearms on the table. 'I've been mulling over that question too,' he said. 'What are your own thoughts on the matter?'

She fingered the corner of her letter to Ellen. 'I'm not sure. On the one hand, Patrick is his flesh and blood. Perhaps he has the right to know that his son is alive.'

'Or perhaps he relinquished that right when he abandoned his son eight years ago,' said Cormac grimly. 'What evidence is there that he would even care to know?'

'None,' she admitted. When Garrett had confessed to being the man who had got Cormac's sister Mary with child, he had exhibited genuine regret for the consequences of his actions but no desire to take any responsibility for them.

'And what benefit would there be to Patrick if Garrett learned of his whereabouts?'

She reflected on Patrick's situation. Under the false name of Edward, he resided in one of the wealthiest parts of Dublin as the supposed nephew of Lord and Lady Anner. Raised as their heir, he was living in total comfort, well fed and well educated. There were regrettable flaws in his character thanks to Lady Anner's supercilious influence, but there could be no denying that his existence was a privileged one. If Garrett sought him out, Patrick's true origins would be exposed and he would plummet from the status of a baron's heir to the illegitimate son of a lower class woman who had taken her own life. Cormac had already tried to tell the boy about his family but he had rejected the notion outright. What material advantage was there to him in acknowledging such an inferior background?

'None,' she conceded again.

'Those are the two conclusions I keep arriving at as well.' Cormac laced his fingers together and stared down at them. 'Therefore I don't consider us to be under any obligation to divulge this knowledge.'

Bridget swallowed. 'Can you hazard a guess as to what Mary might have wanted?'

Cormac's fingers twitched. 'I suppose I can. But Mary didn't always have the soundest judgement, God love her.'

They sat in silence. After a beat, Bridget reached for her new ink pot. Then she let out a little gasp. Cormac looked at her sharply.

'I just felt a tiny kick,' she breathed.

His expression lifted. Even though he wouldn't be able to feel it himself, she grasped his hands and brought them back to her belly once more. His warm palms encompassed the bulge, irrefutable evidence of the life they had created together. She sensed the barely perceptible movement again.

'Our little one can't wait to meet you too,' she whispered.

She pressed her forehead to his and they rejoiced in the tranquillity of the moment.

There was a clatter as a pair of feet came scampering into the room and just as abruptly departed again.

'Let's go somewhere else. Mama and Papa are kissing. They do that a *lot*.'

CHAPTER 6

'McGovern!'

Cormac tried not to wince. He would have to get used to being addressed that way again, even though it was uncomfortably reminiscent of his days working in Cunningham's gang.

He hurried forwards as Mr Walker beckoned to him from the open doorway of Robert Smith & Co.'s warehouse. Next to the foreman stood a tall, black-skinned man with a coil of rope slung over his arm.

As Cormac reached them, Mr Walker said, 'I hope you're ready for a hard day's work. This fellow here will help break you in.'

He bumped a fist on the other man's shoulder and disappeared inside the warehouse.

Cormac stuck out his hand and said, 'Good to meet you. McGovern's my name.'

The man grinned and shook his hand. 'Likewise,' he said in an accent different to Mr Walker's but still clearly American. 'I'm O'Mali.'

'O'Malley?' Cormac repeated in surprise. The fellow didn't look or sound like he had a drop of Irish blood in him.

His grin widened. 'It's what the others call me so I fit in. My great-grandparents sailed here decades ago from the great country of Mali.'

'Ah,' said Cormac with an appreciative chuckle. 'O'Mali. I get it.'

He followed O'Mali along the waterfront to the wharf where a group of dockworkers were assembled next to a moored ship. Cormac recognised Higgins among them; he looked no worse for wear after his altercation with the fallen crate.

'Our new man, McGovern,' said O'Mali, swinging his free arm towards Cormac.

They nodded at him and a few muttered their own names in return. Their expressions were not unfriendly but neither were they warm with welcome. That didn't trouble him too much. He guessed they were not unlike the tenants back at Oakleigh – their trust would have to be earned.

The day's work proved to be loading a quantity of goods stored in the warehouse onto the moored ship. O'Mali showed Cormac how to position pieces of wood to keep the cargo raised out of any water lying in the hold and demonstrated the best way to tie the cargo securely with rope. They carried barrels and crates of all sizes down into the depths of the ship, some of the bigger items needing two or three men to lift them. The wooden crane was used for the very largest goods and the men displayed a noticeable vigilance with it, constantly checking the ropes to make sure they were bearing the weight.

It was backbreaking work. Cormac found himself using muscles he hadn't exercised in a very long time. Besides the recent weeks of inactivity on the ship, his entrance five years ago into upper class society in the guise of Oliver Davenport had introduced him to a well-heeled lifestyle that had demanded no hard labour of any kind. Not since he had worked as a stable hand at Oakleigh had he been obliged to push his body to such extremes.

And he was undeniably feeling the effects of it. His limbs quivered with the strain of lugging heavy objects across his back and shoulders. He scraped his hands countless times on the rough wooden surfaces of the barrels and crates and more than once burned his palms when a rope slid through them too quickly. Thinking back to Mr Walker's initial assessment of him, he was certain his hands wouldn't remain 'as soft as a baby's arse' for long.

He made no complaint. He had known what he was getting himself into, and he wouldn't have received sympathy in any case. He just toiled on in silence, gritting his teeth against the pain and exhaustion.

There was a short break in the middle of the day to allow the men to have something to eat. Cormac sat within the vicinity of the group but did not contribute to the conversation; he didn't want to intrude where he might not be welcome, and he couldn't muster the energy to talk anyway. The others largely took no notice of him. However, as the break ended, Higgins came over to him and held out his hand to help him up. Cormac grasped it and got to his feet, doing his best to conceal the fact that every muscle in his body protested at the movement. Higgins didn't say anything but he gripped Cormac's hand firmly before releasing it.

Some excruciating hours later, when Cormac trudged back to the warehouse with several others to move a stack of casks, O'Mali stopped him in the doorway.

'You wanna take a rest on this one?'

Cormac shook his head. No one else was pausing for a rest so neither would he. As he hefted a cask into his arms, he spotted Mr Walker speaking with O'Mali and caught a few words before he slogged out the door.

'...thinks he's got something to prove?'

'Yes, sir. And he's gonna prove it if it kills him...'

By the time they finished for the day, Cormac's legs felt as shaky as the jelly served in Lady Bewley's favourite trifle. The men started to disperse, calling good-natured goodbyes to each other. O'Mali caught up to Cormac.

'Good work today, McGovern. Will we see you tomorrow?'

Even though the prospect of doing it all again the next day was almost unbearable to Cormac in that moment, he said, 'You sure will.'

O'Mali offered him his easy grin and Cormac responded with a rather lopsided one of his own. They parted and he walked away from the wharf, keeping his back straight. He waited until he was out of sight of the waterfront and then, finding a shadowed side street that was beyond the reach of the setting sun, he leaned against the wall of a nondescript building and slid to the ground with a low groan. He needed to gather himself before he went home. It would get easier, he was aware of that. And the knowledge that this work would support his family was enough motivation to keep him going. But just for a few moments he allowed himself to sink into a pit of physical misery.

'Here, mister, are you coming inside or what?'

A bare ankle came into his line of vision. He looked up into the heavily rouged face of a young woman.

He stood hurriedly, ignoring the aches in his joints. 'No, sorry. I have to be on my way.'

She threw him an irritated scowl and her attention transferred to another man approaching the building.

'Are you coming in, mister?'

'You bet I am, sugar. Are you going to take good care of me?'

'Oh, I hope so.'

She gave a false giggle, hooked her arm through his, and led him inside. Cormac recovered enough strength in his legs to hasten away.

When he got back to Broad Street, he found Emily sitting at the table painting stripes on a page with every cake from her watercolour box while Bridget was perched on the stool at the window, rubbing a cloth around the window frame. The cupboard had been pushed aside and a lit candle sat on top of it – the last traces of daylight were meagre given the proximity of the neighbouring building outside the window.

'What in God's name are you doing?' Cormac demanded.

Bridget glanced over her shoulder. 'I noticed some mould up here. I wanted to get rid of it before it spreads.'

He strode over to her, touching an affectionate hand to Emily's head as he passed. 'That's not the most prudent idea in your condition,' he said, with horrible visions of Bridget losing her footing and tripping off the stool. 'Please come down now.'

He reached for her waist and she didn't resist as, muscles screaming, he lifted her down to the floor.

Looking vexed, she said, 'But I hadn't finished.'

'I'll do it,' he said, plucking the cloth from her grip. He couldn't silence his grunt of pain as he stepped up onto the stool but covered it by asking, 'Where are Orlaith and Tess? They should be helping you with these chores.'

'Downstairs with Derval again,' she said. 'They are becoming fast friends already.' She hunkered down to pull open the doors of the cupboard. 'I have your supper here. Tell me, how was your first day?'

He started wiping at the narrow line of black mould snaking along the window frame. 'It was fine,' he said vaguely. 'They seem like a decent bunch.'

'Papa, look what I painted!'

He twisted around on the stool, prepared to praise Emily's creation no matter what it turned out to be, but was impressed to see that she had painted a very credible rendition of a plump hen over her stripes.

'Superb work,' he said.

Beaming, she said, 'Will I be able to get my hens soon?'

He felt guilty as he recollected the promise he had made to her. 'I'm afraid we can't keep hens here, *a stór*. We have no garden for them to roam in.'

Her face fell. She stared down at her painting and dismally chewed the corner of her nail.

'You mustn't bite your nails, Emily,' said Bridget, rising from her hunkers with a frown. 'It's a bad habit.'

Looking even more downcast, Emily removed her finger from her mouth and sat on her hands.

'Why don't you run down below and show Una and Sorcha your new painting?' suggested Bridget. 'I'm sure they'd like to see it. And tell your aunties they're needed upstairs.' As Emily scampered off with her page, Bridget called after her, 'And then it's bedtime!'

Cormac resumed his scrubbing but his mind strayed from his task. Emily had reminded him of Henrietta Brennan and the way she used to bite the skin around her nails. His cleaning efforts slowed, to the great relief of his throbbing arms, as he grew pensive, recalling that little girl's sad life to date.

Thoughtlessly, he said aloud, 'I wonder how Henrietta is faring these days.'

Bridget shut the cupboard doors with a snap and set his supper plate of bread and cheese on the table with a little more force than necessary. Cormac felt like adding to the rest of his aches by kicking himself. It was impossible to think of Henrietta and not also remember Thomasina, the girl's mother and the only other woman whom Cormac had bedded besides Bridget.

Even though that ill-advised encounter had occurred during the years Cormac and Bridget had been apart, he had later deliberately lied about it to her. While that was bad enough, at least Cormac was not Henrietta's father – that claim lay at the feet of Henry Munroe, Cunningham's chief lackey who had beaten Thomasina to death in a fit of rage. Cormac had no idea where Munroe had vanished to after the confrontation in the Dublin alleyway, so he had taken it upon himself to place Henrietta in the charge of Thomasina's aunt, Biddy O'Hara. It had been the most logical decision to make as Mrs O'Hara was Henrietta's only living blood relative apart from her absconded father, but the woman had never demonstrated a warm-hearted nature in any of Cormac's dealings with her. Was she maternal at all towards her grandniece?

'I think perhaps I would like to write and enquire after her wellbeing,' he said cautiously.

Bridget cast a brooding look at the tabletop. She began to tidy Emily's watercolour cakes back into their box, unmindful of the messy streaks they left on her fingers.

'Why do you feel accountable for her?' she asked at last.

'I don't!'

She arched her eyebrows at him.

'Well, maybe a little,' he said, sheepish. 'I just…I may not have fathered her but I'm the one who decided to put her in Mrs O'Hara's care, which means I've set her on the path that will shape her upbringing. I do feel a sense of responsibility in that. I'd like to think it was the best option for her, but what if I was wrong? It would ease my mind to know if she is safe and happy in the choice I made for her.'

'And what if Mrs O'Hara decides that your concern must betoken a sense of financial responsibility?'

'That's a risk,' he admitted. 'However, I'm willing to take it for the sake of attaining that peace of mind.'

Bridget's mouth compressed into a thin line but Cormac thought he perceived grudging acquiescence in her expression. He was about to return his attention to the mould when Orlaith, Tess and Emily entered the room.

'You look knackered,' said Tess. 'How did you get on?'

'Arrah, grand,' said Cormac. From his vantage point on the stool, he saw Bridget, Orlaith and Tess exchange amused glances and realised what he had said.

'The other workers are rubbing off on you already,' said Orlaith with a laugh.

He shrugged self-consciously. 'Maybe so.'

As Oliver Davenport, he had needed to make a deliberate effort to shake his Carlow brogue and adopt a more polished style of speech. Having spoken in that manner for so many years, he was surprised to hear himself slip unexpectedly into more colloquial language. But then, he had been surrounded by Irish accents for quite some time now – not just his new workmates and the Careys, but also Orlaith and Tess, and the Oakleigh tenants and Dublin denizens a few months ago. Perhaps he couldn't help a little Irishness stealing back into his tongue. He supposed it was no bad thing where his job was concerned as it might help him blend in a little better with the dockworkers. Which reminded him...

'Wait until I tell you the clever name of a fellow I met at the docks today...'

CHAPTER 7

Bridget peered closely at Emily's scalp, suppressing a shudder.

'Hold still, gooseberry,' she said and drew the comb once more through the little girl's damp hair, her golden curls flat and dark on her crown. Emily squirmed on the stool and reached up to scratch her head. Bridget gently batted her hand away and combed again.

Next to her, Orlaith and Tess scoured the hair on Una and Sorcha's wet heads, seeking out the lice and their eggs. Both Carey girls sat passively on the bench, their resigned expressions suggesting that they submitted to this process on a regular basis. Over on the sofa, Derval strove to inspect Brian's hair while Rory, first to be deloused, helped to hold the wriggling child in place.

The door swung open and Cormac strode in, waving a newspaper.

'It's there,' he announced.

The triumph on his face was a pleasing sight. Most nights, he came home to Broad Street with exhaustion written in every line of his body. Bridget didn't push him to talk about his work at the docks – when he plastered on a grin and said all was fine, she understood it was an ordeal he was trying to endure on his own. He probably had some daft notion that it would be a sign of weakness to admit how gruelling it was. So she didn't comment, but she left out a basin of water for him each evening so he could soak his sore hands and she pretended not to hear him groan when he struggled stiffly out of bed each morning.

But today, at the end of his third Saturday as a dockworker, his fatigue had been replaced by enthusiasm. He dropped *The Boston Pilot* onto the tabletop – it was folded open on the advertisements page. They all gathered around, the children particularly eager for a distraction from the task at hand.

Orlaith's eyes scanned the notices hungrily but embarrassment coloured her cheeks as she mumbled, 'Which one is it?'

Bridget hastened to skim the page, spotted Bronagh's name, and pointed. 'There.'

'I'll read it!' said Emily and, wet curls falling over her shoulders, she pulled the paper towards her. Taking care with every word, she enunciated, '"Information wanted of Bronagh McGovern, Ballydarry, County Carlow, Ireland, who may have sailed from Cove to Boston in the year 1834. Sought by siblings Cormac and Orlaith McGovern. They can be found by applying to Father Whitty at the Cathedral of the Holy Cross.".'

Emily looked up proudly, heedless of the water dripping from her hair onto the page.

'Good girl,' said Bridget, sliding the newspaper back out of reach.

'I spoke to Father Whitty about it,' said Cormac. 'He said the church assists many immigrants in finding their family members. We can check with him each Sunday after Mass to find out if he's heard from Bronagh.'

'For sure,' said Derval, bouncing Brian on her hip. 'There's nearly always a line of folk wanting to talk to him at the end of Mass.'

Orlaith nodded. 'Here's hoping Bronagh contacts him.' Then, folding her arms and clenching her teeth, she said to no one in particular, 'I'd like to learn how to read.'

Bridget offered her a kind smile. 'I can help you with that.'

Orlaith cast her a grateful look. They agreed to start the next day.

Later that night, as Bridget shut the bedroom door, she whispered, 'I'm very pleased for Orlaith. She is so full of determination to better herself.'

Holding a candle aloft, Cormac stepped carefully around the sleeping form of Emily, who was splayed out on her mattress with Mabel tucked under her elbow, to reach his side of the bed. He set the candle on the window sill and sat on the bed to remove his boots.

'I do admire her fortitude,' he said in an undertone. 'And I think her behaviour spurs Tess to seek self-improvement too. I've no doubt you will have a second pupil come morning.'

'I'm sure you're right,' said Bridget, although that prospect didn't seem to fill her with quite as much pleasure.

She tiptoed to her own side of the bed and began to undress. Her back was turned as Cormac slid between the sheets but she heard his quiet hiss and wondered what sort of knock he had sustained today.

When she climbed into bed too, she was surprised that he didn't turn to blow out the candle but instead propped himself up on one elbow and regarded her with a very serious expression.

'There's something I've been meaning to discuss with you,' he murmured. 'But it's a rather sensitive matter.'

She lay on her side facing him, one palm curved over her rapidly growing stomach. 'What is it?'

'I don't know the best way to say it.' He chewed the inside of his cheek as he sought for words. 'It's nearing the end of September and you may have noticed that the nights are becoming cooler. As you are aware, we recently purchased decent bedcovers to keep us warm during the coming winter months.'

'Yes, we did,' she said, puzzled as to where this was going.

'I, for one, am looking forward to the warmth those bedcovers will supply.' He took a deep breath. 'So I would humbly request that you refrain from monopolising them for yourself as you have been doing every night thus far with these sheets.'

'E*xcuse* me?' she squeaked.

'Shh,' he said, glancing over his shoulder at Emily, who slumbered on. 'I would hate for our daughter to witness this discord between us.'

When he turned back to her, she caught the hint of devilment glinting in his eyes but he managed to keep his tone grave as he said, 'I regret to report that you have committed this offence so often that I wake most mornings exposed while you are wrapped up snugly beside me. It does grieve me to learn your true nature. I confess I would not have been so quick to run away with you from London had I known how selfish you would be with the bedcovers.'

'You wretch!' she spluttered with as much indignation as she could convey in a whisper. She poked him in the chest. 'You should know better than to tease a pregnant woman.'

He touched the place where she had poked him with an air of wounded innocence. 'I have only broached this issue out of genuine concern.' He paused. 'Concern that my toes will fall off this winter due to frostbite.'

She pressed her face into her pillow to stifle her giggle. 'You are an utter rogue,' she said when she resurfaced. 'Let me tell you that your own sleeping habits leave something to be desired.' At his raised eyebrows, she went on, 'You grind your teeth in your sleep and the sound of it is insufferable. So there.'

'Oh,' he said. 'Do I really?' Looking abashed, he added, 'I'm sorry. I had no idea.'

'Sometimes it's loud enough to wake me up. Thankfully, Emily appears to be able to sleep through it.' She gave him another prod. 'So perhaps we can call it even?'

'Certainly,' he said. 'And if I emerge next spring with at least nine toes I shall be more than satisfied.'

He swallowed her rebuttal in a kiss.

CHAPTER 8

Bridget lumbered into the cathedral pew, doubtfully eyed the kneeler around her huge bump, and opted to sit on the bench instead. Emily knelt beside her, shivering inside her cloak. Cormac, Orlaith and Tess joined them just as the bishop appeared on the altar, accompanied by Father Whitty and another priest, and the celebration of Mass for New Year's Day began.

Bridget did her best to concentrate but in the middle of the Gospel reading she became distracted by a pain in her lower back which steadily worsened as the Mass continued. During the Offertory, she slid a surreptitious hand inside the folds of her cloak and kneaded the sore spot but it didn't help. She breathed out slowly as the bishop faced the congregation and elevated the host.

Emily turned to her and whispered, 'Mama, what do you think Jesus tastes like?'

'Hush, gooseberry. We must be respectful and—ah...!' Bridget let out a stifled gasp as the pain suddenly intensified.

Cormac gave her a sideways glance of alarm.

'I'm fine,' she mouthed at him.

Paying no heed to this, he slid along the bench, lifting Emily over his lap and setting her down on his other side. He leaned in close to Bridget.

'Are you feeling unwell?' he muttered with an anxious glance down at her bump.

She rubbed her belly soothingly. 'No, no. It's just a little backache, that's all. Nothing to worry about.'

'The Careys are only a few rows behind. Do you need Derval—'

'Not at all. Honestly, I'm fine.'

Unconvinced, he watched her like a hawk for the remainder of the Mass and even stayed by her side during Communion, letting Orlaith and Tess take Emily up to the altar. Upon their return to the pew, Bridget squirmed as the pain became superseded by another uncomfortable sensation – a desperate need to urinate. This was not an uncommon occurrence of late, but she was usually at home and thus in the vicinity of the privy at the back of the Broad Street building, rather than stuck in the pew of a cathedral.

She gave thanks as the bishop rose to say the final blessing and she endured the last few prayers by focusing on her back pain as a diversion from the pressure on her bladder. When the congregation started to leave, Cormac took her elbow and helped her to her feet.

'Let's get you home,' he said firmly and this time she didn't object.

Out on the front steps, where the cold January air only made matters worse for Bridget, they met the Careys, including Derval's husband, who had come for Christmas as promised but who stood taciturn even as his daughters hung on to him gleefully.

Derval squinted at Bridget. 'I was watching you during Mass. Are you—'

'I do believe the baby's on the way,' said Bridget, and Emily started whooping. 'But I have a more immediate need to attend to.'

She had never entered the reeking privy at Broad Street with a greater sense of relief.

Afterwards, she joined the others upstairs where they had gathered around the fireplace. The sofa, bench and stool had been moved closer to it for the cold winter months and Orlaith, Tess and Emily sat in a semicircle, hands stretched out to the fire, shaking off the chill after their walk back from the cathedral. Cormac knelt at the hearth, adding more coal to it with noticeable care.

'I saved the sofa for you, Mama,' said Emily, jumping off it with a flourish.

'Thank you, gooseberry, but I'm going to walk about for a little while.'

'Derval said she'll be up once she's settled Brian for his nap,' said Orlaith, excitement filling her features.

'Ah, she reckons you'll be a while yet anyway, if your pains have only started,' said Tess.

While Orlaith and Tess had gained much theoretical knowledge from Derval over the past few months, this would be their first time to receive a practical education. Bridget thought she might have felt more self-conscious about that if it were her first baby, but she had delivered twice before and knew there was no place for prudishness in the messy affair of childbirth. She would be glad of their sisterly support, even if she sometimes doubted whether Tess's was genuine.

She paced towards the window and gazed out at the grimy wall of the next-door building, massaging her lower back. Cormac joined her and clasped her other hand, entwining his fingers through hers, conveying so much hope and apprehension in his tight grasp.

'This is really happening?' he said.

'It is.' She was about to say that this stage of waiting could well be the hardest part but she gulped back any further words in a moan as another strong wave of pain passed through her. Bending forwards, she clutched Cormac's hand and ridiculed her previous notion. When the wave subsided, she let go of him; both of their hands had gone white from the strength of her grip. She released a shaky laugh. 'Oh, yes, most assuredly.'

'Maybe we should fetch Derval right away?' asked Orlaith.

'No need,' said Bridget. 'It's gone again. And I'm sure she'll be along shortly.'

'She might be kissing Mr Carey, like you and Papa do,' Emily piped up innocently.

Bridget tried to muster a smile but, despite their four children, she didn't think Derval and her husband shared many affectionate moments. 'Perhaps. In the meantime I'll try sitting for a bit.'

She crossed the room in an ungainly fashion and eased herself onto the sofa. Cormac didn't take a seat beside her; instead, he crouched in front of the hearth to check on the fire, prodding it with the poker. He hid his fear well but Bridget still sensed its presence. She couldn't blame him – between the conflagration that had burned down Oakleigh Manor last March and the stable fire that had claimed his older brother when Cormac had been only seventeen, he had now survived two large blazes, barely escaping both times with his life. It was no wonder they had left a residue of dread in his bones and instilled in him a heightened instinct for caution.

As Cormac set the poker down, Bridget was pondering what she could say to distract him when the pain hit her again. She whimpered and tried to breathe through it, vaguely conscious of Cormac moving swiftly to her side. He rubbed her back while she fought to ride it out and gradually it eased.

'Good gracious,' she said, stroking her belly. 'That came quite soon after the last one.' Then she felt a trickle between her legs and, fretful, she struggled to stand. 'I think we should ask Derval to come up now.'

'I'm here!' Derval hastened into the room. Her eyes were swollen and red but she beamed around and said, 'How's our expectant mother doing?'

'A little disconcerted at how quickly things are progressing,' said Bridget, leaning into Cormac for support.

Derval clapped her hands. 'The babby's in a hurry? Right, best get the bed ready.'

Orlaith and Tess leapt up and headed for Bridget and Cormac's bedroom. As Orlaith passed Derval, Bridget heard her say in a low, concerned voice, 'What's upset you?'

'All's fine,' said Derval bracingly and she shooed Orlaith on. She turned back to the others and clapped again. 'Men and children out.'

Emily grumbled with disappointment. Bridget looked at Cormac and was touched to see his reluctance so plain on his face.

'I'll be fine,' she assured him, even as she experienced another sharp twinge. Breath hitching in her throat, she said, 'Derval will take good care of me.'

'I sure will,' said Derval. She made a flapping motion towards Cormac. 'Why don't you head on downstairs to Brian Mór? Maybe he'll take you out for a stroll while you wait.'

Cormac took both of Bridget's hands and kissed them. So quietly that only she would hear, he murmured, 'I love you,' against her knuckles before unwillingly letting go.

Tess stuck her head out the bedroom door. 'Are yous coming or what?' she demanded to Bridget and Derval.

'Come along, *a stór*,' Cormac said and Emily came to his side. 'Tess, keep an eye on the fire, won't you?' he added in a casual manner.

Then he and Emily departed with one final exclamation from the little girl. 'I hope I get a baby sister this time!'

Bridget pressed her palms to her bulging belly, clenching her jaw against the deep ache. No matter whether it was a boy or a girl, all she discerned was the child's sudden rush to meet the world.

'Let's go into the bedroom and take a look at you so,' said Derval and Bridget followed her, a chaotic combination of panic and anticipation bubbling under her skin.

A few minutes later, Derval said, 'Jaysus, you'd better get ready to push...'

***

Stomach tied in knots, Cormac led Emily downstairs and through the Careys' open door. The Carey family had only two rooms: a living space similar to the one upstairs and a single bedroom which they all shared. Derval's husband sat at their small table, pressing his fingertip moodily into a crack on the tabletop. He glanced up at Cormac and Emily's entrance and grunted a greeting.

Emily skipped over to the hearth where Una and Sorcha huddled in a palpable state of distress. In the flood of whispers which passed between them, Cormac was just able to distinguish 'Da's leaving *already*...' and 'I never seen Ma cry like that...'

Rory stood with his back to the closed bedroom door, behind which little Brian was presumably napping. He observed his father with slitted eyes and Cormac perceived a level of condemnation in his gaze far beyond his ten years.

An agonised cry burst out overhead. Cormac flinched.

'Arrah, don't worry about it, man.' Brian Mór, the senior Brian of the family, let out a humourless chuckle. 'I've lived through a few of these now. There's always a touch of playacting in it.' He sat back with folded arms. 'They do love the attention.'

A quiet voice cut across the room. 'You weren't here when Sorcha or Brian was born.'

Nettled, Brian Mór wouldn't look at his son. Instead, he jerked his head at Cormac. 'Want to go for a beer? I know a place that'll be open even though it's Sunday. The lad'll keep an eye on the tots.'

Cormac supposed that if he were in Ireland his friend Liam might have taken him to the drinking house. The closest he had to a friend in Boston was O'Mali but, even if he knew where O'Mali lived, he wouldn't seek him out. His gut told him to stay right where he was, particularly when another loud cry came from above.

'Thank you,' he said politely to Brian Mór, 'but I'd rather wait here, just in case...'

The other man shrugged. 'Suit yourself. I'm going anyway.'

He stood and headed for the door, where he ran smack into Orlaith who had just come bounding down the stairs.

'Ah, thank God you're still here,' she said breathlessly to Cormac, ignoring Brian Mór who uttered a mild oath and stamped away into the hallway and out of the building. 'Derval said don't go anywhere. She's never seen such a quick labour in her life.'

Offering no further details, Orlaith vanished upstairs again. Cormac took Brian Mór's vacated seat and ran his fingers through his hair. Was this a good or a bad thing? Might it mean less pain for Bridget? Or could a speedy delivery cause complications, possibly for both mother and child? Not knowing was a torment of its own kind.

The three girls were still clustered around the hearth. Emily was saying, 'I wish I had brought Mabel down with me. She would give you such a big hug to make you feel better...'

Rory sidled over to the table and sat on the opposite side of it to Cormac. He didn't speak and Cormac didn't know what to say to such a grave-looking child. The silence between them accentuated the sounds of turmoil drifting down through the ceiling.

Then Cormac's heart stopped. The sounds had changed. The cries were no longer Bridget's – they were the cries of a newborn. His heart started beating again, so rapidly he thought it might burst from his chest. Was Bridget safe? Was the infant healthy?

He was glad when he heard Orlaith's steps thumping down the stairs again because he didn't think he could wait in the dark one moment more. He was already on his feet when she rushed into the room, her face shining and her round eyes wet with emotion.

'Go on up,' she managed to say and Emily let out a squeal.

Cormac mounted the stairs two at a time, his pulse thrumming in his ears. As he hastened through the doorway, Tess was coming out of the front bedroom, a bloody sheet balled up in her hands.

'Congratulations,' she said, giving him a smile that didn't quite reach her eyes.

He crossed the room with quick strides, hardly able to breathe. Pausing at the bedroom's threshold, he stared in to see a weeping Bridget sitting up in their bed. Derval was placing a small bundle into her arms. She glanced over her shoulder and caught sight of Cormac.

'Well now, here's the da himself. Come over here and meet your babby. You have a beautiful boy.'

***

When Bridget woke up, it was dark but an unseen source of light flickered along the bedroom wall and ceiling. Mindful of the various aches in her body, she twisted cautiously to look over the edge of the bed. The baby basket was empty. Alarm shot through her but then she heard a whisper.

'He's here.'

She looked towards the corner of the room. Cormac had brought the stool in and was sitting there, a candle at his feet and their son cradled in his arms.

Bridget pushed back the covers and gingerly got out of bed. Derval had informed her that there had been some slight tearing which would take a few weeks to heal but, thankfully, the tremors at least had passed. The shock of the swift birth had left her trembling and emotional for several hours afterwards and she had embraced her new baby almost in a daze. Now, in the middle of the night, she felt more alert and ready to drink in every miniature, exquisite detail of him.

As she approached the corner, Cormac kept one arm securely around their son while he used the other to wipe across his face.

'How long have I been asleep?' Bridget murmured, touching a knuckle to his cheek where a little wetness still glistened.

'Only about an hour and half,' he said, his voice thick. 'I don't think he needs feeding just yet.'

He opened his embrace to her and she slid onto his lap, finding a position that would not aggravate her sore parts too much. As she rested back against his chest with his arm around her still-expanded waist, he tucked the wrapped bundle into his other elbow with infinite gentleness. Their son's small face peeped out; he was fast asleep.

Cormac laid his temple against Bridget's shoulder and they sat there for an immeasurable time, simply staring at their extraordinary marvel. She felt full to the brim with joy at being able to share this experience with him. He had never had this with Emily.

When he eventually spoke, his words were laden with a quiet, fierce conviction. 'I swear to you I will do absolutely anything for him. Seeing him so vulnerable like this, knowing that he's depending on us...' She felt the rumble of his emotion against her back. 'Him and Emily both. I will do whatever it takes to keep them safe, even if I have to go to the ends of the earth to do it.'

'Me too,' she said softly. There was nothing she would not do, no crime she would not commit to protect her children.

He bent and pressed his lips to their son's smooth forehead. 'We're here for you, *a mhac*. We promise. Always.'

'Son' was what Cormac's mother used to call him in their Irish tongue, and now he was passing it on to the next generation. Bridget thought of Maggie and how happy she would have been to hold her grandchild.

For a moment, she allowed herself to stray into a wonderful fantasy where she and Cormac entered the McGoverns' cottage back on the Oakleigh Estate and the whole family was there to greet their new baby. The faces of those they had lost swam before Bridget's vision. She pictured Maggie fussing over the boy, sprinkling him with holy water and drowning him in kisses. She imagined Patrick giving Cormac a brotherly nudge of congratulations while their sister Margaret gazed starry-eyed at the endearing creature that had stemmed from Bridget and Cormac's true love. Mary might seem jealous at all the attention they were receiving but then she would probably engulf Cormac in a bone-breaking hug. And Cormac's father, Jack, would clap him on the shoulder, looking as proud as could be of his son's achievements. Bridget knew she had Jack to thank for the earnestness of Cormac's commitment to her for he had grown up witnessing an exceptional example of marital love in his father's sincere devotion to his mother. Theirs had been a special bond, neither radical nor showy, but deep and constant like the base of a mountain.

Heart grieving for the beloved people who had departed too soon from their lives, Bridget sensed their presence all around them in this humble bedroom in Boston.

She placed a tender hand on the bundle. 'Shall we name him Jack?' she murmured.

Cormac's gaze connected with hers and she perceived the way his blue eyes turned hazy with memory. 'Let's do that,' he said and looked down again. 'Welcome to the world, Jack.'

Almost as though their son had heard him, Jack stirred. His face puckered and a fretful whimper escaped his tiny mouth.

'I'd better get ready to feed him,' said Bridget, and she slipped off Cormac's knee with a quiet moan at the painful movement.

As she crossed back to the bed, slid under the covers and set her pillow upright to lie back against it, Jack's whimper turned into a shriek of dissatisfaction. Cormac stood and held the boy to his chest, swaying from side to side. He spoke soothingly to him but Bridget couldn't hear what he said as the shrieks grew louder.

All of a sudden, Emily's head popped up from the other side of the bed, her fair hair in disarray.

'He's crying *again*?' she said.

'You cried a lot too when you were a baby, gooseberry,' Bridget said, accepting Jack carefully from Cormac. 'Try to go back to sleep.'

'I can't,' said Emily petulantly. 'Mabel and I are awake now.'

'Well then, how about a story to help you nod off again?' said Cormac.

The little girl's eyes brightened. 'Oh, yes, please!'

Cormac went around to his side of the bed and propped up his pillow like Bridget's. Pulling back the bedcovers, he reclined against the pillow and Emily climbed up, lying alongside him with one arm and one leg thrown across his torso and thigh. He tugged the covers up over them and she positioned Mabel above his midriff, erect with avid attention. As Bridget adjusted her nightdress and encouraged Jack to latch on to her breast, Cormac began to talk in a low, mellifluous voice.

He described the Irish legend of Tír na nÓg, the land of the young, where the trees and flowers always bloomed and the people never grew old. Stroking Emily's golden curls, he recounted the love story of Oisín and Niamh who travelled to Tír na nÓg on a magical horse, but luckily Emily dozed off which meant he could stop before the tale reached its tragic conclusion. Bridget was glad; it was kinder to let the girl believe it had a happy ending.

Bridget gulped back the tightness in her throat as she remembered Maggie and Jack McGovern, Mary, Patrick and Margaret, all frozen in time, never aging. There had been no happy endings for them. She cupped her little boy's head as he suckled and prayed for good fortune for the next generation of McGoverns.

CHAPTER 9

Yawning, Bridget stirred the iron pot over the fire. Orlaith was the most skilled cook of them all, having been trained in assorted kitchen activities while working as a scullery maid at Anner House, but this evening she was off with Tess and Derval, assisting in the delivery of old Mrs Kane's newest grandniece or grandnephew. It was the third birth on Broad Street in as many weeks, so not only were Orlaith and Tess gaining plenty of midwife experience but Jack had quickly lost the mantle of being the youngest inhabitant on the street.

'You're still a very special boy though,' Bridget cooed towards the baby basket sitting on top of the table. 'Despite your best efforts to keep your mama awake at night.'

Even as she yawned again, she knew she was very lucky. He might wake frequently but he always fell back asleep after feeding, and he didn't make much of a fuss when he soiled himself, lying placidly while she cleaned him. He hadn't even cried when Father Whitty had poured the baptismal water over his head.

'You're every parent's dream, my little lamb,' she said, leaving the stirabout in the pot to lean over the basket and plant a kiss on his nose.

Emily traipsed in from the landing, dragging a broom.

'I've swept the stairs,' she announced. 'And I promise not to leave it until the daylight's nearly gone next time. May I go up to Mr Lorenzo now?'

'What on earth for?' asked Bridget, still peeking into the basket. Jack's fingers were rooting in his mouth and his little body wriggled about beneath his blanket – the child was like clockwork.

'He *told* you, don't you remember?' Emily stood the broom up against the wall next to the fireplace. 'When you met him in the hallway yesterday. He promised to make a cloak for Mabel so she wouldn't be cold.'

'Oh, yes, I remember now,' said Bridget, pushing aside the blanket and lifting Jack out of the basket. She sat on the sofa and untied the slit she had sewn into her bodice.

'Mama?' Emily prodded.

Bridget winced at the first pinching sensation and tried to coax Jack into a better position. 'Hmm?'

'May I go up now?'

'Not just yet. I need you to watch the supper while I feed your brother.'

Crestfallen, Emily picked up the wooden spoon and gave the contents of the pot a half-hearted stir.

'Make sure you do it correctly, gooseberry. The spoon has to touch the bottom so the stirabout doesn't stick.' Bridget smiled down at Jack as his tiny hand fluttered to rest on her breast.

The door opened wide. 'Is that my big girl making the supper for everyone?'

'Papa!' Emily squealed and dropped the spoon into the pot to run towards Cormac.

Even though she was only a few months from her eighth birthday and growing fast, he swung her up into his arms like she weighed no more than Jack. Long gone was the exhaustion that had suffused his body each evening after coming back from the docks. He had acclimatised to the demanding physical labour and was now fitter and leaner than he had ever been. Bridget cast him a sidelong, admiring glance. While he had acquired a sturdy build during his years working as a stable hand, and had developed a well-nourished physique living the privileged lifestyle of Oliver Davenport, now she observed his figure with an altogether new level of appreciation. She felt rather hideous in comparison, given her unattractive excess weight – until his gaze landed upon her nursing Jack and his adoration could not have been more palpable.

Arms around his neck, Emily asked, 'Papa, will you stir the pot so I can go upstairs to get Mabel's cloak from Mr Lorenzo?'

Wisely, he answered, 'That depends on what your mama says.'

From her perch on his hip, Emily peeped over at Bridget. 'Please, Mama?'

Bridget nodded. 'Very well, but don't dally. Mr Lorenzo surely has better things to be doing.'

Emily cheered, slid down to the floor and bolted out the door.

'The poor, persecuted man,' said Bridget.

'To be honest, I don't think he minds,' said Cormac. 'He left behind half a dozen grandchildren in Italy and I do believe he misses them a great deal.' He glanced around. 'Orlaith and Tess?'

'Up at the Kanes' with Derval since about noon.'

He had known they were only waiting to be called upon to assist in the birth so he didn't question this. He took a seat on the sofa, kissed Bridget's cheek and put a gentle palm on Jack's crown. 'And how's our boy doing today?'

'He's been an angel as usual, bless him. Although I caught him looking at me in a particular way today that has me convinced he takes after you.'

'Really? How did he look?'

'It was an expression of pure devilment.'

Cormac's face broke into a mischievous grin.

'Yes, exactly like that. Of course, he might have just been blinking.' She gave Cormac a playful nudge. 'Please do check the pot. I don't want it to burn.'

'I will, but first...' He reached inside his coat and withdrew a couple of letters. 'I collected these at the post office on my way home.'

She let out a gasp of delight. He handed them to her before getting up to fish the spoon out of the pot, stir it and inspect the fire below. The two pieces of correspondence turned out to be a letter for Cormac and a packet addressed to her. Keeping a firm hold on Jack, she fumbled one-handed with the packet until Cormac set down the spoon and came to her aid, opening it for her and revealing the four letters which lay within.

'Good gracious, how marvellous,' she said, even as her heart sank when she recognised the handwriting on two of them.

'Do we know when to expect Orlaith and Tess?' Cormac asked. 'Shall we wait for them to eat?'

'It's hard to tell, but Derval said it's the mother's sixth time giving birth so the baby might arrive quickly enough. Possibly not as quickly as you, my lamb,' she added fondly to Jack. His eyes – would they retain Cormac's shade of blue or might they darken to Bridget's dark brown? – stared steadily up at her as he suckled.

'Let's delay for a little while so.' Cormac moved the pot out of the direct heat of the fire, took off his coat, and rejoined her on the sofa. 'Is there enough light to read by?'

She angled a letter towards the glow from the hearth. 'I think so. Perhaps we might get these two out of the way first. They're from Garrett.'

He had addressed both letters to 'The Right Hon. The Viscountess Wyndham'. It came as no surprise to her at all that he would use her full title, a deliberate and spiteful reminder of who she was really married to.

Cormac broke the seals on the letters for her and she checked the dates on each one. 'They're only three days apart,' she said, mystified. She began to read the one with the older date. 'Oh, for heaven's sake,' she burst out a few moments later. 'The man is insufferable.'

'What does he say?' Cormac asked, frowning.

'Allow me to read it to you.' Affecting a pompous accent, she carried on, '"Madam. It is with the greatest attempt at restraint that I write to you to express my displeasure at your most outrageous conduct. I cannot comprehend the breadth of your arrogance that you would presume to take upon yourself the management of the Oakleigh Estate, a property which is legally *mine*"' – she tilted the page to show Cormac that Garrett had underlined 'mine' three times – '"and which you have no right to administer, either by your own hand or through your proposed third parties. Furthermore, that you should write such a missive and leave no capacity for me to respond is inconceivable."' She paused. 'He must mean my previous letter which I wrote from my uncle's before we left Dublin.' She had instructed Lord Walcott's footman, Simon, to wait at least a month before putting it in the post, ensuring that by the time it arrived in London they would be far across the ocean and well beyond Garrett's reach. 'Hmm,' she said, 'perhaps that was a touch thoughtless of me.'

'He didn't deserve any more consideration than what he received,' said Cormac flatly.

She returned her gaze to the page. '"Having reflected upon your deception at great length, I was contemplating the course of action that would be most beneficial to me when I received today your second communication which you have sent from your undisclosed location on the American continent. While the Earl of Bewley had intimated to me upon his return from Ireland that you intended to travel west, I am astounded that you would conceal your whereabouts and impose the stipulation of corresponding through an intermediary channel. It is wholly beneath me to write to a mere steward in order to convey my sentiments to you. And those sentiments, madam, are fervent and aggrieved indeed." My goodness, he tore a hole in the paper just here.'

Cormac snorted. 'He's always had a fine talent for portraying himself as the injured party.'

Sensing Cormac's mounting resentment, Bridget decided to summarise the rest. 'Let's see..."shall not be tolerated"..."address this abominable situation forthwith"...Oh, no.' She read the final lines with dismay. 'He intends to expose our fraud to Webb & Brereton Solicitors and dismantle our arrangement with Mr Enright and Mr Corbett.'

Cormac looked utterly unsurprised. 'That was always a risk. And if he took immediate action, then any directive sent by him to the solicitors has already reached Ireland long before this letter got to us.'

'How can he be so short-sighted? It's such childish retaliation.' She shook her head. 'I scarcely wish to read his other letter if it will contain more of the same vitriol.'

Jack chose that moment to pull off her breast, his little face calm and content. She offered him to Cormac, who took him and held him against his shoulder, patting and rubbing his back, while she retied the slit in her bodice.

'I shall prepare myself for the worst,' she said, picking up Garrett's second letter with apprehension. She unfolded the page, scanned it, and said, 'Well, that wasn't what I was expecting.'

Cormac arched an eyebrow at her over Jack's head.

'It's an apology,' she said. 'Listen to this. "Permit me to express my regret for the violence of my language in the letter preceding this. I would have retrieved it if I could for I sent it in too much haste without pausing to consider my rash words. I have since taken time to dwell further upon your actions and can now begin to acknowledge the wisdom in them." First it was arrogance, and now it is wisdom!'

Jack spat up on Cormac's shoulder. 'My thoughts precisely, *a mhac*,' Cormac said, rising and fetching a clean rag from the cupboard to wipe the boy's chin and his own shirt.

Suppressing a laugh, Bridget continued to read. '"I concede that, given your deep connection to Oakleigh, you are the one best placed to repair the deplorable damage your mother caused to the estate." I infer that to mean he has come to realise it is a headache he would rather do without. "I have therefore decided not to overturn the contract you had drawn up by Webb & Brereton, despite the reprehensible duplicity perpetrated by the man in your company."'

The corner of Cormac's mouth twisted down. He had taken no pride in impersonating Garrett but it had been the only way to achieve their purpose.

She hurried on. '"In conclusion, even though Oakleigh still belongs to me, I will allow it to be your plaything but I expect to be fully informed of any significant decisions you make."' Relief washed over her that, in spite of his insults, he had come around to their point of view. She glanced down at the end of the letter. 'Oh, and almost as an afterthought he offers stiff sympathy on the passing of my mother.'

Cormac appeared to have stopped listening. He was laying Jack into his baby basket and tucking the blanket carefully around his small form. But then he said, 'There's something I want you to remember, *a mhac*, and I'll remind you of it again when you're older. No man is entitled to be called a gentleman by virtue of his birth. He has to earn it by his conduct. I fully intend to raise you to possess the manners of a worthy gentleman because if you ever wrote a letter like either of those to a lady I'd have to disown you.'

He touched an affectionate fingertip to the boy's cheek and came back to sit next to Bridget.

'At least he did apologise,' she said tentatively.

'In the most detestable manner possible,' Cormac countered, his tone clipped. 'He is a cad and what's worse is he doesn't even have the self-awareness to see it.' Cormac raised his hands and dropped them into his lap in a resigned gesture. 'Did you notice his reference to Lord Bewley? If they are in correspondence with each other, then the earl will have learned that I managed to escape from Cunningham's clutches. I am once again roaming free, unpunished for the offences I committed against him and Lady Bewley.'

A shiver of unease ran down Bridget's spine. 'But you are an ocean away from him. He cannot possibly exert any influence here in America.'

'No, he can't. However, if we return to Ireland in the future and he gets wind of it...' Cormac sighed. 'I don't relish the idea of constantly peering over my shoulder for the rest of my life.'

She put her hand over his. 'At least there is no need to peer over your shoulder in Boston. We are free here.'

He squeezed her fingers. 'And I thank God every day for it.'

She smiled. 'Shall we open the other letters?'

'Please do. They are guaranteed to be more pleasant than the last.'

She picked up the next letter which turned out to be a brief report from Laurence Enright and John Corbett detailing the work that had been happening on the Oakleigh Estate, including progress on the rebuilding of the manor house and the preparation of the land for the coming spring. They also wrote that Ellen Kirwan had asked if her own correspondence could be included in the packet so Bridget opened the fourth letter in high anticipation.

'Ellen gave birth in September!' she exclaimed. 'She had a girl and—oh!' She turned to Cormac, a lump of joyful astonishment in her throat. 'She and Liam have named her Bridget.'

He grinned. 'What an honour.'

Focusing again on the page, she read on, 'They have taken to calling her Bridie for short and look forward to the day when she can meet her namesake. Gracious, I'm overwhelmed.' She was thrilled with the lovely surprise but her heart hiccupped when she saw Ellen's next question. Happiness leaking away, she said, 'She asks if we have had any luck seeking Bronagh.'

Cormac's shoulders slumped. Their primary reason for coming to Boston was also the least successful part of the life they had started to build here. They had found a home, Cormac had secured employment, and their baby had arrived safely, but they were no step nearer to finding his missing sister. The advertisements which he continued to place regularly in *The Boston Pilot* had not yielded any results. He had enquired about her up and down the length of Broad Street and in nearby areas where other Irish communities lived but so far his search had been fruitless. No one had heard of a young woman called Bronagh McGovern nor recognised his description of her.

'I wish we had better news to offer,' he said glumly.

To divert him, she said, 'Why don't you see who the last letter is from? It's addressed to you.'

He took it from her, opened it and, after a quick perusal, grimaced.

'Well, we can't say we didn't see this coming,' he said. 'It's from Mrs O'Hara. According to her, "Henny" is a dear pet but she has a sickly nature. She's been poorly for months and

Mrs O'Hara doesn't have the wherewithal to pay for the best medicine for her.' He blew out his breath. 'She writes that if I had it in my Christian heart to help the child, she'd be very grateful.'

Bridget crossed her arms over her belly, which had decreased in size but was not quite back to normal. 'That does not come as a shock in the slightest.' Biting the tip of her tongue, she added, 'And I have to confess that part of me doubts the truth of what she says. From our interactions with Henrietta, would you have described her as a "dear pet"?'

Bridget herself certainly wouldn't. Though the girl was undeniably a victim of her circumstances, she had been unwashed and uncommunicative and had pinched Emily when there were no adults watching her. Cormac shook his head in reluctant agreement.

'So Mrs O'Hara might also be lying about Henrietta's ill health to play on your heartstrings,' Bridget said cautiously, striving for pragmatism as well as compassion.

Just then, Emily came pounding into the room, holding a piece of fabric aloft. 'Isn't it just perfect?' she exclaimed.

It appeared that Mr Lorenzo had fashioned a doll's cloak out of a shirt tail and a bootlace, sewing the edges with a remarkably neat hand.

'It's charming,' said Bridget warmly. 'Mabel will be so cosy.'

As Emily ran into the bedroom to dress Mabel in her new garment, Bridget looked back at Cormac, who was gazing pensively after their daughter. She knew him well enough to guess the approximate direction of his thoughts, given that he had purchased the same doll for Henrietta back in Dublin.

Her hunch was confirmed when he said, 'It was Henrietta's birthday on Christmas Day. It might be reasonable to send her a little gift to acknowledge the occasion, and perhaps a small sum of money to ease whatever financial burdens they have.'

She might have asked whether they could really afford it but she could tell his mind was made up.

'Just beware this may be a slippery slope,' she said, her own mind already working to consider ways to earn some more income for their family.

Orlaith and Tess came clattering in, looking weary but exultant.

'All's well,' Orlaith declared. 'Except the baby was huge, far bigger than Jack. The poor woman said she refuses to ever have another one.'

'Wait 'til ye hear this,' said Tess, tittering. 'She thrashed about so much she managed to rip not only her nightdress but the bed sheet too. With six children to be minding, she'll likely need a seamstress to get them mended.'

As she rose to get the supper ready, Bridget thought that coincidence really was an extraordinary thing.

***

Emily swept the stairs, gathering the dirt from one step to the next until she reached the hallway at the bottom. She tried, and failed, not to feel sulky as her mama's laughter drifted down from the room above. Baby Jack had learned how to smile and it delighted Mama every single time he did it.

With brisk, resentful strokes, Emily drove her pile of dirt towards the front door of the building. Baby Jack was special to Papa too – yesterday, she had heard Una and Sorcha's mama, whom she had taken to calling Auntie Derval, say to Auntie Orlaith that she had never seen a father so besotted with a child. A stray bit of gravel bounced away and Emily stamped after it, crossly brushing it back to the pile.

As she emerged outside, she spotted old Mrs Kane coming up the street and paused in her labours. It wouldn't do to accidentally sweep the dirt onto the old woman's skirt and risk the sting from her notoriously sharp tongue.

'Good afternoon, Mrs Kane,' she trilled and dropped into a small curtsey as the old woman tottered past.

Mrs Kane gave her a beady-eyed stare. 'You're a quare child,' she said and shuffled on.

Downcast, Emily finished brushing the dirt out onto the street. As she returned indoors, she decided that a hug from Mabel would make her feel better and she climbed back up the stairs in a hurry.

'All done!' she said to Mama and, propping up the broom next to the hearth, she hastened into the bedroom before she could be given another chore.

She knelt next to Mama and Papa's bed and pulled her mattress out from beneath it; she had left Mabel tucked up asleep when she rose that morning. To her surprise, Mabel wasn't there. Frowning, Emily rifled through her blankets and peeked under the bed but there was no sign of her. She stood, hands on hips, and surveyed the bedroom.

'Where are you?' she said, confused and impatient.

She scurried back out to the other room where her mama sat at the table doing some mending while Baby Jack lay in his basket on the tabletop.

'Mama, have you seen Mabel?'

'Is she not in your bed, gooseberry?' Mama asked as she licked the end of her thread to get it through the eye of her needle.

'No,' said Emily with the first twinge of panic. She marched up to the table and grasped the edge of the basket to peer inside.

'*Gently*, Emily!' her mama said.

Baby Jack gave Emily a gummy smile but he was alone.

She proceeded to check each nook and cranny, from the back of the cupboard to the shadowy corners of her aunties' bedroom. Mama helped, shaking out her and Papa's bedcovers and running her hand underneath the sofa, groaning when her fingers reappeared covered in dust. But Mabel was nowhere to be found. Mama admitted that she had brought Baby Jack downstairs to see Auntie Derval for at least an hour that morning, so anyone could have stolen in during that time.

By bedtime, Emily was hysterical. Although she had scoured every place she could think of and enlisted the help of everybody in the building from the Careys to Mr Lorenzo, their hunt for Mabel was as futile as her papa's search for Auntie Bronagh. Even Papa himself couldn't find Mabel when he came home, which distressed Emily almost more than anything else – hadn't he promised he would always look after her? Surely her precious Mabel's welfare had to be included in that promise.

'I've lost her,' she wailed and, unwilling to go to bed without her dear companion, she sobbed until she wore herself out, eventually falling asleep in the circle of her papa's arms.

The next morning, the frantic search resumed. Red-eyed and puffy-faced, Emily charged up the stairs to the top of the building and knocked on Mr Lorenzo's door.

'May I please check again?' she beseeched.

'Of course, *bambina*,' he said in his strong Italian accent.

He let her in and together they looked beneath every piece of furniture in his tiny room, his spine creaking as he bent to peer under the armchair where he had sat while she watched him finish stitching Mabel's cloak.

'She's definitely not here,' Emily said, sniffing. 'Thank you for helping, Mr Lorenzo.'

She trudged back down the stairs, feet heavy with sorrow. As she reached the landing outside her own family's rooms, a figure with prominent ears was ascending the flight of stairs from the ground floor. It was Rory Carey.

And Mabel was clutched in his grasp, his fingers holding her loosely by the neck.

A wave of euphoria washed over her, but it was displaced almost at once by outrage. 'You!' she exclaimed, her skin hot with fury.

She hurtled down the stairs to meet him halfway. Snatching Mabel from him, she pressed her cherished little body close to her chest.

'How dare you take her?' she demanded.

'I was bringing her back to you,' he protested in indignation.

'Did you think it was a joke? Kidnapping is a crime. You are a criminal!' Recalling one of Auntie Tess's choicer phrases, she said, 'In fact, you are a lousy sod!'

Mama appeared on the landing. 'What is this racket about?'

Emily levelled an accusing finger in Rory's direction. '*He* took Mabel!'

And without waiting for any further explanation, she rushed up the stairs and through the door past Mama, a powerful loathing ignited deep in her bones.

CHAPTER 10

Bridget blew out her cheeks as she darned a shirt sleeve at the table, recalling the days when she would have waved a pretty fan to relieve her discomfort. All the windows and doors were wide open, including the door onto the landing, but the June heat sat heavy and still in the air. The unconquerable Boston summer had returned.

'Bridget, how do you pronounce D-E-A-R-T-H?' asked Orlaith.

'Dearth,' she replied. 'Think of it as rhyming with earth. It means scarcity or famine.'

Orlaith and Tess sat on the sofa, heads bent over the Bible, picking out words they recognised and stringing sentences together where they could. Whereas Orlaith had turned into a diligent pupil, quick to grasp the basics and eager to improve, Tess had flagged once learning to read proved to be a tougher challenge than she had expected. She kept trying but grew dour in their lessons when she failed to keep pace with Orlaith. Now, while Orlaith murmured the word 'dearth' several times over, Tess heaved a sigh of boredom and glanced idly towards the doorway, as though waiting for someone to walk through it.

Bridget enjoyed teaching so much that she thought she might have been well suited to become a governess. However, even though the income would have been advantageous, such a position required the candidate to be unmarried and to live in the family's household, and she could meet neither of these conditions. Instead, she had explored the idea of teaching local children how to read, but the inhabitants of Broad Street could see no benefit to it.

'Reading won't get them a job in a mill or a factory,' Mrs Kane's nephew Donie, a joiner by trade, had said dismissively.

So Orlaith and Tess remained Bridget's only pupils apart from regular encouragement to Emily to practise her writing and sums and some casual instruction on the alphabet to the Carey brood. Rory seemed the most interested but he avoided coming up to the McGoverns' rooms as much as possible, lest Emily spear him with her wrathful gaze.

Even though her tutoring had not developed into a lucrative venture, Bridget had managed to pick up pennies here and there thanks to her needlework. Most of the women in the neighbourhood either couldn't afford to send out their darning or had enough competency to do a rudimentary job themselves, but now and then they sought a helping hand and praised her exceptional skills. All those tedious hours learning embroidery as a sullen girl were finally paying off in their own small way.

Her current labour, however, was a shirt belonging to Cormac. He had ripped his sleeve the previous week during an incident at the docks which had left a gouge in his forearm two inches long, though he had been vague on the exact details. Orlaith, keen to explore beyond midwifery, had cleaned and bandaged the cut under the supervision of Tess who had some experience in this area, for she had tended Cormac's pistol wound on the very same arm when he had been shot in the Dublin alleyway. 'You need to take better care of yourself,' Tess had told him, tapping his shoulder with joking reproof as Orlaith had tied the bandage with a triumphant flourish.

Bridget, now bending over her darning and appraising the severity of the jagged tear in the fabric, resolved to reiterate the same caution to Cormac when he came home later.

He had set off after Mass earlier that day to make further enquiries about Bronagh. It was how he spent many of his Sundays, but Bridget noticed that he was heading out with less optimism as time went on. She understood his frustration, particularly as they could well be chasing a dead end if Bronagh had never travelled to Boston in the first place, and yet Bridget didn't regret their decision to come to America. Although they lived in reduced circumstances and she missed Ireland very much, she believed she had never been happier in her life.

Jack burbled near her feet, wearing nothing but a clout on this hot day. At five and a half months, he had mastered the knack of rolling from his stomach to his back and now lay on the floor merrily gurgling up at her. He hadn't succeeded in rolling back onto his stomach just yet but she was positive that it would not be long before he accomplished that too. She adored witnessing those moments of discovery and growth, treasuring each milestone all the more because she had never beheld her beloved James reaching the same small, wonderful achievements.

She bent over to tickle Jack's toes and a complaint rose from the other side of the table.

'Mama! I was in the middle of drawing your ears.'

Bridget straightened and Emily gave a satisfied nod, returning to her work. Using the new pencil she had received the previous month for her eighth birthday, she screwed her mouth up in concentration and made some adjustments to Bridget's ears on her sheet of paper.

'I've got another name for your collection, Emily,' said Orlaith. She held the Bible up closer to her face and read slowly, 'Bar...nab...as. Barnabas.'

Emily looked up. 'I like that one!'

'Collection?' repeated Bridget.

'Auntie Orlaith is gathering the best names from the Bible for me,' Emily said brightly. 'In case I can get hens in the future.'

She bent back over her drawing with renewed focus so she missed Bridget's guilty expression.

'D'yous hear that?' Tess said suddenly, tilting her head.

'Hear what?' asked Orlaith, turning a page of the Bible.

'Sounds like shouting to me,' said Tess, her brow puckered.

Bridget cocked her ear too, while leaving it in full view of the portraitist. An indistinct din floated up from the street through the open window.

'I think Derval mentioned there'd be a funeral procession coming down the street today,' said Orlaith.

Bridget frowned. 'They're being quite rowdy for a funeral.' She glanced down and exclaimed with pleasure, 'Oh, good boy!'

Jack had rolled back onto his stomach for the first time. She scooped him up to reward him with a hug. As she pressed her lips to his sweet-smelling crown, the commotion from outside grew even louder, becoming a cacophony of bellows and thuds.

'What on earth is going on out there?' said Tess, baffled. She hopped off the sofa and darted into the front bedroom. 'Jaysus, Mary and Joseph!' came her startled cry moments later.

Full of alarm, Bridget stood with Jack clutched to her chest and hastened into the bedroom. Orlaith followed her, the Bible still in her hand. They gathered around the open window.

'God Almighty,' Orlaith said and made the sign of the cross.

Bridget gaped at the shocking scene below. Dozens of men, hundreds perhaps, had flooded the street and were fighting each other, yelling and throwing punches and bricks. Those who fell were trampled underfoot and cudgels swung without mercy at unguarded skulls, ribs and knees. Even as they watched, more men poured in from all sides to join the fray and others lined the footpaths, cheering and jeering in a dissonant medley of Irish and American accents.

'I want to see,' Emily's voice piped up from behind them and she tried to squeeze between Bridget's and Orlaith's hips.

Bridget held her back. 'No, stay away from the window,' she said, panic rising in her throat. 'Please close it, Tess, will you?'

Tess pushed down on the sash window, forcing it shut with a groan from its warped frame. It diminished the uproar from below only slightly. She flicked her red hair over her shoulders and pressed her forehead to the window pane.

'Christ,' she said, 'there's Donie Kane giving a fella a right wallop over the head, whoever he is.'

Then they heard the smash of breaking glass.

Orlaith gasped. 'That sounded like it was downstairs!'

She dashed away from the window and out of the bedroom.

'Wait!' Bridget cried after her.

Her shout gave Jack a fright and he started to whimper in her arms. 'Hush, hush, my lamb,' she said anxiously as she towed Emily by the wrist back into the other room. There was no sign of Orlaith. Tess strode past, heading for the door.

'I'll go get her,' she called over her shoulder and she too disappeared.

Bridget stifled her moan of consternation; she couldn't let Emily sense the extent of her fear. She hurried over to the window above the cupboard and closed it even though it didn't face out onto the main street. Bouncing Jack lightly on her hip, she tried to stay calm as visions of what might be happening downstairs bloomed in her mind. The air was sweltering inside the room but sweat of a totally different kind ran down her spine.

'What's going on, Mama?' Emily asked in a very tiny voice.

Bridget wrapped her free arm around her daughter. 'There's just a little argument outside, that's all. It's nothing to worry about.'

Emily's face crumpled with unshed tears. 'I wish Papa were here.'

Bridget's teeth clamped down on the tip of her tongue. 'I know, gooseberry. But he's out looking for Auntie Bronagh and I'm not sure how long he'll be.'

A sudden shriek came from below, followed by scuffling noises and a bang. Heart in her mouth, Bridget hugged her children close and steeled herself to go to any lengths necessary to shield them from harm. She scanned the room and her gaze alighted on the poker next to the unlit hearth. Extricating herself from Emily, she shot over to the fireplace and grabbed the poker.

That was when she heard footsteps sprinting up the stairs. She dashed back to Emily and thrust Jack into her arms.

'Go into your aunties' bedroom and shut the door. Don't open it unless I say so!'

Eyes wide, Emily scurried into Orlaith and Tess's bedroom and slammed the door behind her and Jack. Bridget turned towards the door to the hallway, holding her breath and gripping the poker tightly. The thumping feet reached the landing and came racing into the room.

It was Tess carrying little Brian Carey. Bridget released her breath.

'The others are coming now!' Tess gasped.

More footsteps pounded on the stairs and Rory appeared clutching the hands of Una and Sorcha, both of whom were wailing and sobbing. Hard on their heels came Orlaith supporting Derval, who had several cuts on her cheek.

Orlaith's Bible was tucked into her armpit. Pitching it onto the table with a heavy thud, she said urgently, 'We need to block the door.' A distant Italian expletive caught her attention and she ducked back out onto the landing. 'Stay in your room, Mr Lorenzo,' she shouted up the stairs. 'Jam your door closed whatever way you can.'

She barrelled back into the room and flung the door shut behind her, looking around wildly.

'The sofa!' said Bridget.

She dropped the poker on top of the cupboard and darted over to the sofa. Orlaith and Rory joined her and together they pushed and heaved the sofa across the floor, shoving it up against the door. Tess threw the bench onto it for good measure.

'It'll have to do,' said Orlaith. 'I hope it's enough to keep them out.'

Bridget hurried to Orlaith and Tess's bedroom to retrieve Emily and Jack. By now, all the children were crying apart from Rory, who was valiantly putting on a brave face despite the terror in his green eyes. He took hold of his mother's elbow and guided her to the stool at the table, where Bridget's darning and Emily's sketch lay abandoned.

'Are you badly hurt?' Bridget asked her.

Derval's hand shook as she reached up to touch the scratches on her cheek. 'No, I'm grand. I was standing near the window so a few shards grazed me when it smashed. Jaysus, I'm lucky. An inch higher and I might've lost my eye.' Her voice trembled. She stretched out an arm to Brian. 'Come here, my baby boy.'

Tess handed him over and he buried his blubbering face in his mother's bosom.

Even with the bawling children, Bridget could still hear the clamour of the brawl outside. 'What happened down below?'

Stroking Brian's hair, Derval said, 'We were gathering the youngsters to go upstairs when a strange man barged right through the door. I swear I never screamed so loud in my life.'

'Da would've kicked him out if he'd been home,' snivelled Una, her nose running.

Derval hid her grimace poorly; Brian Mór hadn't been back to Broad Street since he left after New Year's Day.

'Orlaith took care of him though,' Tess said, making an effort to grin. 'Whacked him across the head with her Bible so hard he knocked over the table in his rush to get away.'

Her grin vanished as a blood-curdling cheer rose above the rest of the racket. She stalked into the front bedroom, pursued by a warning from Orlaith to be careful, and returned with a scowl.

'They're throwing people's things into the street. Breaking furniture and ripping clothes. Rotten bastards.'

For once, Bridget didn't worry about Tess's use of bad language in front of the children. Wiping Emily's tear-streaked face with her thumb while holding Jack so fiercely she thought she might never let him go, she asked, 'What in God's name is this all about?'

Derval shrugged. 'Who knows? Some fella probably looked sideways at another and he saw it as an insult. It doesn't take much to spark them off.' She gingerly felt the cuts below her eye again; a bead of blood showed on her fingertip. ''Tisn't the first ruckus we've seen around here. There are always local Protestants itching for a fight with us immigrant Catholics, or the other way 'round. Sure, they drove the nuns out of the city altogether. Did ye hear about the Ursuline Convent in Charlestown?'

'No,' said Orlaith, hovering near the blocked door to listen out for trespassers.

'Must be nearly three years ago, I suppose. The convent had a school for girls where the nuns taught Protestants as well as Catholics. Rumour got out that a woman was being held there against her will. A Protestant mob showed up and ransacked

the place, and the nuns and pupils had to escape out the back.'
Derval's voice grew fainter as though she didn't want to divulge
the rest. 'The mob burned the convent down.'

In the ensuing silence, the noise from the melee outside
intruded louder than ever.

CHAPTER 11

Cormac plodded towards home, a dejected feeling in the pit of his stomach; his day's efforts had been as unsuccessful as all the previous Sundays. He had visited several boarding houses which held a reputation for accommodating newcomers to the city, identifying the ones most open to providing lodgings to Irish foreigners. None of them had recognised Bronagh's description or found a record of her name in their books.

There were so many uncertain aspects to his search for his sister, not least her name itself. The information supplied by the Cork Harbour Commissioners had listed the passenger name on the ticket as Bronagh McGovern. But what if, seeking a completely fresh start in this new country, she had decided to change her name upon arrival? Furthermore, there had been a second ticket with an illegible name – what if her companion had been a man and she had since married him? Her surname could be anything under the sun.

This theory had an additional knock-on effect: some boarding houses were female-only while others accepted both male and female guests. Cormac had been obliged to include both kinds in his search as he couldn't rule out either one. While his brotherly instinct made him instantly dislike this unknown and possibly nonexistent man, he had to admit that Bronagh would probably have had an easier time if she was under a male's protection rather than one of a pair of women travelling alone.

Orlaith, who sometimes accompanied him, had cautiously aired an unwelcome thought at the end of their last fruitless excursion: what if Bronagh did not want to be found? Could she have seen their notice in *The Pilot* and purposely not acted upon it? Perhaps her old life in Carlow and her miserable existence in Dublin were wretched memories which she preferred to keep locked away in the past. Cormac didn't want to entertain the idea that they might have left their beloved Ireland and crossed the ocean for no reason at all.

As he yearned for the smell of fresh turf rather than the stench of the city gutters, his attention caught on the sound of a disturbance somewhere up ahead. He tried to ascertain the location and the nature of it – was it a fight of some kind? Two women came running along the street in his direction; one was carrying a pot and a framed picture of the Sacred Heart of Jesus, while the other's arms were full of bedding. Both had tears streaming down their cheeks.

'Sons of bitches,' one wailed and the other concurred with even more offensive slurs.

They passed him by, furious curses floating in their wake. He kept walking, frowning in puzzlement. Reaching the next corner, he noticed the tumult growing louder and angrier and, now that he was so close to home, he realised with a jolt that it was coming from the general vicinity of Broad Street itself. Suddenly fearful, he quickened his stride until he was sprinting.

As he neared Broad Street, he came upon the source of the noise: men were swarming the area, spilling out from Broad Street in huge numbers. They struck each other with stones and sticks and fists, snarling and roaring obscenities. Any man who fell to the ground was beaten where he lay. More women fled from the scene, some dragging howling children by their wrists.

Cormac skidded to a halt, pressing himself back against the wall of a house as two men tore past chasing a third.

'We're gonna get you!' one screamed.

'You and all the papist Paddies!' his cohort cried.

'Have to catch me first,' hollered the third fellow. Without slowing, he turned and raised both of his middle fingers at his pursuers. 'Yankee Prods!'

Cackling, he spun about and raced away. As the two men pounded after him, spitting oaths, Cormac ran onwards until he reached the top of Broad Street where he looked around frantically. Brawling men thronged the centre of the street, while others goaded them on from the sides. An abandoned horse-drawn fire wagon stood at the corner, the horses shivering and flaring their nostrils at the commotion around them. The sound of shattering glass came from a house close by; a couple of men tossed belongings through a broken window out into the street, their faces leering within the window frame.

A powerful terror gripped him. Where was his family in the midst of all this? Were they safe, or had their building been ransacked too? Dread coiled in his gut. He needed to get to them without delay.

He scanned the crush of people for any trace of a clear path through. Further ahead between the writhing bodies he espied a mound of broken furniture piled in the middle of the street. The intention might have been to make it into a bonfire but whoever had built the structure must have since been diverted back into the affray for no one tended it now. It could serve as a point of shelter as he forged his way through the skirmish. Hunching his shoulders, Cormac darted in its direction, dodging around a pair of men wrestling for control over a long knife. One of them wrenched it from the other's grip and thrust it out wildly; his adversary stumbled backwards and disappeared into the crowd.

'Get back here, you Irish coward,' yelled the man wielding the knife and he pushed Cormac out of his way as he dove after his prey.

Cormac lurched into the back of another fellow who was so muscled it felt like falling against a brick wall. The man swivelled about in rage, hefting a cudgel as thick as a table leg. Cormac put up his hands in a placating gesture but the frenzy had contorted the man's expression into something feral.

'Fire Engine Company 9!' he bellowed like a battle cry and swung his cudgel around.

Cormac ducked and it whipped over his head, missing him by barely an inch; if it had connected, it would probably have cracked his skull. Still crouching, he turned tail and darted away – maybe he was just another Irish coward but he had no weapon with which to defend himself. As he wove between the fighting men, he heard a roar behind him and glanced over his shoulder. The fellow with the cudgel was pursuing him, his face red with fury.

Alarmed, Cormac picked up his pace, running headlong for the mound of furniture. Perhaps there would be some broken piece of wood he could use to resist the cudgel. As he drew nearer, he could see that the architects had begun with a solid foundation of a table sitting on a bed frame, but the structure grew more unstable as it gained height and became a jumble of chairs and stools balanced precariously on top of each other.

He had almost reached it when a growl of triumph resounded in his ears. He chanced another fleeting look and realised the man was right on his heels. He had no time to veer or duck; the fellow struck him hard across his shoulder blades with the cudgel and Cormac fell forwards with a yell, crashing into the stack of furniture.

The tower of chairs and stools teetered and then began to topple. The other man barely had time to look up before a stool hit him squarely on the forehead and he crumpled. Cormac, at ground level, had an extra second or two to scramble out of the way but he didn't escape unscathed – one of the falling chairs smashed on the ground and rebounded with force against his arm. It was the same limb he had injured the previous week at the docks when a hook he was using to lower cargo into a ship's hold had snapped free and sliced his forearm. Grimacing, he felt a warm stickiness inside his shirt sleeve and knew the wound had opened again.

Struggling to his feet, he surveyed the wreckage. His assailant lay collapsed in a heap with bits of broken wood all about him; the stool had knocked him out. Cormac groped through the debris and fished out the man's thick cudgel. He weighed it in his hands.

'Thanks,' he said to the man's prone form.

He skulked around to the far side of the pile of furniture and hunkered down to assess the way ahead. To his confusion, everywhere seemed coated in white. Disorientated, he blinked and looked again. Feathers. They swirled in the air, drifted along the ground, alighted on the men's hair and shoulders, and accumulated in heaps against doorsteps and ankles. A raucous cry of laughter drew his attention to a group ripping up a featherbed and flinging its contents in all directions. Though he had no idea who had started this riot or why, anger burned in him that they were being so ruthless with people's precious belongings. Folk around here had little enough as it was.

A cry of an altogether more panicked sort reached his ears. He squinted through the storm of feathers and spotted Donie Kane, blood trickling down his temple, backing away from two fellows who were approaching him from either side. As Cormac watched, one of them lunged forwards and grabbed Donie, twisting his arm behind his back. He yelped in pain.

Cormac gripped the cudgel tightly and, abandoning the shelter of the pile of furniture, he charged towards the trio. He swung at the man who held Donie and the cudgel connected solidly with his shoulder. The man shrieked and let go at once.

'Son of a whore!' he spat as he clutched his shoulder, his face contorted in such agony that Cormac wondered if he had dislocated it from its socket.

He raised the cudgel in a threatening stance. 'Stick around and I'll do the other one for you too,' he said roughly.

The fellow gave him a baleful glare before vanishing into the squall of feathers with his companion.

Donie massaged his arm. 'Cheers for that,' he said to Cormac. He eyed the cudgel greedily. 'Where'd you get that?'

Cormac gestured behind him to the fallen stack of furniture. 'Have you seen my family—' he said urgently but Donie had already barged past him, pelting towards the furniture to see what he could dig out of the remains.

Exasperated, Cormac looked down the street in the direction of his home. Bridget, the children, Orlaith, Tess – they could all be in danger. He couldn't wait about for Donie.

Keeping the cudgel raised, he took off, zigzagging between pockets of tussling men and kicking up feathers in his path. He swerved around another group of looters who had emerged from a building with armfuls of clothing and were tearing the garments to shreds. It reminded him of the tales he had heard as a young lad back at Oakleigh of evictions on the neighbouring Rathglaney Estate where the constables had been pitiless in turfing tenants out of their households. It made him sick to his stomach.

Racing onwards, he came within sight of his family's building at last but, instead of feeling relieved, his stomach turned over once more. The front door gaped open and several panes of glass in the Careys' downstairs window had been broken. To make matters worse, a skirmish between four or five men was happening right in front of the building, blocking his way to the entrance. Halting, he glanced anxiously upwards but there was nobody visible at the upstairs window, the one that looked out from his and Bridget's bedroom. Were other looters inside? Could they have already been and gone, leaving destruction and trauma in their wake? Fear tightened his throat so he could hardly breathe.

An exclamation of fright burst from the centre of the skirmish below. Four of the men had surrounded the fifth, who looked scarcely more than a boy, and were pummelling him with their fists. He crumpled beneath their blows, dropping to his knees and lifting his arms to protect his head. They started kicking him, aiming their heels at his back and his thighs and his chest. Even at a distance, Cormac could hear the youngster's groans of pain and weak protests. His fingers clenched on the cudgel. He couldn't tell who was on which side of the fight, but four grown men attacking one defenceless lad was contemptible.

He started in the direction of the group, so intent on going to the youngster's aid that he didn't see the punch coming towards himself until it was too late. A set of knuckles connected with his cheekbone and his head snapped to the side. This was followed by a vigorous uppercut to his ribs. Reeling from the impact, he whirled to his attacker, a stumpy man with bloodlust in his eyes.

'Get off our street, you Yankee scum!' he bawled at Cormac.

'You goddamn fool, I'm Irish,' Cormac barked back. Wheezing at the ache in his ribcage, he pointed at the building across the way. 'That's where I live.'

'Ah, Jaysus, I'm sorry,' said the man with a grimace. 'No hard feelings?'

Without waiting for an answer, he hurtled on down the street, his fists raised in readiness for his next foe.

Maddened, Cormac spun back towards the cluster of men surrounding the youngster but the stumpy fellow had caused a crucial delay. The lad now lay prostrate on the ground and, even as Cormac hastened forwards, the men delivered their final blows, stamping on the lad's back and legs before sauntering away, laughing. Cormac worried that they had beaten him unconscious – or worse – but the lad's limbs quivered and, with what looked like a monumental effort, he crawled towards the building's doorway, removing himself from the main fracas on the street. He slumped onto the doorstep just as Cormac reached him. When Cormac's shadow fell over him, he cringed as though expecting another assault.

'I'm not going to hurt you,' Cormac said, crouching next to him.

He could be no more than eighteen years old. A meagre strip of bristles dusted his upper lip and his black hair was matted with sweat and dirt and feathers. He was bleeding in several places, including a nasty cut on his left ear which dripped blood down the side of his face. He gazed up at Cormac with scared eyes.

Cormac made a quick decision. He couldn't brook any further delay in getting upstairs to confirm if his family was safe. But neither could he step over this youngster on the doorstep like he was a piece of rubbish blown in from the street.

'Can you move?' he asked.

The youngster shifted a little. 'It hurts to breathe,' he rasped. His accent was American.

Cormac berated himself for his split second of hesitation. That didn't change anything. 'You've probably got a cracked rib or two,' he said bracingly. 'It'll hurt like hell for a while but you should heal fine. Try to stand, will you?'

The lad bent his knees and, leaning heavily on Cormac, struggled to his feet. His whole body shook with the exertion and he let out a moan.

'Put your arm over my shoulders,' Cormac said and, when the lad did that, he grasped him firmly around his waist, tucking the cudgel into his other elbow so he could clutch the lad's wrist hanging loosely around his neck. 'There are a few steps to climb but you'll be grand. I've got you.'

Bearing the bulk of the youngster's weight, he manoeuvred him across the threshold into the building. He had some difficulty with his own breathing and reckoned his ribs were bruised at the very least. He glanced towards the Careys' rooms and his heart plummeted when he saw the open door, the overturned table, and the fragments of glass all over the floor. Wanting to dash upstairs at once, he compromised by half carrying the youngster up the steps, muttering words of encouragement while dreading what scene might greet him above.

They reached the landing and discovered that the door to his family's rooms was closed. He could hear nothing beyond it. As he stretched out his hand, his elbow lost its grip on the cudgel and it clattered to the floor. A gasp burst from within but was quickly smothered. He pushed on the door. It wouldn't budge. He tried again, putting more force into it, but the door resisted.

Then came a shout. 'Clear off, you rats, or we'll gut you!'

'Orlaith?' he exclaimed.

There was another cry, this one of eloquent relief. 'It's Cormac!'

At the sound of Bridget's voice, he exhaled, some of the tension leaving his body in a rush. 'Let me in,' he called.

Something heavy scraped across the floorboards to the accompaniment of grunting and then the door cracked open.

Orlaith peered out warily, holding up her Bible almost like a weapon, before pulling the door wide.

'You're safe,' she said, looking pleased until her gaze fell upon the youngster he was supporting. She scowled. 'Who's that?'

'To be honest, I've no idea,' he said, easing through the doorway, the lad's limbs trembling as he strove to stay on his feet.

Emily said excitedly, clutching Mabel, 'Papa, I wished that you were here and my wish came true! It was real magic!' She wiggled Mabel about like she was cheering.

Next to her, Bridget stood with a dozing Jack nestled in the crook of one arm while grasping the poker with her other hand. Her gaze connected with Cormac's. 'Thank God,' she murmured.

The sofa was behind the door, pushed back at an angle with the bench sitting on top of it. Tess leaned against the end of it, her expression almost as bright as Emily's. 'Can't believe you got through that lot,' she said admiringly. 'You must be made of iron.'

Derval Carey was sitting on the stool at the table, little Brian in her lap and her other three children gathered around her. Given the state of the room downstairs, he was very glad that they had taken refuge up here. Derval had a few scratches on her cheek but otherwise everyone seemed unharmed.

When Derval saw the burden he was bringing into the room, she hopped up. 'Put him here,' she said, staring at the youngster with curiosity but without comment.

Orlaith had no such reservations. 'We need to block the door again,' she said, one hand on her hip. 'Is he staying?'

'Yes,' said Cormac as he set the lad down on the stool, propping him back against the table. 'Will you grab the cudgel from the landing? Better for it to be in here than out there.'

'Fine,' huffed Orlaith. She retrieved the cudgel before shutting the door with a snap. Then she, Tess and Rory shoved the sofa back into place.

In the silence that followed, adults and children alike eyed the newcomer. The lad cast a nervous glance around at them all.

'You won't come to any harm,' Cormac assured him. 'What's your name?'

'Charlie.' The youngster's voice came out in a hoarse whisper. He cleared his throat and said more clearly, 'Charlie Adams.'

His American twang seemed to echo as the others turned to Cormac in disbelief.

'Did you get a hard knock on the head after all?' said Tess.

'Throw him out!' said Orlaith, outraged. 'We don't want him here.'

Derval didn't speak but she pressed Brian tighter to her bosom, while Una and Sorcha shrank behind her skirt. Rory's green eyes glittered.

Bridget swallowed. 'I'm sure Cormac has a perfectly good reason for doing what he did,' she said, her expression conveying a mute plea for enlightenment.

He crossed his arms, even though the action aggravated the wound on his forearm. 'I couldn't leave him. He was literally bleeding on our doorstep.'

'So?' said Orlaith. 'He's a Yankee. Let him bleed.'

Cormac set his jaw. 'Come on, he's just a lad. You can patch him up and we'll let him go when he's able to stand on his own two feet.'

'I'll do no such thing,' she said, full of indignation as she wielded the Bible in one hand and the cudgel in the other. 'Those Yankees are out there attacking decent Irish folk who've done nothing wrong.'

Charlie's troubled gaze flicked back and forth between them as blood seeped onto the collar of his shirt.

'It was four Irishmen who beat him up,' Cormac retorted. 'Do you think four toughs taking on one lad is commendable behaviour? Our side isn't made up of saints either.'

'I don't care,' she said mulishly. 'I won't help him.'

'Is that how Ma raised you?' he demanded, astonished at her lack of charity.

'Ma didn't raise me for long, thanks to you.'

It was like she had struck him with the cudgel. Over the past year, he had believed they had been fostering a reasonable sense of sibling amity but it could never be genuine if she continued to harbour resentment towards him for their family's terrible history. Anguish swelled inside him and he pushed it back down, locking away the memories and the unending guilt in the darkest, most ravaged corners of his soul. Wordless, he let his arms fall to his sides. Bridget took a step nearer like she wanted to embrace him but her hands were full with their baby son and the poker.

Orlaith bit her lip, remorse filling her features. 'I...' she began before trailing off.

Without responding to her, he turned to Derval. 'Will you tend him? He can't hurt any of us. He's barely upright and he's outnumbered.'

She mumbled her assent but then Charlie spoke, his gaze still on Orlaith. 'No, I'll go,' he said, his breath escaping in a wheeze. 'She's right, I don't deserve any help.'

He started to rise, leaning on the table for support as his legs shuddered with the strain. The shame in Orlaith's expression intensified. Covering it up, she clicked her tongue.

'Stay where you are,' she said brusquely.

When he still struggled to get up, she let the cudgel drop to the floor with a dull thump and crossed over to him, pressing lightly on his shoulder to make him sit down again. He wavered and fell back onto the stool.

'We'll bandage you up before you go,' she said, her voice tight. She peeped over at Cormac. 'Better take a look at you too.' She jerked her chin at the redness soaking through his sleeve.

He gave her a stiff nod, acknowledging the olive branch she offered him.

She disappeared into the back bedroom, returning with a small bag in place of her Bible. Removing a few strips of rolled cloth from the bag, she asked, 'Do we have much water?'

'Enough for now,' said Bridget. She pointed a finger towards the pail sitting next to the cupboard. Derval handed Brian to Una and went across to get it. 'But it would be advisable to ration what you use. We don't know how long we'll be trapped in here and we're all going to be thirsty in this heat. There's a basin inside the cupboard,' she added to Derval.

Derval took out the basin, poured a conservative quantity of water from the pail into it, and brought it over to the table. She put it down and Orlaith dipped a cloth into it. Standing over Charlie, she said primly, 'Please turn your head to the side.'

Casting her a doubtful look, he nonetheless did as she asked. She touched her wet cloth to his injured ear; he flinched but didn't make a sound.

As she wiped at the blood, she said, 'So, Charlie Adams, can you tell us what started all this?'

He hesitated. 'I'm not quite sure. The church bells rang for the fire alarm but when we got here there was no blaze, just all the men fighting.'

Tess had settled herself on the bench on top of the sofa and now said from her lofty perch, 'You're a fireman?'

He nodded. 'Company 14. I only joined two weeks ago.'

Derval made a noise of displeasure deep in her throat. 'Y'know, the fire companies were called to the scene back when the Ursuline Convent was going up in flames but they just stood by and let it burn.' She glanced hastily at Charlie. 'You obviously

103

had no involvement in that. I'm just saying this goes back a lot further than today.'

Even though Charlie couldn't be implicated in that event, the side of his face that Cormac could see still appeared mortified at his fellow firemen's actions. Orlaith pulled her cloth away, revealing his red and misshapen ear.

'That looks sore,' said Bridget in a sympathetic tone. 'Are you having any trouble with your hearing?'

He reached up to touch his ear but Orlaith flapped him away, soaking the cloth again in the water and reapplying it.

'I'm getting a faint ringing,' he said, 'but it doesn't feel like any serious damage has been done.'

'You're luckier than most so,' said Orlaith tartly, rubbing hard at his ear and making him wince. 'Plenty of people on this street are losing everything as we speak. Did you take part in any of the looting, hmm?'

'No, I did not,' he answered, horrified. 'And I swear the other firemen didn't either, at least none that I could see. There are vandals out there taking advantage of the situation.'

From her somewhat precarious position, Tess leaned closer to the door. 'I'm keeping an ear out for them,' she said with a giggle and a wink at Charlie.

To everyone's surprise, a hoot of real laughter burst from him. Even through the bruises and the blood and his grimace as the laugh hurt his cracked ribs, his boyish innocence shone out. Cormac could practically see the steam of hostility dissipating into the air.

Bridget smiled and, bringing the interrogation to an end, said, 'I think it's time we all drink some water. Children first. Line up, please.'

They obeyed, forming a ragged queue in front of the pail. Emily, realising that she was right in front of Rory, haughtily removed herself from the line and joined it at the end behind

Sorcha, making a show of patting Mabel soothingly on her head. Rory twisted his mouth in irritation but kept it closed.

Bridget propped the poker up against the wall but she still held Jack.

'I'll take him,' said Cormac, reaching out.

She responded with an emphatic shake of her head. 'You're injured, and filthy besides. Can you get his basket?'

He went into the front bedroom where the noise from the riot increased. How much longer would it go on? They were essentially prisoners until it ended, a notion which gave him a decidedly queasy feeling. Hoping their barricade would hold out, he picked up the baby basket, brought it back to the other room and set it on the floor. Bridget laid Jack into it; he squirmed a little but didn't waken. He was getting so big that he had almost outgrown the basket and would soon be needing a cot.

'He rolled back onto his stomach for the first time today,' Bridget informed Cormac proudly. 'Just before the bedlam began.'

As he showered whispers of praise over their son's sleeping form, Bridget extracted a cup from the cupboard and gave each child a sip of water. Then she said, 'Casualties of the battle next.'

She wouldn't listen to Cormac's protests but agreed to offer the cup to Charlie first before forcing it into Cormac's own hands. Surrendering, he drank; the water, despite being tepid, was a great relief to his parched throat. Finally, Bridget passed the cup around among the women. Once everyone's thirst had been somewhat slaked, she peered uneasily into the pail and then set it aside with a general warning to the room that no one could go near it without her permission.

As Derval helped Orlaith make a bandage for Charlie's ear, and the children, apart from a taciturn Rory, started to play a game where the objective was to save Princess Tess from her

105

locked tower, Bridget seized the opportunity to have a moment of relative privacy with Cormac. Facing away from the others with Jack's basket at their feet, she laced her fingers through his with one hand and reached up to his face with the other, her fingertips hovering over but not quite touching his cheekbone.

'Does it look bad?' he asked.

'I expect you will have a magnificent bruise,' she replied. She plucked a feather out of his hair before her gaze travelled down to his forearm.

'That's mostly from my injury at the docks last week,' he said reassuringly. 'The wound reopened when I took a knock, that's all.'

'I see. Anything else?'

He took an experimental breath. 'Sore ribs,' he admitted. 'But there's nothing to be concerned about.'

'That's not quite true,' she said, inclining her head towards the continued din from the brawl. She released his hand and, rolling up his sleeve, said in a low voice, 'What are we to do?'

He pondered their options. 'If anyone tries to bludgeon their way through the door, we'll confront the crisis. But I think while there is no immediate threat to us we should just wait. The city can't allow such a brawl to continue for long.'

She sighed as she drew back the sticky fabric to expose the gash on his arm. 'We'll clean this up just as soon as Orlaith is finished with Charlie.' She peeked up at him. 'Have you an opinion on what you should like to do with our guest after that?'

He chewed the inside of his cheek. 'Do you think I ought to have left him where he was?'

'No, you did the decent thing, which is no less than I would have expected of you.' She gave him a rueful grin. 'Though it does rather complicate matters in terms of our water and food supplies.'

'Not to mention diplomatic relations.'

He glanced over to the table where Orlaith was wrapping one of her longer pieces of cloth around Charlie's head, making sure to cover his ear. She wasn't saying much to her patient but at least she had dampened her animosity enough to help him. For his part, he didn't seem too put out by her frosty attitude and sat meekly through her ministrations.

When she tied off the end of the bandage, he looked up at her. 'Thank you,' Cormac heard him say with palpable sincerity.

'You're welcome,' she replied reluctantly.

Chapter 12

By dusk, Broad Street had fallen silent. After hours of fighting, Irishmen, firemen, spectators and vandals alike had scattered when the militia had arrived, sweeping through the mob on horseback and on foot with rifles and bayonets. Wary that an overenthusiastic shot from a militiaman or a wild brick thrown in retaliation could easily go astray, Cormac had insisted that everyone stay well away from the front bedroom until the danger had passed.

Only when the shouting had ceased and the last hoof beats of the cavalry had faded away did he go to the window to look out. The street was a sea of dirty feathers, broken furniture and torn clothing but, rather remarkably, no dead bodies. He lifted the sash to let some cooler air into the stuffy bedroom and returned to the others.

'It's definitely over,' he told them and a collective sigh rippled from them all, with one noticeable exception.

Charlie slumped over the table, his arms crossed upon its surface and his forehead resting on his wrists. The pale strip of cloth wrapped around his head stood out starkly against his black hair, a faint blush of red showing on the part that covered his damaged ear. The only sound he made was the soft, rhythmic breathing of sleep.

Everyone stared at him, at a loss as to what to do.

'We could wake him with a bang,' said Tess, picking up the cudgel and dangling it teasingly.

'Ah, that'd be cruel.' Derval barely suppressed a chuckle.

'Let him alone,' said Bridget. 'The poor boy is shattered.'

'It was just a bit of fun.' Tess's tone was indifferent as she set the cudgel back down. 'What d'yous want to do about him?'

Cormac contemplated their slumbering guest. 'I reckon we should leave him be. Aside from the fact that he's in no fit state to move yet, it's getting dark and tonight of all nights is not one to be walking the streets. He can stay here and go back to wherever he lives in the morning.'

'If he still resides with his mother, she will be worried sick when he doesn't come home,' said Bridget, looking agitated on behalf of Charlie's mother.

Cormac raised his palms, resigned. 'In these circumstances, it can't be helped.'

Following that, they discussed the sleeping arrangements. There could be no question of the Careys returning downstairs that night, given the broken window in their front room, although they did go down to fetch what bedding they could. Emily refused point-blank to share a sleeping space with Rory so Una and Sorcha were assigned to the front bedroom, their blankets laid out on the floor alongside Emily's mattress, while Derval, Rory and Brian joined Orlaith and Tess in the back bedroom. As for Charlie, Bridget left a folded blanket on the table next to his head; if he woke, he could curl up on the sofa for more comfort.

Cormac wished they had arranged things differently when the three little girls exchanged animated whispers until dawn, desisting only temporarily after each remonstration from him or Bridget before resuming with unquenchable enthusiasm. Turning restlessly in the bed, he tugged a corner of the sheet back from Bridget's side and decided it would be best to fix the broken window with all possible haste.

To that end, by midmorning he had scavenged the detritus on Broad Street for pieces of wood that would be suitable for his mission and equipped himself with a hammer and some nails from Donie Kane, who sported a huge lump on his temple and a wide grin as he reminisced on the previous day's activities. Now Cormac stood outside the Careys' window, boarding up the lower panes. The upper half of the window was intact which meant that some light could still reach inside, although it would be quite dim. He was assisted by Rory, who seemed determined to help even though he couldn't do much apart from handing Cormac the nails. There was a great deal of bustling behind them as other residents roved the street, seeking belongings that could be salvaged and sweeping smashed glass away from their doorsteps.

Rory was his usual quiet self but Cormac was happy to labour in silence. He found himself taking great pleasure in working with the wood, simple though the task was, and he savoured the familiar feel of a hammer resting in his palm and a nail poised between his fingertips. He thought again about the fact that Jack would be needing a cot before too long. Derval had offered to give them Brian's cot as the boy would soon be too big for it ('And God help us all when that scamp can no longer be penned in'), but Cormac wondered if he might relish the challenge of building one instead, provided he could get the right tools and materials for the job.

Suddenly, Rory spoke. 'I let my ma down yesterday.'

Startled, Cormac paused in the action of lining up another nail against the piece of wood over the window frame. 'What on earth do you mean by that, lad?'

Rory blew out his cheeks, his shoulders hunched with despondency. 'She got hurt. I'm the man of the family when Da's away. I'm meant to protect her.'

Cormac didn't know the nature of the discord between Derval and Brian Mór which seemed to keep him away from home for reasons beyond his occupation, but he regretted the burden that the man's absence had placed on this young boy's shoulders.

'It's not that long since you turned eleven, Rory,' he said. 'You aren't expected to be a man just yet.'

'Who'll look after Ma and the small ones if not me?' Rory demanded.

'Do you think your ma needs looking after?' Cormac asked. 'It seems to me like she can stand up for herself pretty well.'

'But she's just a woman,' said Rory.

Cormac felt uneasy. How many times had the boy heard such a remark uttered with the same matter-of-factness? Maybe Brian Mór was better off staying away after all. Cormac hesitated, examining the point of the nail in his grasp. Rory wasn't his son so it wasn't his place to educate him, and yet he couldn't let the comment pass.

'Tell me,' he said casually, glancing from the nail back to the boy, 'did you notice that it was four women who kept you out of harm's way yesterday?'

Rory's brow scrunched up. 'You were there too.'

'I did nothing,' Cormac said, his tone firm. 'It was your ma and Bridget and Orlaith and Tess who made sure that you were all safe behind that blocked door, long before I got there.'

Rory stared moodily at the bunch of nails resting in his palm. 'What if someone had knocked down the door? What could they have done then?'

'It's true that most women don't have the same physical strength as men,' Cormac acknowledged. 'But they are strong in other ways. And you'd be surprised what a woman can do when her children are in danger. I don't know about you but I certainly wouldn't like to face one brandishing a poker.' When Rory didn't respond, he added, 'Will you pass me another nail? The point of this one is bent.'

He handed back the crooked nail and took the new one Rory offered him. Lining it up in the same spot as before, he said, 'My advice to you would be to never underestimate a woman. She'll show you what she's capable of and she'll put you in your place pretty sharpish if you make an assumption to the contrary.'

He drove the nail home with the hammer and then tugged at the piece of wood to ensure that it was securely attached to the window frame. There was only one more pane to board up. When he looked again at his young companion, Rory's expression was pensive as he gazed absently through the remaining gap in the window. Setting down the hammer, Cormac picked up the last bit of wood at his feet and held it up to the gap to assess its fit, even though he had already measured it earlier. It broke Rory's line of sight and he blinked. His green eyes cut back to Cormac.

'Why'd you save the Yankee? He's a Prod.'

Feeling like he was only a hair's breadth away from pontificating at this point, Cormac replied, 'His name is Charlie. And he may be a Protestant but he's also a human being who eats and breathes and laughs and bleeds the same as us. A man's religion shouldn't be a factor in choosing whether or not to save his life.' Plucking another nail from Rory's outstretched hand, he added gravely, 'You have to remember the personal cost too. How do you think I would have felt if I had come downstairs this morning to find Charlie sprawled dead on the doorstep, knowing that I had had the chance to keep him alive? I would have had to carry that guilt with me for the rest of my days.'

It was perhaps a touch blunter than he had intended, not to mention a slight exaggeration of the extent of Charlie's injuries, but it made an impression. Face reddening, Rory dropped his gaze to the ground, abashed.

Cormac wanted to put a kind hand on the boy's shoulder but doubted whether Rory would welcome the gesture. Instead, he said, 'Don't feel bad for having those thoughts. As we witnessed yesterday, many folk judge others that way. However, I believe it's wiser for a person to have an open mind. What do you think?'

Rory didn't say anything but when he looked back up there was a new awareness in his expression. He gave a sombre nod and Cormac wondered if the eleven-year-old had just become a man after all.

Turning back to the task at hand, he said, 'Will you hold the wood in place?'

Rory pressed his free palm flat against the board, keeping it lined up with the window frame. Cormac lifted the hammer again, adjusted his grip, and knocked in the first nail. He repeated the action with several more nails until the piece of wood was immovable. As they stood back to admire their handiwork, a figure emerged from the doorway of the building.

'Rory, your ma needs you to help with the clean up inside,' said Orlaith. 'She doesn't want the young ones near the broken glass.'

Rory relinquished the remaining couple of nails into Cormac's possession and scurried indoors, leaving an awkward silence in his wake. Pocketing the nails, Cormac avoided Orlaith's eye and busied himself with gathering the discarded bits of wood into his arms; they hadn't proved to be a good fit for boarding up the window but they would make decent firewood once winter came.

'I'm very sorry, Cormac.'

He glanced up. Orlaith's hands were clasped in front of her skirt, fingers twisting together so hard that they appeared bloodless. She was biting an equally pallid lip, and her round grey eyes roiled with a jumble of emotions like a turbulent sea.

'I want to take back what I said,' she mumbled. 'It was unfair of me to throw that in your face.'

He shifted the bundle of wood and felt a splinter slice into his thumb. Suppressing a grimace, he said, 'You had grounds for your accusation. The consequences of my past actions, however unintentional, did leave you without a mother.' He took a breath. 'But the shame of that will crush me unless I keep it buried. I must overcome it, for my family's sake if not my own. We have, I hope, many years ahead of us and it will serve no one if I squander them by languishing in my sins until they have consumed me whole.'

'I know,' she said, looking deeply anguished. 'It'd be a waste of a life and I'd hate to see that happen. You're a good person and you didn't deserve that cruel knock from me. I'll never say anything like that again, I swear.' She unclenched her wringing hands and, to his surprise, placed one over his own, despite the load he carried. 'I'm so glad you found me in Dublin. I won't ever stop being grateful for that.'

Tears glistened in her eyes and in that instant he was forcibly reminded of Bronagh; not only did she and Orlaith look alike, but they were both his tough little sisters who only ever showed emotion when it truly mattered to them.

'I'm exceptionally glad of that too,' he said.

He offered her a tentative smile and she returned it with a watery one of her own.

'Now that we're on good terms again, could I beg you for a personal favour?' he said solemnly.

'Anything,' she responded with earnestness.

He wiggled his thumb. 'Would you help me remove this splinter?'

She blinked before a laugh burst from her. 'You're such a clown. 'Course I will.'

Upstairs, Cormac deposited the wood in a pile next to the fireplace and then sat at the table to let Orlaith examine his thumb. The sofa had been pushed back in front of the hearth and Charlie sat on it, looking dishevelled and disorientated.

'Do you remember what happened yesterday, lad?' Cormac asked.

'Yes,' Charlie mumbled, his gaze flicking to Orlaith whose back was to him.

'And do you remember where you live?'

'Yes.'

'Grand,' said Cormac. 'If you're able to walk, I'll accompany you home after this. Your family must be worried about you.'

Charlie extended his legs one at a time and stood cautiously. 'I expect my mother in particular is in hysterics,' he admitted, taking a few experimental steps from the sofa to the fireplace. 'But you don't need to come with me. I'm fine.'

'I can see the splinter,' Orlaith announced. 'I'll use one of Bridget's needles to get it out. Give me a minute.'

She bustled into the front bedroom in search of the sewing kit; through the open door, Cormac could see Bridget nursing Jack on the edge of the bed, Emily playing with Mabel by her feet. He turned back to Charlie.

'I'd rather go along if it's all the same to you,' he said. 'I feel like you're my responsibility until you're home safe.'

'I honestly don't need any help,' the lad insisted, sounding like he was doing his best not to get rankled. Then he swayed a little and grabbed hold of the mantelpiece. He cast Cormac a sheepish look.

'We'll keep that between the two of us,' Cormac promised.

'And me,' said Tess, emerging from the back bedroom with a wink. She clicked her tongue at Cormac's outstretched arm on the tabletop. 'Injured again?' Crossing over to the table, she peered at his thumb, so close that her red hair spilled over his wrist. 'I think we can agree this one isn't life-threatening.'

She stepped back as Orlaith returned, wielding a sharp sewing needle. While Orlaith poked at the skin on Cormac's thumb, trying to ease the splinter out, Tess sauntered over to Charlie.

'Heard you say your ma's probably having a conniption 'cause you didn't come home last night. What about your girl? D'you have a sweetheart who'll swoon when she sees your heroic wound?' She batted her eyelashes at him.

'No,' said Charlie rather uncomfortably. He raised his voice a little to address Orlaith. 'Can you tell me how long I should keep the bandage on, Miss McGovern?'

He had persevered with this formality even though they had all told him their first names. With Orlaith's head bent over his hand, Cormac couldn't glimpse her exact expression but he thought he saw the corner of her mouth curving up. When she spoke, however, her words were clipped.

'I'll replace it now before you go. After that, get your ma to change it every day or two, or sooner if the blood soaks through again.'

Presently, with splinter removed and wound re-dressed, Cormac and Charlie stood ready to go. Everyone had gathered except for Rory who was nowhere to be seen. Charlie looked around at them all.

'Thanks,' he said self-consciously. 'For, you know—and—well, thanks.'

'We wish you the best,' said Bridget, offering him a warm smile.

Derval and Tess echoed her in slightly cooler tones. Orlaith said nothing, only crossed her arms and stared at the floor.

116

Turning away with a somewhat crestfallen air, Charlie limped to the door and Cormac followed him through it.

At the bottom of the stairs, they met Rory sweeping broken glass over the threshold from the Careys' front room into a neat mound in the hallway. He stopped and surveyed them.

'You leaving?' he said curtly.

Charlie nodded.

Rory hesitated, glancing at Cormac. 'G'luck then,' he said to Charlie with a respectful nod in return. 'Mind yourself.' And he resumed his sweeping with vigorous strokes of the broom.

Chapter 13

'We're going to end up spending a fortune on candles,' said Derval. 'Or go blind squinting in the gloom.'

Bridget tutted in sympathy as she sat opposite her friend at the Careys' table, bouncing Jack gently on her knee. 'It is exceedingly unfortunate,' she said, experiencing a fresh surge of resentment towards the reprobates who had wreaked so much damage along with its subsequent inconveniences.

Cormac's efforts to board up the window had certainly made the room secure again but even now, on a sunny June day, the light was dim. She could just imagine how murky it would be on a dreary winter afternoon. Not to mention that it was no longer possible to lift the sash which meant that an oppressive heat had pervaded the air until Derval had thrust open both the door to the hallway and the front door of the building.

Through the gap in the door, they saw Emily, Una and Sorcha charging up the stairs and heard Emily's animated voice floating back, 'This time I'll play the Yankee and you're the ones chasing me!'

Little Brian, tottering after them, slipped as he clambered onto the bottom step and let out a howl. Derval jumped to her feet and hurried to comfort him. A faint breeze drifted in, tickling Bridget's cheek as she in turn tickled her son under his chin. He babbled at her with a happy smile.

'You are a little rascal,' she murmured.

After accomplishing the feat of rolling onto his stomach just before the pandemonium broke out on Sunday, it had taken him three whole days to repeat the performance for his father. This triumphant act had happened at last that morning before Cormac had left for the docks. He had swung the boy up into his arms in delight and promised him a special gift as a reward. Bridget had had no inkling of what Cormac was alluding to and he had not elaborated, although he had said that he might be home later than usual that evening.

As Derval came to sit back down, settling a sniffling Brian on her lap, she said, 'Mrs Kane heard it supposedly started with Company 20. Some sort of spat between one of the firemen and a few of the mourners from the funeral. He was smoking a cigar and they demanded that he put it out to show some respect for the dead but he refused.'

'Perfectly acceptable grounds upon which to instigate a riot,' Bridget said scornfully.

Derval wiped away a smear of blood from Brian's knee. 'It seems the foreman at the engine house feared the Irish would rise up and kill them, so that's why he sounded the alarm and the church bells rang.' She shrugged. 'All rumours, of course. Could well be a different tale tomorrow, and no doubt 'tis another story altogether in Yankee circles.'

From the hallway came the distinct sound of someone clearing his throat. Bridget glanced up.

'Charlie?' she said, baffled. 'What are you doing back here?'

The youngster approached the doorway but didn't step over the threshold. The bandage still crossed over his black hair, covering his ear, though it was slightly askew. Nevertheless, despite the ripened bruises on his face, he held his body straighter than before.

'Good day, Mrs McGovern, Mrs Carey,' he said politely. 'I hope I find you both in good health?'

'You do indeed,' Bridget responded with equal civility. 'May I enquire as to your own wellbeing? Have you recovered from your recent injuries?'

'Yes, thank you.' He cast a fleeting look over his shoulder in the direction of the stairs before repeating, 'Thank you. I'm feeling much better.'

Beginning to perceive his real purpose in returning to Broad Street, she said, 'Perhaps it would be advisable to examine your wound while you are here. Derval could check it for you.'

'Oh,' he said, making a poor attempt to conceal his disappointment. 'I'd be very much obliged.'

Bridget strove to curb her smile. 'Having said that, I do recall seeing Orlaith roll up a fresh set of bandages yesterday. So she may be better equipped to attend to you instead.'

He brightened. 'If you think that would be best.'

Exchanging an amused glance with Derval, Bridget said, 'I'll take you up to her now.'

She hoisted Jack into a comfortable position against her chest and rose to her feet. Charlie stepped back from the doorway to let her pass and she started to climb the stairs. As he followed her, she said casually, 'Orlaith truly is a remarkable young woman. Even at her age, she already has the makings of a fine nurse.'

'I agree,' he said, his voice eager.

'In fact,' said Bridget, 'she is so mature that one could easily forget she is only fourteen.'

There was silence behind her. Then, quiet and resolute, he said, 'I understand.'

She knew it was the warning Cormac would have delivered to the boy if he had been here himself. It was preferable to be prudent about such matters from the outset.

Reaching the landing, she preceded him into the room, saying gaily, 'Look who's here!'

Orlaith and Tess were supposed to be scrubbing the floorboards – in the interest of fairness, they and Bridget had divided the task into three sections, although they had both dawdled over the chore while Bridget had already finished her portion the previous day – but she found them instead sitting on the floor with their backs against the wall, their brushes abandoned beside them as they chattered. When she entered, Orlaith jumped up guiltily but Tess stood with less urgency.

'Who's here?' she said lazily. Then Charlie stepped through the door. 'Our hero returns!' she exclaimed with a clap of her hands. Her cheeks flushed pink and she seemed genuinely pleased to see him.

However, after a respectful greeting of 'Miss O'Leary', Charlie's gaze slid past her. 'Miss McGovern,' he said.

Orlaith's forehead creased in confusion. 'Why are you back?'

Undeterred, he lifted his chin. 'I wanted to say a proper thank you. I didn't express myself very well before so I felt it was best to come back and do it right.' He paused. 'I'd also like to apologise for my part in the events of Sunday last.'

'What use are words?' Orlaith muttered, toeing the brush near her foot. 'The damage is done.'

'I haven't brought only words,' said Charlie. 'I come with a pledge to replace the glass in the window downstairs at the earliest opportunity.'

Bridget couldn't tell if this had been his intention all along or a spur-of-the-moment idea but either way he maintained his composure as Orlaith stared at him.

'Why would you do that?' she asked. 'You didn't break it yourself, did you?'

'I didn't, but it's the only thing I can think of to make up for being involved in what happened,' he said, his expression candid.

'No one would expect you to replace it,' protested Bridget. 'And the cost would surely be too great for you to cover.'

'I'll ask the other fellows in Company 14 to chip in. It might take us a while to gather the full amount but we'll manage it.'

'You're soft in the head,' said Tess. 'Sure, why would they bother?'

'Because they're embarrassed,' Charlie said simply. 'I am too. We got swept up in the chaos of the brawl but that's no excuse. This is a small way to make amends.'

Bridget, Orlaith and Tess gaped at each other.

'Well...' Bridget said, patting Jack's back as he made a small noise of discontentment. 'I know Derval would be over the moon. But if it doesn't prove feasible—'

'It will,' he said.

Orlaith folded her arms, frowning, then released them, letting them swing at her sides as she tapped her fingertips against each other. 'Right so. Want me to have a look at your ear while you're here?'

He took a seat meekly on the bench, his wince indicating that his body was far from healed just yet. With a flick of his eyes towards Bridget, he angled his knees sideways so they didn't brush up against Orlaith's skirt when she moved to stand in front of him. She leaned over and started to unwrap the bandage. When she pulled away the final strip of material, he let out a hiss through his teeth as it parted from the congealed blood on his ear.

'Arrah now, be tough,' she said. 'You were tough enough to go rioting with the other sheep, weren't you?'

It was unnecessarily harsh after the generous promise he had just made. Bridget wanted to reprimand her but didn't feel she had the authority to do so – while they were essentially sisters-in-law and Bridget was fourteen years the senior, Orlaith had clearly demonstrated her unwillingness to be under anyone else's thumb following her servitude at Anner House. Still, she seemed to recognise the unfairness of what she had said. Her face went red and she peered at Charlie's ear with excessive concentration.

'It looks like it's on the mend but it'll take some time.' She hesitated before saying gently, 'I don't think it'll go back to its normal shape.'

He gave a resigned shrug. 'I could have ended up in a much worse state, so a deformed ear is acceptable if you ask me.'

'I'll put a fresh bandage on it,' she said and went to retrieve her bag of rolled cloths from the back bedroom.

While she was gone, Tess flopped onto the bench next to Charlie. 'That's a really nice thing you've offered to do,' she said. 'Does this mean we'll be seeing you again?'

He discreetly shifted an inch or two away from her. 'I suppose it does.'

Orlaith returned with her small bag and Tess got up, flouncing away to the sofa. Bridget couldn't fathom why Tess felt the need to turn every situation into a game of flirtation. In any case, Charlie was a bit young for her. What age could she be? Twenty-two maybe, or twenty-three? Given her unfortunate circumstances growing up on the streets of Dublin, Bridget wasn't sure if Tess even knew the answer to that herself.

As Orlaith shook out a strip of cloth, she said, 'Will you tell us, Charlie?'

'Tell you what?'

'Why do the Yankees loathe the Irish so much?'

123

His gaze travelled from her nimble fingers up to her grey eyes, which demanded understanding.

'I'm not able to speak for anyone else,' he said, 'but I can't think of a single reason.'

CHAPTER 14

'—price of cotton's plummeted. It's a dang disaster.'

Cormac secured a rope around one of the cotton bales, readying it to be transferred from the deck of the ship onto the wharf. Having lived in Boston for over a year now, he was beginning to recognise the differences between the diverse range of American accents and could identify this one as possessing a distinct Southern cadence. It belonged to the merchant of the ship that had just docked in the port and the man was gesticulating as he stood on the wharf and griped to Mr Walker.

The foreman nodded gravely and replied, 'We're feeling the effects of it here too, though not yet quite as severely...'

O'Mali was working alongside Cormac, tying a rope around another bale. He shot Cormac a dark look. 'It's bad news and it's only gonna get worse.'

Cormac felt the familiar ripple of unease in his gut. In recent months, there had been much talk at the docks about the financial crisis sweeping the nation. Garnering information from those who could read the newspapers, the men discussed it constantly and panic mounted among them as banks and businesses collapsed and they feared they might lose their employment. Mr Walker did his best to assuage their concerns but he could make no guarantees that Robert Smith & Co.

would not also fold. The foreman's own role was equally at risk for the calamity did not discriminate, affecting Irish and Americans alike, not to mention the other assorted nationalities who called this country their home.

Knotting his rope deftly around the bale, Cormac contemplated the uncertainty of his own job. If Mr Walker was obliged to reduce the number of dockworkers and operated on a 'last in, first out' basis, Cormac had a cushion of just two men who had been taken on after him. If, on the other hand, dismissal was determined on a scale of satisfactory performance, he believed that might put him in a more advantageous position. Aside from his hardworking attitude, which had earned him the esteem of his fellow workers, he had gained additional favour with Mr Walker by entirely different means.

Once he had concocted the idea of building a cot for Jack, he had asked the foreman for permission to glean unwanted wood from the warehouse – broken crates might no longer be able to serve their original purpose but he hoped he could give the wood a new lease of life as humble furniture. Mr Walker, intrigued by his request, had agreed on the condition that Cormac also build a second cot – though he referred to it as a crib – as his own wife was expecting their first child before the end of the year. He had even furnished Cormac with some of the necessary tools for the task. The arrangement had resulted in many late evenings but had eventually produced two plain but sturdy cots which had been presented to a delighted Mrs Walker and an ecstatic Bridget, while Brian's old cot was gladly welcomed in the Kane household, where three of their big brood were still under the age of four. Cormac had even gathered from some of Mr Walker's comments that he would not be adverse to commissioning further pieces in the future. Perhaps that would be enough incentive for the foreman to keep Cormac's job safe for now, although there would be no protection if the whole company went under.

O'Mali's expression was solemn, no trace of his usual easy grin, as he tugged at his rope to test its tension. 'Might be only a matter of time before we all get the heave-ho. I'm gonna have to send my eldest out to find work just in case. She could probably get a place in one of them fancy houses.'

'Which houses?' asked Cormac.

'Over on Beacon Hill. Lots of rich folk up there needing maids to do their laundry and wash their dinner plates.' O'Mali straightened with pride. 'My Tilly's a strong girl. She wouldn't shy away from hard work.'

'What age is she?'

'Ten.'

Cormac baulked. His sisters Margaret and Bronagh had been sent to work as scullery maids at Oakleigh Manor when they were aged only twelve and ten. It had been out of sheer necessity as he had been unable to support his whole family on a stable hand's wages after the deaths of his father and brother. Now he thought of Emily, his beloved treasure, almost eight and a half years old. Refusing to tolerate the notion of sending her out to work in just a couple of short years, he swore to himself right there and then that he would do everything in his power to avoid such a scenario. He was managing at present as Bridget made small contributions through her sewing and even Orlaith had started to pick up sporadic amounts for bandaging wounds in the local community. But his was the only steady income of the family – what if at some stage in the future he found himself becoming as desperate as O'Mali?

Dispirited, he and O'Mali worked on with an air of gloominess as if a bank of thunderclouds hung low over their heads, even though it was a sunny, crisp autumn day – or fall, if he was to use the term he had discovered was more prevalent in this country. The changing of the season was not so easy to recognise here in the city, beyond the cooling of the temperature and the shortening of daylight hours. When he had lived in the countryside, its full effects had always been a feast for the senses. With an unexpected wrench of nostalgia, he remembered the oak tree in the orchard at Oakleigh. It had signalled the onset of autumn each year with a slow, steady dignity, its leaves turning gold and russet before falling to the ground, the earthy scent of the leaf litter pleasingly pungent. In contrast, the strongest smells he could currently detect were ubiquitous all year round: the salty tang of seawater, the pitch that sealed the ship's timbers, and, when he went down into the hold, the rather less pleasant odour belonging to the unwashed bodies of sailors.

It was a gruelling day spent unloading cotton bales from the ship and the men were all shattered by the end of it, but that was a good complaint to have under the present circumstances. After bidding farewell to O'Mali and the others, Cormac departed from the docks and headed to the post office where he waited in line, shoulders drooping with fatigue. There was only one letter to collect – it bore the seal of the Walcott title and the postage had been paid in advance. He tucked it into his pocket and made his way home.

When he reached Broad Street, he found his whole family standing outside the building, along with the Careys and even Mr Lorenzo. Everyone was gaping at the downstairs window where the wooden boards had been removed and brand new panes of glass had been fitted. Charlie Adams stood next to it, beaming around at them all. Bandages and bruises gone, he exhibited no sign of the beating he had taken during the riot back in June, apart from his slightly misshapen ear.

Cormac joined the group. 'That's a fine job,' he said and gave Charlie a clap on the shoulder.

The youngster's grin grew wider. 'One of the men in the company has a brother-in-law who's a window fitter. He agreed to do this for half his usual fee.'

'Thank you, Charlie,' said Derval, her voice thick. 'I never seen anyone do a good deed like this, not for people outside of their own.'

'Perhaps we could claim him as an honorary member of the Irish community,' suggested Bridget, bent over as she held Jack's wrists, helping him to balance on his own two feet.

'Like me,' said Mr Lorenzo with a chuckle.

Bridget smiled up at him. 'Indeed, *signore*.'

Emily, Una, Sorcha and Brian galloped about with excitement while Rory stood at his mother's elbow, his jaw nearly on the ground. Charlie's delighted expression dimmed as he looked towards Orlaith, who showed no indication of her approval. She continued to stare at the window, her eyebrows raised in incredulity. Then her mask fractured and the corner of her mouth twitched. She jerked her chin at Charlie.

'Want a bite to eat? You might as well come up while you're here.'

A wave of relief rolled across his face. 'That would be nice.'

'About time. I'm starving,' Tess said and led the way indoors.

As the others followed her, Cormac said, 'Orlaith, would you mind taking Jack up? Bridget and I need a minute before we go in.'

Both of them looked confused but neither protested. Bridget passed Jack to Orlaith and they disappeared inside along with everyone else until only Cormac and Bridget remained on the street, twilight beginning to fall around them.

'What is it?' she asked, her brow furrowed.

He drew the letter out of his pocket. 'I thought you might prefer some privacy when you open this.'

She took it and inspected the seal. 'My uncle? How strange. I only received his last correspondence a couple of weeks ago.'

She inhaled sharply, peering up at Cormac with sudden anxiety. She easily comprehended his suspicions without him having to say a word.

'Oh, no,' she whimpered. Fumbling, she broke the seal of the letter. She read the first few lines in the waning light and pressed her hand to her mouth. 'He's gone,' she said between her fingers and started to weep.

Cormac had feared that would be the case, given how soon this letter had come after Lord Walcott's previous communication. He led Bridget over to the doorway and coaxed her down onto the step. The hallway beyond was empty but chatter drifted down the stairs from the room above. Sitting beside her, he put his arm around her shoulder.

'I'm so very sorry to hear this,' he murmured.

He truly meant it. Lord Walcott may have been an Englishman but the fire of Irish freedom had burned in his not inconsiderable belly and with his secret funds he had assisted the tenants at Oakleigh in resisting the tyrannical behaviour of Bridget's ruthless mother. In light of Lord Walcott and Lady Courcey's conflicting views in this world, Cormac wondered how they might greet each other in the afterlife.

Bridget looked at the letter again and said through her tears, 'His heart gave out while he was in the library, enjoying a glass of whiskey after dinner. His footman, Simon, found him when he came to bring his lordship to bed.' She gulped. 'Brutus died only two days later. Oh, that just makes me even sadder.'

She turned to Cormac and sobbed into his chest, the page crushed between them. He remembered the small, aging dog that had hardly stirred from Lord Walcott's side and imagined the poor creature hanging on until his master had breathed his last. The temperature dropped as the sky darkened towards deep dusk but he just rubbed Bridget's back and let her cry.

At length, she pulled away a little, wiping her eyes with the heels of her hands. 'I don't know why it has come as such a shock. We knew when we took our leave of him in Dublin last year that he was living on borrowed time.'

He brushed a kiss on her temple. 'News of a loved one's death is always distressing, no matter how prepared you may be for it.'

A lamplighter passed them by and continued along the street, his dark silhouette illuminated as he lit the nearest lamp with his staff. Its glow reached them, revealing Bridget's damp cheeks. She sniffed and flattened out the page against her thigh.

'I had better read the rest of it. It is my uncle's second cousin who has written. Of course, that is why he used the Walcott crest on the seal—the title is now his.' Bending over the letter, she scanned it down to the end. After a long pause, she said, 'Good gracious, am I reading this right?'

She handed the letter to Cormac and he glanced through it. Stunned, he blinked and scrutinised it more thoroughly. 'Yes, I think you are,' he said, even as he found it hard to believe himself.

The opening lines bearing the news of the deceased were delivered in a rather detached tone by the new Lord Walcott, and the reason for this became clear in the subsequent paragraph. With concise language that bordered on churlish, he described his dismay when, upon inheriting Lockhurst Park and coming into possession of its accounts, he discovered that his predecessor had frittered away much of the estate's wealth on expenditure of an unexplained nature and that, even after such negligence, his lordship had seen fit to leave a substantial sum to an individual named Cormac McGovern residing at an address on Broad Street, Boston, in an incontestable addendum to his will.

'The poor man is incensed, isn't he?' said Bridget. 'Could you imagine his fury if he were to learn that the unexplained expenditure had actually been siphoned from the English estate for an Irish uprising?' She made an odd sound somewhere between a hiccup and a laugh. 'And the bequest is beyond astounding.'

Cormac rubbed his jaw. 'It is highly generous and also very clever. We both know that this legacy is intended for you. But if Lord Walcott had designated you as the recipient, then Garrett would have had a legal entitlement to it. Whereas bequeathing the money to me guarantees that it will reach us here—'

'—and he trusted you enough to have faith that you would then give it to me,' Bridget finished. She squeezed Cormac's arm. 'What a mark of respect to you. But such a sum! My dear uncle, what can he have been thinking to act with such outrageous benevolence?'

Cormac stared at the figure on the page. 'He was evidently very fond of you.'

A few more tears leaked from her eyes. 'And I of him.'

They sat on the step in silence. Further down the street, the lamps flickered into life one by one until the lamplighter turned the corner and went out of sight.

'What shall we do with it?' Her voice was barely a whisper.

He passed the letter back to her and pressed her hand over it. 'That choice is yours. He left the money to you—I am only the conduit.'

She bit the tip of her tongue, nibbling on it for several moments. At last, she said, 'My choice is that we should decide together. And that, whatever we may choose, it will be for the benefit of our family.'

He nodded, thinking of a hundred ways that this gift could help their family. What a godsend that it should come to them at such an unstable time for the country. He sent up a silent message of thanks to Lord Walcott and hoped the gentleman was savouring a prime glass of whiskey wherever he might be now.

Shifting on the cold step, he glanced down and noticed a dark stain in a crevice between the step and the door jamb. It looked like dried blood, crusted into a brownish smear, the spot sheltered enough that it had never been washed away by rain. This was where Charlie had slumped bleeding on the day of the riot so he was the most likely culprit, unless there had been further altercations on the doorstep of which Cormac was not aware.

In the weeks following the riot, he had questioned the wisdom of bringing his family to Boston. The search for Bronagh was turning into a fool's errand as the months went by without a shred of progress, and they had all been in very real danger when Broad Street had become a battleground for the simmering hostilities between the Protestant Americans and the Catholic Irish.

And yet, they were not unhappy. There were disagreements at times, certainly, like when Orlaith and Tess shirked their chores or Emily hardened into a block of ice if Rory came anywhere near her. But, despite all that, genuine warmth existed within the walls of their three rooms, cramped though those quarters may be. What detracted from it was the temporary nature of it all, the feeling that they were waiting – waiting to find Bronagh, waiting to move on to...what?

He leaned back against the doorframe. 'Given the current climate, I wouldn't advocate spending the whole lot and leaving ourselves short. It would be prudent to save a portion of it. But let's not be miserly about it either.' He reached out and curved his hand over hers, the letter of deliverance beneath them. 'I think it's time to embrace our life here, instead of acting like it's a transitory step to something else. What would you say to getting ourselves a proper house?'

She tilted her head. 'You mean...leave Broad Street?'

'Only if you wish it,' he assured her. 'But wouldn't it be nice to have a little more space? Four of us in one bedroom is very tight, and Emily and Jack are only getting bigger.' Not to mention, moments of privacy were virtually nonexistent.

She pondered the idea, her expression brightening as the appeal of it took hold. 'It would be lovely to have a small garden they could play in. Where could we find a place like that?'

'I don't know,' he answered honestly. 'I've walked through many different neighbourhoods in my search for Bronagh but I'm not sure where there might be houses available, particularly in the present circumstances. We would have to investigate further. You'd like to consider it though?'

She gazed down the quiet street, the glow of the nearby lamp casting a shadow on the far side of her face. A burst of laughter floated down the stairs behind them.

'It would be quite a commitment, wouldn't it?' she said softly. 'There would be no returning to Ireland anytime soon.'

A pang of homesickness tugged at his heart. 'I suppose not,' he said, striving to prevent his tone from becoming wistful. 'But we are establishing our lives here so perhaps this is where we should concentrate on putting down roots.'

She looked back at him. Tears shone in her eyes again but she was smiling. 'I think it's a wonderful plan. We must make the best life for our family right where we are.'

***

'Moving?' repeated Orlaith, staring from Bridget to Cormac.

They had waited until Charlie had left and the children had been put to bed before raising the subject with Orlaith and Tess. Bridget sat on the stool with the letter open on the table before her. Cormac stood at her shoulder, while his sister and Tess occupied the bench opposite them, both slack-jawed.

'Yes,' said Bridget. Her throat hurt from crying and her emotions were a tangled mess of grief and excitement but she tried to keep her voice steady. 'We don't know how long we shall remain in Boston while we try to find Bronagh so we should like to settle in a more permanent abode for as long as we are here.'

Tess pursed her mouth. 'Well, I suppose we couldn't expect you to slum it with the poor folk forever,' she said coolly.

Bridget bristled. 'That isn't the case at all, I assure you.'

'You are mistaken, Tess,' Cormac agreed, a slight edge to his words. 'We're thinking especially of Emily and Jack. They would thrive in a bigger space. I'm sure you can agree that this place is a bit small for growing children.'

'Seems to suit the Carey brood just fine,' Tess muttered. 'Don't see why it's not good enough for yous.'

'We didn't realise you weren't happy with the way things have been,' Orlaith said more neutrally.

'On the contrary, we have been very content here,' said Bridget. 'But the opportunity has arisen to improve our situation and we think we should seize it.' Guessing the source of Tess's petulance, she added, 'We have no intention of leaving either of you behind. We hope you will be willing to come too.' Even as she said it, she knew she did not mean it where Tess was concerned.

Tess immediately looked mollified. Orlaith, on the other hand, gnawed on her lower lip, her expression pensive.

'I think,' she said slowly, 'I might prefer to stay here.'

Tess shot her a sideways glance. 'Really?'

Orlaith nodded. 'I'm ready to rely on myself. It's time to step out from under my brother's wing.' She gave Cormac a smile which conveyed both her gratitude and her determination.

He dipped his head in acknowledgement. Though he couldn't conceal the regret that was plain in his features, he said, 'I understand. Much as we'll miss you, I won't attempt to convince you to change your mind.'

Bridget watched Tess for her reaction. It would be inappropriate for her to accompany the family without Orlaith. She seemed to recognise this too for she shrugged and elbowed her friend.

'I like the sound of that,' she said jauntily. 'A pair of independent women with not a care in the world.' Bridget doubted whether the floor would ever be scrubbed after she left.

Orlaith frowned. 'We sure would have cares. Keeping up the rent on this place, for one thing. We'll have to start earning proper money, not just odd pennies now and then. We should make it more widely known in the local area that both of us can nurse wounds. If we help enough folk, we'll gain a reputation for it.'

That would likely do better for them than the midwifery route. They didn't earn anything when they accompanied Derval to births as observers only, and neither of them had felt confident enough yet to deliver a baby themselves. Apart from that, Derval was well established as a midwife in the community so they would need to go much further afield to find custom. However, Orlaith had developed a flair for bandaging injuries, greatly helped along the way by both Cormac and Charlie who had given her ample occasion to practise her nursing skills. Tess didn't quite have the same zeal for it but her aptitude matched well enough as she had been obliged to bind more than one wound while living in the shelter for homeless people in Dublin.

It was feasible that they might be able to fend for themselves to a certain extent. Would it be enough though?

'If you find that you require additional support at any time,' Bridget said as delicately as she could, 'we would be very glad to help you.' She fingered the corner of the letter, both saddened by and grateful for its contents.

'Ah, we'll be fine,' said Tess. 'Sure, there's always another guaranteed way to make money if needs be.'

No one spoke. Bridget peeked up at Cormac; he had a face like thunder and she could imagine exactly what he thought of his sister engaging in such unsavoury exploits. Orlaith, too, looked disgusted.

Tess turned scarlet. 'I was only making a joke,' she huffed.

Orlaith put an arm around her shoulder. 'Not your funniest,' she rebuked gently. 'But y'know what is funny?'

'What?'

'We're going to have a bedroom each after they're gone.'

Tess cracked a crooked grin at that. Cormac, his countenance calm again, touched a hand to his chest in an offended manner.

'So now you want to be rid of us as soon as possible, is that it?' He emitted a theatrical sigh and then winked. 'We'll start seeking a new place right away.'

CHAPTER 15

A chilly March wind tugged at the ends of Bridget's cloak but she didn't feel the cold as she hugged Jack close in her arms, her lips pressed to his soft hair. Those fine locks were so light that they were almost the colour of milk and his eyes peering out below had remained a striking shade of blue, so at over a year old it seemed fair to say that Jack had taken after both his father and his namesake grandfather in his features. He had also started walking with tentative, wavering steps but, unlike the audacious Brian Carey, he was still content to stay within his mother's embrace too, for now at least.

'Don't grow up too fast, my lamb,' she murmured. 'Your mama can only handle so much upheaval at once.'

A significant source of such upheaval stood before her. Right there on a weedy footpath in South Boston, her heart swelled as she took in the two-storey wooden structure with its walls painted light grey and its shutters dark grey. The paint was a little faded but the shutters were whole and hung properly from the window frames. Four steps led up to the brown front door which swung open while she gazed at it.

'Come back inside, Mama! I've found a squeaky step on the stairs. I'm going to name him Barnabas!'

Jack stretched out a pudgy hand towards his sister and burbled, 'Emmy! Emmy!'

'We're coming, gooseberry. Jack and I just wanted to take another look from the outside.'

Bridget climbed the steps and entered the house again. A faint odour of tobacco indicated that the previous owner had been a pipe smoker but she hoped that would diminish with time. Cormac was standing in the doorway which separated the two downstairs rooms, one front and one back, knocking at the lintel as though to confirm its soundness.

'Come meet Barnabas,' Emily said and beckoned Bridget to the narrow staircase rising on the left of the front room. The rest of the space was empty apart from a decent-sized fireplace on the right wall.

Emily ascended seven steps up the stairs, paused for dramatic effect, and then pressed her foot onto the eighth step. It creaked loudly. She bent low over it.

'Nice to meet you too, Barnabas!' She looked over her shoulder expectantly at Bridget.

Still at the bottom of the stairs, Bridget curtseyed in the direction of the step. 'A pleasure to make your acquaintance, Barnabas.' As Emily skipped back down the stairs to her, she added, 'I thought that was a name you were saving for your future hens?'

Emily turned solemn. 'Barnabas is a boy's name but Papa told me hens are only girls. The stairs is a boy though,' she finished confidently. With that, she bounded across the room and squeezed past Cormac in the doorway, exclaiming, 'I want to see the garden!'

Bridget followed with Jack and joined Cormac at the threshold into the back room. A door in the far wall led out into the garden and Emily's golden hair whipped out of sight through it but Bridget paused before going after her. This was the aspect of the house which had excited her the most when they had come to visit before – it was a kitchen area with a table in the centre but, more importantly, it contained a cast-iron stove which the previous owner had elected to leave behind. She crossed over to it, shifting Jack so she was gripping him with one arm, and lovingly stroked the stove's cool surface with her other hand.

'What a luxury you will be,' she said to it.

'Perhaps we should give it a name too,' Cormac suggested behind her. She could hear the smile in his voice.

'I think christening one inanimate object in the house is probably enough,' she said with a laugh.

They continued on out into the garden, although she supposed they should probably call it a yard instead. It was not much to speak of, just a patch of thin grass surrounded by a peeling fence, but she experienced another thrill when she remembered that it was now *theirs*. Less appealing but still necessary, a privy stood in the far corner – the fact that they would not have to share it with numerous others was an additional luxury.

Emily was spinning in circles, her arms outstretched and her face turned up to the sky. Fat drops of rain had started to fall.

'We should go indoors, gooseberry,' Bridget called to her.

'Join me instead!' she replied, still spinning.

Cormac didn't hesitate to obey, dashing over to grasp Emily's hands and whirl her around. She shrieked with glee. Bridget clutched Jack tightly and twirled him about too, causing him to giggle and cry, 'More!'

It wasn't until the heavens opened and a deluge poured down that they ran back inside the house, shaking off droplets of water and weak with laughter.

No one was laughing later that night when, not long after the children had been put to bed, Emily let out a scream which had her parents tearing up the stairs with a new glass-covered oil lamp. There were three rooms on the upper floor: a bedroom at the front for Bridget and Cormac and two smaller spaces at the back, one no bigger than a box room and the other large enough to fit Emily's mattress and Jack's cot. When they ran in, Emily was sitting bolt upright, her face wet. She pointed a tremulous finger upwards and Bridget glimpsed rainwater leaking from the ceiling directly above the mattress. Emily's scream had also woken Jack and, although his cot was dry, he was wailing at the top of his lungs. Bridget hurried to soothe him while Cormac slid Emily and her mattress out of range of the dripping water and assured her that the house would not flood and float away down the street. Then he fetched the basin, which was one of the few belongings they had brought with them from Broad Street, and set it on the floor beneath the leak, while Emily wondered aloud if they would have been able to sail all the way back to visit Auntie Orlaith and Auntie Tess.

The room was unusable until the roof could be repaired. The box room would fit Emily's mattress but not Jack's cot and Emily decided she didn't want to sleep alone after her traumatic experience – 'I could have *drowned*!' – which resulted in the mattress, the cot and the two children taking up residence in Bridget and Cormac's bedroom for the night. They didn't have alternative bedding to replace the damp bedcovers so they bundled up Emily in Bridget's cloak instead.

'So much for getting some privacy at last,' Bridget said in an undertone as, after an extended period of stories and lullabies, she gently closed over the door on the two sleeping figures, leaving it ajar.

'I'll make fixing the roof my first priority,' Cormac promised.

He led the way with the oil lamp and they crept back downstairs, stepping carefully over Barnabas to prevent the squeaking stair from causing any further disturbance above.

Tiptoeing into the kitchen, they left the door open just a fraction and breathed simultaneous sighs of relief at the continued silence. Bridget glanced around – excepting the stove and the table, the room was bare of furnishings.

'Chairs will be my second priority,' said Cormac.

'You're going to be busy,' she said. 'I shall prepare a list for you.'

Grinning at him, she crossed to the table and gathered her skirts to perch on its surface, transforming it into a makeshift chair for now. He followed suit, placing the lamp on the tabletop before sitting next to her and resting his forearms on his thighs.

'Can you believe it?' he said. 'Our very own home.' He shook his head as though he couldn't quite believe it himself.

She tucked her arm inside his and laid her temple on his shoulder. 'I can't even begin to describe how joyful I am.'

'It does require some sprucing up,' he went on. 'Roof leak aside, that door into the other room is hanging a bit crookedly. As for furniture, we'll have to purchase some pieces but I'd like to make what I can.'

Apart from chairs for the kitchen table, they would need a sofa of some kind for the front room as well as furniture for the bedrooms – at present, only a mattress awaited them upstairs when they went to bed. Bridget didn't mind. They could furnish and decorate in time; right now, she simply exulted in the four walls that enclosed a happy future for her family.

'Higgins at the docks has a brother living in the area. He says South Boston's got a substantial Irish community like Broad Street and he recommended Saint Augustine's as the local Catholic church. It's only a few streets from here so it would be convenient for us but we could always attend Mass back at the cathedral for special occasions. And of course it will remain the contact point should Bronagh see one of the notices in *The*

Pilot.' Cormac paused. 'He also mentioned Hawes School as a local school which takes both boys and girls. I was wondering if we should consider it for Emily?'

Bridget lifted her head to stare meditatively at the wall. 'That's certainly an idea. She is without a governess but just because we no longer move in upper circles doesn't mean that she ought not to still receive an education.'

'I agree. Insofar as is possible, I don't want her to be disadvantaged by this way of life we've chosen.'

When she glanced back at him, he didn't disguise the apprehension in his expression. How much did it prey upon him that he had taken her and Emily – or so he seemed to perceive it – from their privileged situation in London? She preferred to view it as a liberation. She felt she was his equal, whereas she had always been Garrett's inferior. While she missed some of her acquaintances as well as her labours at St Swithun's Workhouse, she did not pine for a society where she had been treated first as marriage fodder and later as property, and neither was it an existence that she wished for her daughter. She clasped Cormac's hand reassuringly.

'Near drowning notwithstanding,' she said, 'I think Emily is very content with our circumstances. Our initial move to this country had no detrimental effect upon her and I doubt this relocation will either. She will miss Una and Sorcha but she's an exuberant child and I'm convinced she'll make new friends in this neighbourhood.'

'I'm sure you're right.'

Twisting to face him, Bridget raised their hands to brush a kiss against his knuckles. Then she touched her mouth to his. When he kissed her back, she felt a tug deep inside and lamented the fact that their bedroom was already occupied. His lips were warm and his tongue was tender and she relaxed into his embrace, releasing his hand so he could wrap both of his arms around her. Rain battered the window behind them in a comforting staccato beat.

They broke the kiss ever so gently and she let out a blissful sigh. 'I know we have only just arrived but I haven't experienced such a sense of "home" since I lived at Oakleigh. It feels like the house is welcoming us with open arms, so to speak.'

He nudged his nose against hers. 'Though it is rather more humble than the manor, you have to admit. A mere acorn in comparison to that mighty oak.'

She smiled. 'It may not be so grand but I think it still deserves a name. What do you think?'

In the next heartbeat, their gazes locked together. 'Acorn House,' they said at the same time.

They beamed and held each other close, cradling the cherished past and the precious future between them. Bridget rested her palm on his chest and prayed that Emily and Jack would have as happy a childhood in Acorn House as she and Cormac had enjoyed at Oakleigh.

He loosened his grasp a little and his lips found a sensitive spot on her neck, caressing it softly. It tickled at first but then he increased the pressure, producing a sensation altogether more pleasurable. She emitted a small moan and he sucked harder until her skin was singing with arousal. When she dropped her hand to his lap, she realised that he was getting great pleasure from the experience too.

He interrupted his endeavours to grumble, 'God, I wish the roof hadn't sprung a leak.'

She was inclined to disagree for she had just had an idea. Bringing her mouth close to his ear, she murmured, 'If only there was another flat piece of furniture in the house.'

She drew back in time to see his eyes widen. His gaze cut downwards and then returned to her. 'If only,' he repeated, the fire in his expression unmistakable.

She tightened her grip. With a renewed sense of purpose, he resumed his attentions on her tingling neck, while his own hand roved down her back to clutch her backside. She rolled towards him to provide more of it for him to grasp and he rumbled his approval, squeezing firmly. He nipped at her skin with his teeth and she responded by biting his earlobe, before soothing the hurt with a lick of her tongue.

He slid off the table and moved to stand in front of her. Maintaining smouldering eye contact, he hiked up her layers of skirts until they gathered in folds around her waist. He stepped in closer and she wrapped her legs around him, pulling him tight against her exposed region below. He braced his fists on the tabletop on either side of her and, with an almost bruising force, they kissed passionately.

How freeing it was to be physical with each other without fear of intrusion. The rooms at Broad Street had offered no privacy whatsoever and even fumbles in the dark of night had run the risk that one or both children could awaken at any moment. They had groped hurriedly, in hushed, fleeting moments, repressing the sounds of their satisfaction and rushing to finish before they might be discovered.

Not tonight. A whole floor separated them from the only other inhabitants of the house and, with any luck, the two children would stay fast asleep, worn out after the earlier upset. Even if Emily woke and chose to venture downstairs, Barnabas, whom Bridget now recognised as a blessing in disguise, would alert them to her presence in sufficient time for them to part and fix their clothing. The two doors remained ajar but, while that prevented exclamations of the most energetic nature, it did not deny them the opportunity to articulate their gratification in at least louder terms than their near silent activities at Broad Street.

To prove the point, she let out a delicious groan as any lingering inhibitions dwindled away. The vigour of their kissing

145

bent her backwards and she hooked her feet around his thighs to keep herself braced against his body.

'I want—' she gasped.

He pulled back. 'Tell me,' he said, his ardent blue eyes promising to grant her anything she desired.

'I want to see you naked,' she said breathlessly.

He gave her a lopsided smile and, stepping back, started to unbutton his waistcoat. 'If we get disturbed, I'll escape out the back door to spare everyone's blushes. Just be generous and throw my clothing out after me.'

His waistcoat dropped to the floor. He tugged his shirt from the confines of his trousers, drew it over his head and let it fall too. Greeted with a fine view, she reached out to skim her fingers over his lean torso, greatly appreciative of his industrious labours at the docks.

'Everything,' she implored.

He obliged and, once the rest of his clothes and his boots lay scattered by his feet, the soft glow of the oil lamp illuminated his bare, eager body. She drank in the sight, her yearning for fulfilment mounting with each passing second. Unwilling to wait any longer, she took a persuasive hold of him and urged him to her.

'Not yet,' he said with a wink.

He knelt before her, compelling her to release him. He removed her boots and then, hands burrowing under her bunched-up skirts, he sought out the drawstring of her drawers. She adjusted her position on the table to allow him to undo the drawstring and slip the drawers down her buttocks and legs, easing them over her stockings. After casting them aside, he returned to her skirts, pushing them back to reveal the trio of freckles that adorned her right hip.

'I love these,' he murmured, planting a kiss upon them. 'One of them is just a fraction larger than the other two but other than that they make a perfect triangle.'

He brushed his mouth against them once more. His fair hair spilled over his forehead, grazing her skin, and she idly reflected that he needed a haircut. In the next instant, that thought vanished as his lips trailed down her outer thigh, leaving gooseflesh in their wake, and a frisson of excitement ran along her spine. He hooked her knee over his shoulder and continued his kisses, this time up the inside of her thigh, and further...

She tilted back on the table, only dimly registering its hard surface. All of her awareness became narrowed to just one point, that nub of heat and sensation and intensity that was receiving the most rigorous attention from his mouth and she felt the anticipation building and her hips thrust against him and a wave was coming and she couldn't contain it—

Her back arched off the table as she quivered and a high-pitched gasp erupted from her. She bowed over him, trembling. Unhooking her knee, he rose and held her in his arms.

'That was rather spectacular,' she mumbled, her head spinning like she had drunk a glass of wine too fast.

He bent his head to kiss her and she tasted herself on his lips. With a great effort, she pulled her senses together and cocked an ear to listen for any indication of movement above. All seemed quiet. She tried to rest again against his chest but he was detaching himself from her.

'Where are you—'

He sidled around the corner of the table to grasp the oil lamp which had shifted and was now sitting perilously close to the brink.

'I'm just going to take this out of harm's way,' he said, twinkling at her, and set it on the floor.

Its light cast different shadows around the room as he returned to her, tucking himself once more inside her embrace. She pushed his hair back and touched her mouth to his, squeezing her thighs around his hips to communicate her readiness.

He leaned over her, his tongue flicking across that spot on her neck again. Putting his hands under her backside, he drew her towards him until she was balanced on the edge of the table. She lay back, stretching her arms above her head to grip the far end, and received him with joyous welcome. She closed her eyes, revelling in the union that made her feel utterly whole. When she opened them again, her gaze connected with his.

'*A rún mo chroí*,' he whispered, and she knew he knew how those words set her aflame, like a spark to tinder. She clenched her muscles around him in a fervent plea.

He moved, first with slow, lingering strokes and then with more urgency. Her pulse pounded to the same rhythm and his breath came in fast, shallow pants. That familiar wave grew between them and her heart soared as he crested it too but, right at the pinnacle, the table, which had been mute until now, gave an almighty creak and a distinct lurch and Cormac's deep groan became swallowed in a muffled fit of laughter as he collapsed upon her, his face pressed to her bosom. Convulsing with uncontrollable giggles, she rested her hands on his head and they lay there, shaking and hoping that the table wouldn't give way beneath them.

When he surfaced at last, he gasped, 'That'll be the third priority.'

'Perhaps we ought to advance it up the list a little?' she returned, panting.

Once they had recovered their wits, he eased away and helped her gingerly descend from the table. It remained standing but exhibited a noticeable slant that hadn't been there before.

Cormac threw on his shirt and trousers and, barefoot, padded over to the oil lamp to pick it up off the floor and place it on top of the unlit stove rather than the now-untrustworthy table.

'Can you believe that neither of the children woke?' Bridget said, rearranging her skirts around her ankles.

'A miracle,' he agreed. He tossed her a mischievous look. 'Good to know for the future.'

She shook her head with a half-smile. 'You're insatiable,' she said, but secretly she was of the same mind. She gathered the remaining strewn clothes up into her arms. 'Shall we go to bed? You'll have an earlier start in the morning now that we're further from the docks.'

'I'll have a later finish too. I promised O'Mali I'd take him for a pint in return for his help moving the bits of furniture today.'

'Why don't you invite him back here for supper?' she said. 'I'm sure I'll have figured out how to work the stove by then.'

'Good idea, I'll do that so.'

He grabbed the lamp and crossed to the door leading to the front room, holding it open for her. She passed through but he didn't follow, lingering instead on the threshold. She glanced back over her shoulder; with his free hand, he reached up to the lintel as he had done before but this time he just gave it an affectionate pat.

'Despite the leaky roof and the creaky table, we are grateful for the warm welcome, Acorn House.'

CHAPTER 16

Emily caught herself chewing on the end of her pencil again. With a conscious effort, she removed it from her mouth. She needed to be more careful – it was only an inch and a half long now but there were still a couple of weeks to go until her ninth birthday so it had to last a bit longer yet.

She had been eyeing the ceiling dubiously but Papa had promised her lots of times that it would not leak again since he had fixed it. So instead she returned to scrutinising the page laid out on the floor of her and Jack's bedroom and, after a meditative pause, she drew a smooth curve to add to her creation. She was practising faces but they were hard to do.

'Emily!' Papa's voice came floating up the stairs. 'Can you come down here, please?'

She got up off her knees at once, wondering if she had forgotten to do one of her chores. But no, she had already fetched water from the public well and swept the front steps and minded Baby Jack while Mama used the stove. Tucking her page and pencil beneath her mattress, she hurried out of the bedroom and down the stairs. Barnabas produced a satisfyingly loud squeak when she sprang onto him with both feet and, delighted, she ran on into the kitchen. Papa and Mama were looking out the window while Baby Jack was pulling himself to his feet by holding onto the leg of the new table Papa had recently finished building out in the back yard.

'Yes, Papa?'

He turned to her with a big smile. 'I have a surprise for you, *a stór.*'

She bounced on her toes with glee. 'What is it?'

'Follow me,' he said, crooking his finger at her, and he disappeared through the back door.

She scampered after him and emerged into the yard. The smelly privy was there as usual but in the opposite corner stood an unfamiliar wooden structure with a ramp leading up to a small door and in front of it—

'My hens!' she squealed.

Three plump hens pecked in the grass, two with brown feathers and one sporting magnificent white plumage. She dashed towards them but they flapped out of reach.

'You'll have to be a bit gentler with them, *a stór,*' said Papa. 'But once they get to know you, they won't shy away.'

She stood stock still, hoping they might come back to her. The brown pair huddled near the coop but the white one meandered nearer again. She extended a tentative hand and, when it didn't retreat, she touched its beautiful feathers. Rapturous, she turned to scurry back to Papa and flung her arms around his waist.

'Thank you!' she exclaimed. 'I'm so happy!'

'I'm very glad,' he said. 'You can consider them an early birthday present.'

She pulled back, suddenly anxious. 'Will I still get my new pencil too?'

He plucked at her chin. 'You will.'

Mama joined them with Baby Jack in her arms. 'Now you'll have to decide what to name your new charges,' she said.

Emily spun around to contemplate her brood. She tapped her fingertips on her cheek, trying to recall all the names Auntie Orlaith had supplied from the Bible.

'Delilah,' she said, pointing at one of the brown hens who had fluttered up onto the ramp of the coop. 'Jemimah,' she continued, her finger swivelling to the other brown one. 'And Beulah!' she finished jubilantly, bestowing her favourite name upon the white hen.

'Well done,' said Papa. 'I believe that makes them the most elegant hens in all of Boston.'

She thought so too and maternal pride swelled within her.

'We have another surprise for you, gooseberry,' said Mama. 'There is a school near here called Hawes. How would you like to go to school with the other local girls and boys?'

Emily remembered her governess, Miss Davison, whom she had admired for her broad knowledge of history and geography and her pretty French words. She had taken much pleasure in their lessons together. Would she enjoy going to school?

'Yes!' she said. 'I would like that.'

***

'What's that stink?' said Tess, wrinkling her nose.

Bridget gritted her teeth. Orlaith and Tess had barely stepped over the threshold and already Tess's thoughtless tongue was at work. Keeping her tone level, Bridget said, 'The night soil men came last night to empty the privies on this street. We do apologise for the poor timing but the odour ought to dissipate before too long.'

'Not to worry,' said Orlaith, unconcerned. 'Sure, it's nothing we haven't smelled before on Broad Street.'

'Auntie Orlaith! Auntie Tess!' Emily came barrelling forwards and gave them both tight hugs. 'Come meet my hens!'

She seized Orlaith's hand and dragged her across the front room, which was still empty of furniture, and through the door into the kitchen. Bridget and Tess followed and they all went out into the back yard. The stench became a touch stronger here but an obliging breeze carried the worst of it away. They found Cormac leaning over a bench, sawing at a length of wood. Shirtless under the warm May sun, he blew out his cheeks in the heat and sweat gleamed at the base of his spine where a small blemish was just visible in the shape of a leaf. Bridget was glad when, upon the appearance of the visitors, he grabbed his shirt from the end of the bench and donned it. That secret blemish was for her eyes only and she hoped Orlaith and Tess hadn't spotted it.

'Welcome,' he said to them with a grin. He waved at his labours. 'I'd invite you to take a seat but I'm still in the process of making them.'

Having completed the new kitchen table, which was much, much sturdier than the last, he had started working on a set of chairs to go with it. He had sourced proper timber for these jobs rather than using scraps from the docks and, when he was not out making increasingly desultory enquiries about Bronagh, he toiled on Sundays and in the evenings after work as the days grew longer heading towards summer. Bridget couldn't wait until he had finished them; all they had to use at present were a couple of rudimentary stools which he had cobbled together to tide them over until the chairs were ready.

'I'm happy to sit on the grass anyway,' said Orlaith, flopping down. Delilah was scratching in the grass near her but flapped a few paces away at the sudden movement. 'Where's Jack?'

'Napping upstairs,' said Bridget, joining her on the grass, which was patchy in places but dry. 'I'll bring him down shortly but we might go inside for a little while if he's cranky when he wakes.' She lowered her voice. 'We wouldn't want to disturb the neighbours.'

Cormac chuckled at Orlaith's raised eyebrows. 'There's an older couple living next to us,' he explained, also speaking in an undertone, 'and they're not terribly fond of children. You should have seen the way their faces fell when they met us and realised we possessed not one but two little fiends.'

He dusted off the bench and gestured to Tess if she wanted to sit on it. She took it at once, scooting to the edge so there was still enough space for him. He sat too, while Emily occupied herself at the hen coop, Beulah in her arms and Jemimah's head poking out of the coop's door.

'Did the owners before yous not have any children?' asked Orlaith.

'As we understand it,' said Bridget delicately, 'the previous owner was a bachelor who only entertained gentleman callers. Mr and Mrs Hill were rather tight-lipped about him.'

'Ah. And your neighbours on the other side?'

'A boarding house with a fairly high turnover of lodgers by the looks of it,' said Cormac. 'It's a disappointment for Emily not to have other children as near as the Careys were.'

'But I'll make lots of friends when I go to school!' she chirped, skipping over to drop Beulah into Orlaith's lap.

Orlaith hesitated before gently stroking the hen's feathers and a faraway expression came over her face. All at once, Bridget felt transported back in time to a warm cottage smelling of turf with a solemn, round-eyed girl sitting on the hearth. She half expected Maggie to appear around the corner of the house and offer her a cup of milk.

The spell was broken when Tess said, 'Y'know, Broad Street is so much quieter these days. I'm getting great sleep with no bawling in the middle of the night.' She elbowed Cormac. 'We do still miss yous though.'

'We miss you both too,' he replied. 'And Broad Street as well.'

'Ah now,' said Tess, 'how can you say that with the size of this fancy house and its fancy stove and all the fancy furniture you're making? I suppose yous'll start wearing fancier clothes too.'

This touched a nerve as Bridget had indeed been contemplating the idea of sewing some new garments for the family. 'It would be nice to get new fabric at a later stage,' she said stiffly, 'but we will not be leading extravagant lives by any means. If you noticed the stove, you might also have noticed the lack of any sofa yet in front of the fireplace.'

'Speaking of modest living,' Orlaith interjected before Tess could respond. Her vague expression disappeared as she sat up straighter. 'I have some news. A few of the Ursuline nuns have returned to Boston. They are hoping to restore the convent and the school.'

'Tell them the rest of it,' Tess prodded.

Orlaith flushed. 'Well...I'm thinking of joining them.'

Cormac tilted his head, his features full of astonishment. 'You want to become a nun?'

'Maybe not right away,' she said. 'I thought I might start off as a laywoman first. I've already spoken to Sister Annunciata and she said it's possible. It's not just about faith—they engage in healing in the community. We could learn a lot from them.'

Bridget stared at Tess. 'Are you considering it too?'

Tess laughed. 'Not in a hundred years. They probably wouldn't take me anyway, soiled as I am. But I'd be open to gaining more nursing skills from them.'

'There's great appeal in the way they live their lives,' Orlaith added. 'Humble, uncomplicated, devout, and they've got such a generosity of spirit in giving their time and help to others.'

Bridget conjectured that some of those words must have first come from Sister Annunciata's mouth, but there was no denying that the zeal was all Orlaith's. She held her chin high and her eyes shone with enthusiasm.

'I can't say this isn't a surprise, but good for you,' said Cormac. He ran his hand through his hair and a few flecks of sawdust spiralled away on the breeze. 'I imagine your efforts with them will be on a voluntary basis?'

Orlaith nodded. 'All donations have to be handed over to the Ursulines. But we can still earn money for any nursing we do outside of our work with the order.'

'Do let us know if you ever need a helping hand,' said Bridget. The house had depleted much of her inheritance from her uncle and there had been extra expenses like the unexpected roof repairs, but they were not on the breadline. And the sofa and fabric could wait, after all.

'I hope we won't but thank you,' said Orlaith with a genuine smile and Bridget felt a tiny strengthening of their sisterly bond. Orlaith had created a fortress around herself a long time ago but she was cracking open its doors bit by bit.

In the companionable silence that followed, the only sounds were the contented clucking of the hens and some indistinct chatter drifting over the fence from the boarding house next door.

'How's Charlie these days?' Cormac asked suddenly. 'Have you seen him much?'

'He called by a couple of times recently,' said Orlaith. 'Once 'cause he was in the neighbourhood after putting out a fire a few streets over, and another day he asked me to bandage a burn on his arm. Why?'

'No reason,' said Cormac, his voice light.

CHAPTER 17

Bridget slid her fingers through Cormac's hair, still damp after he had dipped his head in the basin of water. She gathered a portion of it between her forefinger and middle finger, lined up her scissors, and snipped. Several inches of the fair strands, the wetness making them a few shades darker than usual, wafted onto his shoulder and she brushed them off onto the kitchen floor.

'We shouldn't have let it become so unkempt,' she remarked. 'You're a holy disgrace.'

She separated out the next segment of hair and the scissors sliced again. Cormac remained still beneath her hands, seated on one of the new chairs he had finished building. The window was open; through it, they could hear Jack's high-pitched giggles as he watched Emily playing with the hens from his cot, which Cormac had brought out into the June sunshine earlier. Bridget clipped once more and another lock of hair fell.

'There's more of it than I realised,' she said. 'Did you ever let it grow this long before?'

'I didn't have much occasion to visit the barber during my time in Dublin,' he answered, his tone dry.

'Oh, I'm sorry, that was quite thoughtless.' She pressed an apologetic kiss to the nape of his neck. Then she set her scissors down on the table. 'Wait there a moment. I need to check on the soup.'

She crossed over to the stove and found that the pot of soup had stopped simmering so she opened the stove door and used the tongs to lift some lumps of coal from the scuttle and place them inside. As she shut the door again, still holding the tongs, she was arrested by a sudden, distressing memory and with it came the realisation that she had never imparted that grievous loss to Cormac. Heart squeezing with unexpected sorrow, she hung the tongs on its peg next to the stove and turned back to him.

'What's the matter?' he asked, startled.

'It's nothing,' she said, her clogged throat belying her words. 'I just remembered...' She stepped up to him and took his hands. 'Do you recall the wooden bird you carved that summer at Oakleigh? Garrett gave it to me the day we had the picnic in the grove.'

He nodded, his forehead creased.

'It was a lifeline for me all through my early days in London. You were gone—forever, I believed—but I still retained this one tiny link to you, something you had created with these gifted hands.' She tightened her grasp on his fingers. 'When Emily was born, I realised I held an even greater part of you and I gave her the bird as she grew during her infancy, wanting her to share that connection too.' Bridget swallowed. 'Garrett discovered the bird and burned it. It was a devastating stroke. I tried to retrieve it from the fire with the tongs but it broke apart and it felt like another piece of my heart crumbled along with it.'

Cormac's blue eyes clouded over. 'I'm sorry you suffered that grief.'

'I don't know why the memory is having such an effect on me now.' She smiled, even as tears trembled on her eyelids. 'After all, you're right here in front of me.'

'And I'm not going anywhere,' he assured her. He extricated his left hand to touch his fingertips to her right hip, directly over the spot where her trio of freckles lay hidden beneath the fabric of her skirts. A gesture of affection, a pledge.

She bent to kiss him, her lips lingering over his, before releasing him and returning to her station behind the chair again. She picked up the scissors and resumed cutting his hair, which collected in small mounds at her feet.

After a minute or two, he said, 'I could carve a new figurine. Perhaps not a bird this time, but something else with a special significance.' He straightened without warning, obliging her to snatch back the scissors to avoid nicking his scalp. He half turned his head and she could see the upward curve at the corner of his mouth. 'I've got it. I'll do one of our family with four figures—a man, a woman, a girl, and a boy. What do you think?'

She paused. Now was the time.

'I'm not sure,' she said casually. 'I think you should wait.'

'Wait for what?'

'Until we know whether the fifth figure will be a boy or a girl.'

He went motionless and it seemed as though he had stopped breathing altogether. Then an exclamation of utter delight burst from him and she had the presence of mind to put down the scissors just in time before he swung around in the chair and pulled her into his lap.

'Truly?' he said eagerly.

'Yes,' she replied, beaming.

He hugged her so closely that she almost stopped breathing herself. When he drew back, he rested his palm on her stomach even though there was no telltale swell yet.

'What a blessing,' he said, his wonder clear in his voice. 'You're certain?'

She laced her fingers through his over her belly. 'I believe more than two months have passed. It's my fourth time. I've learned to recognise the signs.'

Two of those joyful arrivals were laughing right now beyond the window but, still rather overwrought from reliving the destruction of the wooden bird, she couldn't help but dwell upon the one who was no longer with her. Had he lived, James would be six years old now. What would he have been like at that age? How she ached for what could never be known.

Garrett, too, hovered at the forefront of her thoughts. In all their years together, whether by unlucky chance or some defect in their own bodies, she had conceived only once. Did he ever think of the beloved boy they had lost? Or of the illegitimate son he had rejected prior to that? Patrick lived, but in reality Garrett had no children at all.

Cormac touched a gentle knuckle to her chin. 'Where are you gone?' he murmured.

Realising that she had been staring off into the distance, she dragged her gaze guiltily back to his.

'What were you thinking about?' he asked.

She bit the tip of her tongue. 'Reflections inappropriate to our happy occasion.'

He didn't say anything but, rather than getting the impression that he was waiting for her to divulge, she understood that he was allowing her the space to tell him if she wanted to.

It gave her the confidence to admit without shame, 'James.'

He cast her a sympathetic look. 'That's only natural.'

'And Garrett,' she added.

His expression became more resigned. 'That's to be expected as well. He's the only other person with whom you have shared this experience.'

That was true, although disclosing to Garrett that she was with child had followed right on the heels of his burning the wooden bird so that event had little in common with today's joy. It wasn't until James had been born that they had established a form of reconciliation.

'You know, despite his flaws, he so dearly wished to be a father,' she told Cormac. 'Which makes it all the more astounding that he had it within him to spurn Patrick the way he did. I'm sure he could have found a way to support Mary as his mistress if he had tried.'

Cormac shrugged a shoulder and single strands of hair drifted down between them. 'He probably thought there would be ample opportunity to sire legitimate progeny in the future and that he had no use for a by-blow.'

'I wonder how bitterly does he regret the choice he made, now that he has no wife?'

Cautiously, as though he didn't want to offend her, Cormac said, 'Perhaps he will seek another lady to provide him with children.'

That gave her pause. 'Of course, I hadn't considered that. If he decides to remarry, he will need to obtain a divorce from me first.'

'We can live in hope that he'll remove that noose from around our necks.'

Cormac stroked her stomach and she thought of the growing baby inside who would be born illegitimate, just like Jack. None of their acquaintances in Boston were aware of that fact so it would likely only prove an issue if they ever returned to Ireland. Still, even if the truth did emerge, she was determined to do everything she could to ensure it would not prevent either of them from leading fulfilling lives. And that was rooted first and foremost in raising them and Emily in a loving home, which was an absolute guarantee.

161

She curved her hand around Cormac's cheek. 'Noose or not, we are fortunate in so many other ways,' she breathed.

'We are,' he said. He turned his head and kissed her palm. 'Jack won't understand but shall we go tell Emily the good news?'

'Yes, let's.' As she got off his lap, she said, 'I've thought of someone who won't welcome it, however.'

He raised an eyebrow in question.

'Mr and Mrs Hill,' she said with a chuckle. 'They will be unimpressed to learn that there's going to be a third fiend next door to them.'

Emily, on the other hand, received the news with enthusiasm, albeit with one earnest stipulation. 'A sister this time, please!'

CHAPTER 18

There was such a coil of nerves twisting up her throat that Emily could hardly swallow. The schoolmaster, Mr Miller, had turned from her to berate two girls who had arrived late to the classroom and subsequently appeared to have forgotten about her altogether, occupied instead with digging papers out of his satchel behind his desk at the top of the room.

She coughed to clear her throat of some of the nerves. 'Excuse me, Mr Miller?'

He looked up in irritation. He had a square-shaped face with close-set eyes and a hairy growth on the side of his nose.

'Where should I sit, sir?'

He glanced around the classroom. 'Do you have good eyesight, Miss McGovern?'

Eyes wide, she nodded fervently.

'Can you see an empty desk?'

Fearful, she peered along the rows of desks; a girl perched primly on a chair behind each one, save for a vacant space by the far window.

'Yes, sir.'

'Then take it and stop wasting my time.'

She scuttled over to the empty seat and sank into it, her cheeks flaming. A bushy-haired girl at the next desk over gave her a fleeting look of compassion but didn't speak, instead swivelling to stare forwards as Mr Miller began the morning lessons.

Her first day at Hawes School was not what she had expected it to be. The schoolmaster's barking voice was nothing like the gentle tones of her governess back in London and neither did his temperament match Miss Davison's. She had been patient with Emily's mistakes but Mr Miller seemed to treat every error committed by his pupils as a personal affront and he made sure that they were fully aware of his disappointment. Before two hours had passed, she had witnessed three different girls crying.

The nerves in her throat dropped into her stomach, squirming inside her like wriggling worms. When she imagined the soft, slimy worms writhing about, she felt quite ill and glanced out the window to distract her mind from the image. A light September rain hit the panes.

'Eyes to the front, Miss McGovern!' Mr Miller snapped.

She jerked her gaze back to the blackboard at once, her chalk slipping across her slate in her fright. How she longed for a hug from Mabel. Mama had explained that it wasn't appropriate for Mabel to attend school too but Emily had compromised by drawing a picture of her which was currently tucked into a pocket of her pinafore. As soon as an opportunity presented itself, she would take it out and press it to her heart, which would be as close to a hug as she could possibly get until the school day ended.

Lessons stopped at noon for lunch. The pupils produced a variety of tin buckets and metal pails while the bushy-haired girl seized the chance to greet Emily, leaning across the space between their desks.

'Don't mind grumpy Miller,' she said kindly. 'He's a beast to everyone. I'm Emmeline.'

Emily's breath hitched with excitement. 'I'm Emily! Our names are really alike!' She felt an immediate, deep conviction that they would become the best of friends.

'Your hair's so pretty,' said Emmeline, reaching out to tug one of Emily's golden curls. 'Mine could never look so pretty as yours. What did you bring for lunch?'

'Eggs from my hens,' Emily replied proudly and extracted two hard-boiled eggs from her own pail.

'Oh, they look tasty! Can I have one?'

She generously handed an egg over. To her delight, Emmeline seemed to enjoy it so much that she gave her half of the second one too. The worms were still fidgeting inside her stomach so she wasn't all that hungry anyway. What she truly wanted was that hug and her hand twitched several times near her pocket.

Emmeline noticed. 'What've you got in there?'

Eager to share her secret with her new friend, Emily drew out the page and unfolded it. 'This is my doll, Mabel. I miss her so much and I can't wait to get a proper hug from her when I get home.'

Emmeline's eyes went round and Emily thought she really liked the picture. But then she gave a flippant wave towards it. 'You still play with dolls, do you? They're just for babies.'

Crushed, Emily didn't know what to say. Could that be true? Was she still a baby? 'I d-don't,' she stammered. 'N-not anymore.'

She hastily folded the picture and put it away, her features blazing as hotly as when Mr Miller had told her to stop wasting his time. Emmeline didn't seem aware of her embarrassment; she was squinting past Emily out the window.

'See them?' she said, pointing.

Emily looked out and glimpsed two children trotting past the school on the opposite side of the street. Both had black skin and bare feet and, as she watched, they raised their faces to the sky to catch raindrops on their tongues.

Emmeline clicked her own tongue. 'My father says black folk are people who didn't bother washing themselves for so long that God just went and gave them filthy skin. Now they can't get rid of it no matter how hard they wash.'

Emily had no time to respond because Mr Miller called for quiet so that the afternoon lessons could commence, but Emmeline's remark added to the slithering nest of worms inside her.

The afternoon was worse than the morning because this time she was one of the girls whom the schoolmaster made cry. They were writing out spellings on their slates and he was going from desk to desk to examine each girl's work. When he reached Emily, he pointed at her slate.

'That's wrong,' he said snidely.

An awful dread bloomed inside her. 'But it's how my governess taught me to spell it,' she said, her voice not much more than a whisper.

'Your *governess*?' he repeated, his lip curling. He turned to the rest of the class. 'You'll have to mind your manners around this little lady. She's got airs and graces. She probably won't even want to be your friend.'

Horrified, Emily saw some of the other girls throw contemptuous looks in her direction. Even Emmeline shifted a little in her seat as though to physically distance herself.

'No, I do,' Emily squeaked. 'I do want to—'

But Mr Miller cut her off. 'Remove that "u". It's C-O-L-O-R. You will write it out one hundred times to make sure you don't forget it again.'

She trembled. 'But I won't be able to fit one hundred words onto my slate.'

He swung his arm in an exaggerated gesture towards the blackboard, the hairy growth on his nose bristling. 'Up there. This instant!'

She leapt out of her seat and scurried to the top of the room. As she scraped her chalk along the board, writing the same word over and over, she felt the burn of her classmates' eyes upon her back and tears leaked from the corners of her own, even though she tried her hardest to stop them. How she yearned with all her might to be anywhere else but here.

When she had completed the hundred spellings and Mr Miller had given her permission to sit down again, she shot back to her chair and shrank as low in it as she could, wiping at her cheeks. She prayed to God that time would speed up or that school would finish early or that the schoolmaster would praise her or that another girl would offer her a smile. None of those things happened.

The conclusion of the day's final lesson brought with it a colossal wave of relief. She picked up her pail and filed out of the classroom with the other girls, her feet shuffling miserably one after the other. Nobody spoke in Mr Miller's presence but once they had reached the corridor and were out of his earshot, Emmeline gave her a nudge.

'I'll still be your friend when no one's looking,' she promised. 'Bring more eggs tomorrow, won't you?'

With a grin, she ran away along the corridor.

Emily trudged home along the route Papa had walked with her twice the previous day; the rain had mostly petered out and only a drop or two fell on her bonnet. Thankfully, the worms had settled into a drowsy state but whenever she envisaged returning to school tomorrow they stirred and made her queasy again. She climbed the steps of Acorn House, her pail knocking against her knee. The door swung open and she saw Mama's protruding belly first and then her smiling mouth above it.

'Welcome home, gooseberry!' she exclaimed. 'I was watching for you from the window. Come in and tell me all about it!'

She drew Emily into the front room which now boasted a plain sofa facing the hearth. The fire was lit and Baby Jack played on the hearthrug, stacking square-shaped wooden blocks which Papa had made for him. He held one up and cried, 'Emmy! See!' Then he dashed the block against the rest of his tower and they tumbled in a heap. He laughed delightedly. Emily wished she had been at home all day building towers with Baby Jack.

Mama towed her over to the sofa and they sat down side by side.

'Well?' she said as she rubbed her palm over her swollen belly. 'How was your first day?'

Emily took a breath, prepared to recount the whole wretched disaster. But then she caught the optimistic expression on Mama's face and hesitated. She could tell that Mama was hoping to hear that it had been a success. Emily gulped. She didn't want to disappoint her.

'I-it was fine,' she said. That wasn't a strong enough word; she needed to sound happier. 'It was great! Mr Miller taught us lots of interesting spellings and the other girls were so nice and I made a new friend called Emmeline. Isn't it wonderful that our names are so alike?'

She endeavoured to beam brightly and when Mama's shoulders relaxed she knew she had done the right thing.

'That's remarkable!' said Mama. 'I'm so glad to hear you had a good day and that you made a friend already.'

She kissed Emily's forehead before rising from the sofa with a grunt of effort to tug Baby Jack away from the fireplace. 'Not too close, my lamb. Hot.'

'Hot!' said Baby Jack, his open mouth revealing little teeth which jutted out of his upper and lower gums and which had very nearly clamped down on Mabel's head last week. At the thought of Mabel, Emily's heart hiccupped. However, rather than seeking her out, she chose to fetch her pencil and paper instead and sat at the kitchen table to draw her memories of the day, thinking they might not clog her mind so much if she transferred them to the page.

Mama peeked over her shoulder as she sketched. 'These are so lifelike. Is that you writing on the schoolmaster's blackboard?'

'It was a reward for getting my spellings correct,' said Emily, shocked at how quickly the lie came to her tongue.

'My talented girl in so many ways,' said Mama proudly and the worms inside Emily roused and slithered about.

Papa agreed with Mama when he came home from the docks that evening. He was late but he didn't say why. He gave Emily a warm hug to celebrate her first day at school and picked up her sketches to admire them.

'I feel like I'm right there in the classroom looking out the window with you,' he said, sounding impressed, and she realised he was holding the drawing of the two black children.

Of all the confusing things that had happened that day, she decided that was one question she could ask. 'Papa, Emmeline said something today...'

When she repeated her new friend's words, Papa looked disgusted. Mama, who was darning at the other end of the table, exchanged a glance with him.

'I wasn't sure if it was true,' Emily said uncertainly. 'Mr O'Mali looked clean when he helped to move the furniture and when he came for supper.'

'Of course he was clean. What Emmeline said was entirely untrue,' said Papa, his tone firm.

'But then why is their skin that colour?'

'They were born with it, just like you were born with blue eyes, or Auntie Tess was born with red hair.' Papa sat next to her at the table, still clutching her picture. 'Everyone in the world has different features but that's no reason to say unkind comments about them. Different doesn't mean dangerous or bad.'

She chewed on her lip. 'But it isn't normal. There were no black people in Ireland, or in London either.'

'There were *fewer*,' he corrected. 'There are many here in America and you would see even more if you visited the continent of Africa. In fact, *you* would stick out there as being in the minority of white people. Would you like to be accused of not being "normal" just because a part of your body doesn't appear the same as everyone else's?'

'No,' she said in a tiny voice.

She feared that he was angry with her but he smiled and shunted his chair over so that he could put his arm around her shoulders.

'How we look on the outside doesn't matter, *a stór*. Who we are on the inside does, and so does the manner in which we behave towards others.'

Mama set her darning down in her lap. 'Do you remember back in Dublin we told you that some people didn't like the idea of your father and I being friends because we were raised under differing circumstances? But it wasn't fair-minded for them to think that way instead of judging us by our characters, and this is the same sort of belief. The most important thing is always to be good and kind and generous and helpful to everybody you meet.'

Emily nodded seriously. She had been generous with the eggs. She could continue to do that.

'And do bear this in mind: we would love you even if you had a beak and feathers.'

She giggled. 'Don't be silly, Papa.' Still, she felt better...about that, at least.

When she went to bed that night – she had a proper bed now, not just a mattress, and a small cupboard for her clothes too – she waited until Papa had left the bedroom with the oil lamp. Then, in the darkness, she listened to Baby Jack burbling in his sleep and hugged Mabel close to her chest. She couldn't see Mabel's face but that was probably for the best.

'I'm sorry,' she whimpered, her voice cracking. 'I'm going to miss you so much.'

After one final squeeze, she drew back the bedcovers, stepped down to the floor, and knelt in front of the cupboard. She opened its door, felt inside to lift up the pile of neatly folded clothing, and placed Mabel at the bottom of the space. Rearranging the clothing by touch, she made sure all of Mabel's limbs were tucked underneath. For a moment, she faltered and didn't think she could go through with it, but at last, with a sob, she shut the cupboard door.

She crawled back under the bedcovers and wept, her hands pressed to her mouth so she wouldn't wake Baby Jack. It was one of the hardest things she had ever had to do. But she was desperate to keep her new friend. And if Emmeline didn't play with dolls anymore, neither could she.

She dreaded returning to school the next day to face the frightening Mr Miller. What other mistakes had she learned from Miss Davison that had yet to be inadvertently exposed before the entire class? She would have to work very hard to improve at her studies and earn the schoolmaster's approval.

In the midst of her despair, one sudden thought gave her comfort, enabling her to stifle her tears and eventually drift off to sleep.

When Mr Miller conducted an art lesson, that would be her chance to shine.

CHAPTER 19

A vague surprise filled Cormac as he opened his eyes and found that he wasn't greeted by the usual pitch black darkness he expected early on an October morning. Instead, a flickering light illuminated the bedroom. When he rolled over, he saw that Bridget had already risen before him and, still in her nightdress, had lit a candle on the bedside table, its glow casting the silhouette of her curved belly across the wall behind her. In a further burst of astonishment, he realised that the bedcovers were actually wrapped around him rather than bunched on her side of the bed as was customary.

'Am I deceived?' he said, plucking at the covers in exaggerated amazement.

'I threw them back over you before you woke,' she confessed. 'In honour of the occasion. How do you feel?'

He grinned. 'Hardly a day over twenty-nine.'

Hand tenderly cupping her belly, she knelt onto the mattress – despite his industrious work over the past seven months, he had yet to finish their own bed – and gave him a kiss. 'Happy birthday, old man.'

He cleared his throat. 'Do I need to remind you that there's only a month between our ages? Come November, you'll be languishing in your thirties too.'

'True,' she said, twinkling, 'but for now a whole decade separates us.' Tilting back on her ankles, she rubbed at her bump and grimaced.

'Are you in pain?' he asked.

'No, no, just a little discomfort, that's all. Would you like your present?'

Intrigued, he sat up, propping his back against the wall. 'Where are you hiding it?'

She bent forwards again, her lips hovering enticingly over his, and he began to assume the gift was of a carnal nature, to which he had no objection, but then she said, 'It's in the drawer. Jack will wake soon and I want to give it to you before I have to get him up out of his crib.'

'Crib, is it?' he said, momentarily diverted. 'Whatever happened to calling it a cot?' He leaned over her bump. 'I believe your mother might be falling prey to the local vernacular, *a leanbh*.'

She squinted at him, amused. 'So what if I am? Do you object?'

'Certainly not. It's a sign that you feel at home which makes me very glad. I'm just wondering what will be next. Candy instead of sweets, perhaps, or who knows what else?'

She arched a lofty eyebrow. 'Do you want your present or not?'

'Yes, please,' he said, sitting back with angelic meekness.

'I shall get it then, if you're quite finished with your jests.'

He bowed his head solemnly. 'I give you my word.' His curiosity was piqued; they generally only marked Emily's birthdays with presents.

Bridget shuffled off the mattress and opened the drawer of the bedside table, angling her body in such a way that she shielded the item from view, before returning to him with it concealed in her closed fist. She started to look nervous.

'I'm not sure what you'll think of it. If you would prefer not to—well, let's see.'

She unfurled her fingers. A braided leather band lay in her palm. He picked it up and noticed the strange texture at once. Two of the braids were leather and the third—

'Is that...' He lifted it closer to his eyes, goggling. '...your hair?'

Silky chestnut strands made up the third braid, weaving in and out between the ribbons of leather.

'Yes, and there's some of yours in there too. Let me bring the light nearer.'

She reached back to the bedside table and brought the candlestick over, holding it above his hands so he could see the candlelight glimmering on the seam of fair hair entwined among the chestnut.

'I saved it when I cut your hair, although it wasn't quite long enough to stretch the whole way around the band like mine.'

At each end of the band, she had sewn a small leather flap to bind the braids neatly – an acorn was stitched onto the surface of one, a miniature oak tree on the other.

'I thought I had better make it now before our hair starts to turn grey,' she said lightly. 'Old age is upon us, after all.' She hesitated. 'Do you like it?'

He dragged his gaze from the band to her dark brown eyes. 'I love it,' he said. 'I can't even begin to tell you how much.'

She smiled with relief. He pressed his forehead to hers.

'Thank you,' he whispered. 'Will you put it on for me?'

He held out his left arm. She set down the candlestick and took the band, tying it around his wrist so that the leather flaps rested on the inside where only he could see them and only she would know about them. He raised her left hand and touched the band to the two rings on her finger, leather and hair meeting thread and gold.

'I will never take it off,' he vowed.

He felt quite overcome with emotion and expressed it by kissing her deeply, her face cradled in his palms. How he adored her, the mother of his children and the secret of his heart.

She tugged at the bedcovers, pulling them back so she could slip under and join him. He traced his fingers down her body, letting them come to a stop on her belly.

'I hope you're asleep, *a leanbh*,' he murmured. 'We don't want you paying attention for this next part.'

Bridget laughed when his hand came back up to rest on her breast. Then she cut herself off as a wail rose from the children's bedroom. They both groaned.

'We'll save your second birthday gift for later,' she promised and slid off the mattress.

CHAPTER 20

Bridget left the shop with new spools of thread in her basket, pleased that the good reputation she had gained in Broad Street had followed her to South Boston, with several of the denizens from their old neighbourhood still willing to come to her thanks to the quality of her needlework. It would be a good idea to earn a name for herself in their new locality too and she pondered how she might do that as she adjusted Jack's little cap down around his ears to protect them from the November chill.

'Take my hand, my lamb,' she said and he obediently did so.

She winced as they started walking along the footpath; the baby was causing her a great deal of soreness under her ribs but there were still two or three weeks to go until the birth. She hoped she would not have to suffer this pain for the whole of the intervening period.

All of a sudden, the skin on the back of her neck prickled and she had the strangest feeling that someone was watching her. She glanced around the street. Wagons and carriages rolled by with rattling wheels and jangling harnesses. Two women passed her and Jack on the footpath, chattering and heading in the direction of the shop they had just left. A man stood on the opposite side of the street, the collar of his coat turned up high against the cold weather and his back to them as he stared into a shop window.

She frowned and carried on, but at the next corner she cast a fleeting look over her shoulder and caught sight of the man with the high collar again. He had crossed over to their side of the street and was much nearer to them but he stepped towards an open shop door as she turned her head.

Now she was very uneasy. She increased her pace, urging Jack to hurry beside her. His short legs couldn't keep up and he began to complain. She wanted to lift him into her arms but that was an impossibility with her basket and her pregnant mound.

She peeked behind her again. The man was still there and this time he kept striding forwards instead of changing course. Her heart pounded faster. She forced Jack onwards, almost dragging him along. His toe stubbed on a crack in the footpath and he pitched forwards. She dropped her basket and managed to break his fall, but his cap went flying and her spools of thread rolled away into the gutter. Although he wasn't hurt, he started crying. She knelt and clutched him to her.

'You're safe, my lamb, all is well,' she said soothingly, running her fingers through his fair hair.

She chanced another look back up the street, panic constricting her throat.

The man was gone.

Even as relief flooded through her, she knitted her brows. Had she imagined it? It had truly felt as though he had been pursuing them.

'Here you go, miss!'

A boy of perhaps seven or eight beamed at her, his two front teeth missing and his hands grasping her dropped spools. They were ruined from the muddy gutter but she thanked him and gave him a penny for his efforts. He skipped away, delighted with himself. As she placed the spools back into her basket, the baby kicked low down and she grunted with pain.

'Let's go home, my lamb,' she said to Jack, wiping away his remaining tears and retrieving his cap from the ground.

When they reached Acorn House, Emily greeted them at the front door. She had been a little quiet of late but right now she seemed back to her usual self, bouncing on her toes.

'There's a surprise but it's not ready!' she burst out. 'You need to wait a few minutes.'

Bridget wanted nothing more than to lie down and massage her aching belly but she attempted a strained smile and said, 'May we at least warm ourselves by the fire while we wait?'

Emily gave an imperious nod of consent just as Cormac's voice sounded from the floor above. 'It's ready!'

She yelped with excitement. Hoisting Jack into her arms, she led the way up the stairs and Bridget trailed after her on tired, shaky legs. Barnabas squeaked underfoot as they climbed. At the top, they found Cormac on the landing, standing in front of his and Bridget's bedroom door, which was closed.

'You can open it now!' cried Emily, setting Jack down on his feet.

Cormac swung the door back and ushered Bridget into the bedroom. Her jaw dropped. The mattress was no longer lying on the floor. Instead, it rested upon a striking wooden bed frame, the top of each of its four posts shaped like an acorn and an oak tree carved into its arcing headboard. It was an outstanding piece of craftsmanship.

Emily and Jack scampered in and climbed up onto the bed, laughing.

'Happy birthday, *a rún mo chroí*,' said Cormac. 'Mr Walker let me build it at the warehouse so I could keep it a secret.'

'Oh, it's—it's magnificent,' said Bridget, struggling to catch her breath.

He peered at her, alarmed. 'What's wrong?'

She wanted to tell him about the stranger who might have been following her and Jack. But her other fear felt far more urgent.

'I think there's something amiss with the baby,' she whimpered and sat heavily on the new bed, her legs unable to support her any longer.

With all possible haste, Cormac left to fetch Derval Carey from Broad Street. Emily looked after Jack while he was gone, giving Bridget the opportunity to nap uneasily on the bed. Her nerves mounted ever higher and she felt a surge of thankfulness when the front door banged downstairs at last. Cormac hovered out on the landing while Derval bustled into the bedroom. Her countenance was cheery at first but she grew more serious as she examined Bridget, pressing her fingertips firmly all over her round belly.

'What is it?' said Bridget. 'I can tell that it feels different this time.'

Derval nodded gravely. 'The position of the head's causing the pain under your ribs and that makes sense 'cause you're feeling the kicks lower down.' She hesitated. 'Your babby hasn't turned.'

A ripple of apprehension ran through Bridget. 'What does that mean for the birth?'

'It could make for a difficult delivery,' Derval admitted. 'There's a greater risk—for both of you.'

Bridget swallowed. 'Is it still possible for the baby to turn before my labour begins?'

'A slight chance, maybe. But at this late stage, 'tis best to make preparations based on the way things are right now.'

'Preparations?' Bridget repeated.

With absolute frankness, Derval said, 'I wouldn't feel confident doing this by myself. I think you'll need an accoucheur. A male midwife,' she added at Bridget's blank expression. 'They've got more skill in this area.'

Bridget felt her sense of control slipping but she did her utmost to stay calm as she said, 'Very well, if that's what you think is best. Could you please call Cormac in? He will need to be involved in these arrangements as well.'

Cormac, too, maintained his composure as he listened to Derval explain the situation but Bridget discerned the tightness in his jaw and the carefully measured tone of his voice as he asked, 'And is there an accoucheur you would recommend?'

'Dr Wolfe,' Derval answered. 'He's a German fella with a temper like a bear but he's the one I always go to in cases such as these.' She looked at Bridget. 'If there's anyone can get ye through this safely, he will.'

Bridget bit the tip of her tongue. 'Are there any other arrangements you would advise?'

'Don't go too far from home, and don't be on your own. You want to be ready to send for help when it happens.'

'I wonder should we ask Orlaith and Tess to come stay with us until then?' said Cormac.

'That's a good idea,' Derval agreed so Bridget didn't protest. 'I'll speak to Dr Wolfe and get him to visit ye beforehand. He'll want to do his own examination in advance.'

'Will you still attend the birth too?' asked Bridget, thinking back longingly to the simplicity of Jack's rapid arrival.

'For sure,' Derval said with a reassuring pat on Bridget's arm, but her green eyes could not mask her concern.

As she opened the door to leave, the boisterous sounds of Emily and Jack playing with the building blocks downstairs drifted into the bedroom. Both of them had been delivered safely, and so had James; the measles had not taken him until three months after he was born. Bridget had done this three times. She could do it again.

But she feared this fourth one much more than the previous three.

CHAPTER 21

Emily puffed out her breath, enjoying the sight of the misty swirls in the cold morning air. As she opened the door of the hen coop, mindful of the dish of water in her hand, she ran her tongue along the inside of her mouth.

'I can feel another loose tooth,' she announced to Mama, who carried a plate of vegetable scraps over her big bump. Jack was marching around the yard behind them, his feet crunching on the frosty grass. There had been no snow yet but ever since December had begun Emily had leapt from her bed each morning to look out the window in the hope that some might have fallen during the night.

'Another one, how exciting,' said Mama, even though she sounded tired rather than excited. She hardly ever wore her happy face these days. 'Those back teeth are catching up at last.'

Mama said that Emily had lost her front teeth just before she turned six in London. She dimly remembered it but London seemed like a very long time ago now. She bent close to the door of the coop.

'Delilah!' she called. 'Jemimah! Beulah!'

She set down the dish of water, then took the scraps from Mama's plate and tossed them onto the ground in front of the coop. Beulah was the first to appear, perching on the ramp and ruffling her feathers. As her two companions also emerged, Mama cleared her throat.

'Gooseberry,' she said. 'I found Mabel.'

Emily felt a pinch of anguish around her heart. 'So?' she said indifferently.

Mama's eyebrows rose. 'Did you and she quarrel?'

'No,' said Emily. 'She's just sleeping.' She lifted her chin. 'And I'm getting too old for dolls anyway.'

Emmeline hadn't called her a baby again but she had also drifted away a little when the hens stopped laying for the winter and their eggs no longer supplemented her lunch fare, so Emily wasn't willing to risk doing anything that might provoke an outright severance of their meagre association. Mabel would have to remain buried in the cupboard. Distressed anew by the memory of what she had done, Emily wished fervently for a distraction.

In the next instant, Mama gasped with pain, dropping the plate and clutching her belly.

'Mama?' Emily said anxiously, struck with tremendous guilt.

'I'm fine,' Mama panted. 'But will you go get your aunties?'

Emily dashed to the house at once, darting through the back door into the warm kitchen. Auntie Orlaith was stirring a pot on the stove while Auntie Tess sat yawning at the table.

'Mama needs help!' Emily exclaimed.

A short time later, she sat on the stairs with Jack at her side, her feet resting on Barnabas as she listened to the discussion going on in the front room below.

'—too early to fetch the doctor,' said Mama. Emily could only see the back of her head and shoulders through the banisters; she was sitting on the sofa while she looked up at Auntie Orlaith and Auntie Tess standing on either side of the lit hearth. 'We can wait a little longer.'

Auntie Tess crossed her arms. 'You remember how fast the last one came, right?'

'Yes, but he warned me not to summon him too soon. He was quite blunt about not wanting his time wasted.' Mama let out a chuckle that was more like a bark. 'He said this after he had tried, and failed, to turn the baby so he was in rather an irritated mood.'

'What about Derval?' asked Auntie Orlaith. 'D'you want her to come yet?'

Mama's shoulders curved inwards and she made a hissing noise of pain. 'I think that would be prudent.'

'And Cormac?' said Auntie Tess.

'He has scarcely started his day at the docks,' said Mama. 'There's no point dragging him back home prematurely.'

Looking dubious, Auntie Tess left to go to Broad Street. Everyone seemed to have forgotten that Emily was supposed to be at school, but she wasn't going to remind them – it had proved to be a drudging repetition of reading, writing and arithmetic, and nothing so enjoyable as an art lesson had ever transpired there. She put her finger in her mouth and touched the loose tooth. It wobbled but didn't come free.

Auntie Tess did not return but Auntie Derval arrived, along with Rory. Emily hadn't moved from the stairs; she glared down at him from her high position and he gave her a surly look in response.

'Tess stayed behind to mind the young ones,' said Auntie Derval. 'I'm here now until the babby comes.'

'Oh, thank you,' said Mama. Her voice sounded strange, like she had something stuck in her throat. 'I'm ever so grateful.'

There was more talking in quiet tones and Mama walked around a lot, her hand kneading her lower back. Jack fell asleep on the stairs, his head pillowed on his arms on the step above Barnabas.

Emily didn't know what prompted it, but after a long wait there seemed to be a great deal of activity all of a sudden. Auntie Orlaith fetched a towel while Mama doubled over the back of the sofa and Auntie Derval asked her questions. Amid a flurry of words, Emily caught 'very quick after the last one' and 'waters'. Auntie Derval waved Rory over to her.

'Go for Dr Wolfe,' she told him and he hurried out the front door. She touched Mama's shoulder. 'What about Cormac?'

Mama turned her head and Emily gulped; she looked really scared. 'Yes,' she said. 'I need him.'

Auntie Orlaith was wiping at something wet on the floor. 'I'll head to the docks right now,' she said as she dropped the towel and she, too, disappeared from the house, swinging her cloak around her.

'Where are the children?' Mama asked.

'Here,' said Emily tremulously. Leaving Jack slumbering where he was, she crept down the stairs and clung to the newel post at the bottom. 'Is the baby hurting you, Mama?'

'Just a little. You did too when you were born, and so did James and Jack. It's the way it's meant to be.' Mama gave her a weak smile and held out her arm. 'Come here, gooseberry.'

Emily scurried across the room. She wanted to hug Mama but was afraid to hurt her more so instead she nestled cautiously into her side. Mama squeezed her.

'I need you to be a big girl and look after Jack. Can you do that?'

'Yes, I can.'

'When Auntie Orlaith comes back, she's going to take you to Broad Street and she will mind you both until the baby arrives.'

Emily peeked up, alarmed. 'I don't want to leave you.'

Mama's eyes were full of worry but she smiled again. 'It will be for the best.'

Auntie Derval went upstairs to get the bedroom ready while Mama asked Emily to rouse Jack so she could give him a cuddle too. He grew fractious upon waking and whined as Mama buried her face in his hair. When she pulled back, her cheeks were wet. Why was Mama crying? Emily didn't understand what was happening.

After some time, Rory returned without Dr Wolfe. 'He's attending another birth,' he told his mama who had come tearing down the staircase with a loud protest from Barnabas. 'His servant said he'll come when he's ready.'

Auntie Derval clicked her tongue. 'Everything has to be on his terms,' she muttered before saying to Mama, 'Shall we get you upstairs?'

Mama had barely nodded when the front door opened again and this time it was Auntie Orlaith and Papa who came rushing in. Emily was relieved to see Papa because he almost always knew how to make things better, but he appeared just as worried as Mama. They looked at each other and seemed to speak with only their eyes so Emily couldn't grasp what passed between them.

'I'll take the children to Broad Street now,' said Auntie Orlaith.

Mama embraced Emily and Jack once more, so tightly that Emily thought she would never let them go. When she finally released them, she said, 'Be good for your auntie and I-I'll see you again soon.'

Her face started to crumple and Papa hastened to tuck them both into his own chest. 'Take care of your brother, *a stór*, and listen to your sister, *a mhac*. We'll send Rory when we have news.'

Emily drew back. 'Rory?' she said incredulously. 'How come he's staying and we're not?'

'He'll be needed to run messages. He's done this before for his mother.'

She glowered in Rory's direction but he didn't look smug, only uncomfortable. She hated that he could remain there even though she and Jack had to leave. It was yet another reason to loathe him.

There was no time for any more hugs. Papa bundled her in her bonnet and cloak and gloves while Auntie Orlaith struggled to wrap Jack up because he had begun to cry in earnest, flailing about in a fussy way that was most unlike him. He cried when Mama gave him one last kiss, and continued crying as they went down the front steps, and kept crying all the way to Broad Street.

Emily supposed she ought to feel excited about getting to see Una and Sorcha but she couldn't muster any enthusiasm. As she walked along the familiar street that used to be their home, she wished she was back at Acorn House. She poked her tongue at her loose tooth and, to her surprise, it detached from the gum and rolled around in her mouth. She spat it out onto her glove and stared at it.

Then she let it drop into the gutter. It didn't seem important anymore.

Chapter 22

Cormac sat on a chair next to their bed and gazed down at Bridget's wan, sweaty face. She looked back up at him, her hand gripping his, the pace of her rapid breaths gradually easing.

'It's slowed down,' she mumbled. 'It feels like it's almost stopped altogether. He was right.'

When Dr Wolfe had at last made his appearance, he had hardly taken a glimpse at Bridget before pronouncing with certainty that the birth was a long time yet from happening. Predicting that the labour would halt in its progress during the night and that his services would not be needed until at least the next day, he had promptly left the house.

Incredibly, he had been correct. Bridget had struggled through intense pain for hours but now, as the dark sky outside began to lighten and the glow of the candles weakened, she lay still on top of the bed, her body sagging with fatigue but not as much physical distress.

Those hours had been a nightmare Cormac wished never to repeat, even though he knew it was not over and the worst might still be to come. Witnessing his beloved in the throes of labour was unbearable when he could do nothing to alleviate her suffering. The baby was causing her appalling agony...and it was his fault. He had done this to her.

On the other side of the bed, Derval said, ''Tis a blessing the doctor knows what he's about. You take a little rest and gather your strength for the final push.'

She inclined her head meaningfully in Cormac's direction and he made a move to rise but Bridget's tight grasp kept him seated.

'No,' she rasped. 'Stay with me a while longer. We need to speak.'

'I'm going to go see where Rory put his head down for the night,' said Derval and she tactfully withdrew from the bedroom.

Cormac reached out to brush Bridget's damp hair away from her forehead. 'Do you want some water?' he asked.

She nodded and he took the glass from the bedside table, holding it to her lips. She swallowed gratefully, then leaned back on the pillow as he set it down again.

'Cormac...'

She gave him an intent look and for some reason he found it difficult to hold her gaze. Focusing on her collarbone above the hem of her nightdress, he said, 'Dr Wolfe should be back soon. I swear I'll barricade him in this time. He won't leave again until the baby's here safe and sound.'

'Cormac...'

Her voice was soft. He forced himself to meet her eyes.

'I have to say something,' she said gently. 'And then you have to promise me something.'

His hand twitched involuntarily over hers. Perhaps she took the reflexive pressure as encouragement, because she went on without waiting for any further response.

'I've never had such complications before. I realise now how lucky I was with the previous three. God, Jack was so easy in comparison to this.' She shook her head, marvelling at the memory. Then her expression grew serious. 'But there is always

189

a risk in childbirth, everyone knows that. And the longer this labour goes on, the greater the risk becomes.'

'It's going to be fine,' he said, his tone bracing. 'You heard Derval. She trusts the doctor to bring you through this safely.'

Bridget's teeth nipped the tip of her tongue in her habitual way. 'She certainly holds his expertise in high regard and he may well be deserving of such esteem. But expertise can only take him so far.' She took a deep breath. 'Should the situation turn grave, he may ask you to make a choice.'

Every inch of Cormac's skin tingled with dread.

'And if that happens, you must choose to save our baby over me.'

He was sure his heart stopped beating. A blank silence echoed in his head. He tried to pull back his hand but she clutched it all the harder, her grip unexpectedly strong despite her exhaustion.

'That,' she carried on relentlessly, 'is what I need you to promise me.'

His heart resumed beating and now its pulse was thunderous in his ears, hammering in outraged protest. He yearned to take the glass of water and smash it against the wall.

'Promise,' she repeated. She pressed her fingers fiercely into his palm.

'How can you ask that of me?' he said, so angry he could scarcely get the words out.

'Because I want to make it easier for you,' she said, her gaze earnest. 'Dr Wolfe might find himself in a position where he can preserve only one life. If so, I doubt he will consult me, a hysterical woman succumbing to the delirium of pain. He will put the burden of that decision upon you. And I am making the decision simple. You will choose to save our baby.'

'It's that easy, is it?' he demanded.

He succeeded in wrenching his hand away and stood abruptly, the chair scraping backwards across the floorboards and the candles on the bedside table flickering. Her empty hand rested on the bedcovers; the other curved over her round belly.

'You know I'm right,' she said calmly. 'I have had thirty years on this earth. Could we really snuff out our child's life before he or she has existed for even thirty seconds? Our little one deserves the chance to live, to thrive, to experience the world.'

He clenched his jaw. 'What about Emily and Jack? You would be happy to leave them without a mother?'

'Of course not.' Her chin trembled. 'It destroyed me to say goodbye, wondering if it might be the last time I ever saw them. But they would still have their father.'

'And what about me?' he burst out in sheer selfishness. 'Do you believe I could survive without you? That I could endure the rest of my life alone, knowing that I had sanctioned the doctor's actions to tear you out of it?'

She swallowed. 'But you would remember that you had done so upon my persuasion and with my blessing. Your conscience would be clear.'

'Is that what you think?' he retorted.

'Consider the alternative,' she entreated. 'If I should be saved and our baby should d-die.' The exquisite torture in her features made him think that her labour had begun again but she just raised her arm in a despairing gesture. 'How could you and I face each other afterwards in the knowledge that we had relinquished the opportunity to let our child live and breathe?'

He dropped back into the chair, his legs weak. 'It's impossible,' he whispered without being sure which terrible prospect he was referring to. He covered his face with his hands in desperate denial.

She touched his knee. 'Look at me, my love.'

Desolate, he let his hands fall into his lap.

'I understand that it will require a tremendous amount of strength to do this,' she said. 'But you have that strength within you.'

Lips barely moving, he said, 'It may not happen. Dr Wolfe could still deliver the baby safely and with no harm to your own health.'

'And please God that is how it will transpire. We shall pray for good fortune.' She paused. 'But if the worst should come to pass...'

A storm of rage battled inside him as he endeavoured to come to terms with the awfulness of losing his child or losing the love of his life. Both visions were intolerable.

But how could he deny her heartfelt plea?

After a long, weighty silence, he exhaled heavily. 'Very well.'

'I need to hear you say it.'

'I promise,' he said. She gave him an encouraging nod and he gritted his teeth. 'I promise that if the doctor declares that he can only save one life, I will choose our baby's over yours.'

The tension in her body relaxed and her countenance became tranquil. While he abhorred the very thought of what he had just committed to, he was glad that it had given her a measure of peace in the midst of her suffering.

He, on the other hand, felt far from peaceful. After all, they had not even entertained the fourth possible outcome – that both lives would be lost in the attempted delivery. His stomach roiled with nausea.

Emitting a small sigh, Bridget adjusted her position on the bed.

'Do you want to try to get some sleep?' he asked.

'I'd rather stand up and walk around actually. My backside is numb from lying down.'

He helped her slide off the bed onto her bare feet and she took a turn about the room, leaning on his arm. Although it was the biggest bedroom in the house, it was not overly large and they could only take a few paces in one direction before circling back again.

She offered him a small smile. 'We should discuss what to name the baby.'

In case there would not be time afterwards, he inferred bitterly.

With a colossal effort, he returned her smile. 'Do you have any suggestions?'

She rubbed her bump with affection, as though it wasn't the very thing that might kill her. 'If it's a boy, I would like to call him Angus after my father, as Jack is named after yours.'

'I'm perfectly happy to agree to that,' he said. 'And if it's a girl?'

Still stroking her bump, she said, 'What would you say to Margaret? In honour of your mother and sister?'

His throat constricted. 'I like that too,' he managed to reply.

'It's good to keep names in the family,' she said softly. 'It allows those who have passed before to live on.'

He thought of Liam and Ellen's daughter, Bridie, born two years previously and named after Bridget. Would the little girl soon be bearing the name of someone who had passed before? His heart ached and he pushed the idea away.

As they circled the room once more, Bridget grimaced.

Alert, he said, 'Is the pain returning?'

'No, I don't think—oh, good gracious, yes,' she said, groaning.

She reached out and grabbed onto a bedpost, her palm clutching the acorn carved on top.

'I'll get Derval,' he said. As wretched fear mounted within him, he added with a growl, 'And I'll send Rory to go again for that damn doctor.'

But when he hastened out onto the landing he heard a deep voice reverberating from the lower floor and realised that Dr Wolfe had already arrived. Cormac descended the stairs swiftly and found the doctor striding from the kitchen across the front room, his sleeves rolled up as he wiped his hands on a cloth. Derval followed on his heels, while Rory skulked just inside the kitchen doorway holding a basin of water.

'...cursed icy footpaths,' Dr Wolfe was complaining in his subtle German accent. 'It is fortunate that I did not break my hip when I fell. Although a handful of horse manure was quite bad enough.' He dropped the cloth into Derval's hands, grumbling, 'At least I had forgotten my gloves so they are not ruined.'

A dark fury eclipsed Cormac's fear. How dared the doctor be concerned about his gloves when the lives of Bridget and the baby she carried hung in such a precarious state? As the man reached the bottom of the staircase, Cormac seized him by the collar and shoved him up against the banister. Derval gasped.

'You're needed upstairs right now,' Cormac snarled into the doctor's shocked face. 'And don't even think of leaving again until the birth is over.'

'Unhand me at once!' exclaimed Dr Wolfe in indignation.

Cormac released his grip. His shoulders slumped as terror coursed through him once more.

'Save them,' he said, his voice cracking. 'Please, save them both. Don't make me a liar to my wife.'

Because, if it came to it, he didn't know how he could keep his promise to her.

Dr Wolfe straightened his clothing in a huff. 'I shall do my best, sir,' he said haughtily and sidestepped Cormac to climb the stairs. Derval laid a compassionate hand on Cormac's arm and then followed the doctor.

Cormac remained where he was, dread pinning him to the spot. What if the doctor's best wasn't enough? What if he presented Cormac with that horrifying choice? He couldn't conceive of a world without Bridget in it. But the loss of their child would be equally abominable.

He fingered the braided leather band on his wrist. While he and Bridget might have spent thirty years on this earth, it was only within the last three that they had found their way back to each other after so long apart. The intervening time had passed so quickly; they had hardly begun to build their lives together. It was right that parents should go before their children, but this was too soon. Far too soon. He implored God to let them have more time.

Caressing the chestnut hair that wove through the leather band, he wondered with a sickening lurch if he ought to have asked Father Whitty or a priest from Saint Augustine's to be present in case the last rites were needed. But surely that would be tempting a wholly undesired fate.

When he looked up, Rory was still in the kitchen doorway, propping open the door with his foot.

'Ma always picks Dr Wolfe for a reason,' the lad said. 'He really does care.'

A cry of distress broke out from above. Cormac spun on his heel and dashed up the stairs. He had stayed away for Jack's birth, but he was damned if he was going to be absent from Bridget's side this time.

When he entered the bedroom, her expression filled with relief. She was still hanging onto the bedpost but she put out her other hand and he took it, trying to pour strength and hope into his grip.

'It is highly unconventional for the father to be present,' Dr Wolfe muttered.

'He's staying,' said Derval, her tone quiet and firm. Cormac cast her a glance of gratitude.

The doctor gave a resigned jerk of his head and said, '*Frau* McGovern, let me assure you of two things. The first is that this will be a difficult, painful birth, there can be no doubt about that. But the second is that I will do my utmost to see you and the child through it safely. I shall only use the forceps if there is extreme need and will otherwise rely upon you to do as I instruct at all times and to push when I tell you. Your husband may stay to support you but I shall expect him not to interfere in any way. Is this acceptable?'

'Yes,' Bridget panted.

Dr Wolfe arched a challenging eyebrow at Cormac and Cormac responded with a respectful nod. They would put their faith in him.

He lost all concept of time during what followed next. It became a blur as Bridget moved restlessly from one position to another, walking again about the room, leaning over the back of Cormac's chair, or even kneeling on all fours on the bed, accompanied throughout by her agonised moans and heavy breathing. He held her hand or massaged her back or, for a stretch, stopped touching her altogether when she snapped and said it was vexing her. Shortly after that, she begged him to rub her back again, her previous outburst forgotten. Derval fetched a fresh basin of water and applied a cool, wet cloth to Bridget's forehead and neck when she wanted it.

Dr Wolfe brought up his medical case and made sure it was close by but he didn't extract any alarming instruments from it. He checked Bridget at regular intervals and, at last, said, 'You need to lie down now.'

Bridget lay back on the bed and from that point Cormac didn't look anywhere except at her face. He sat on the chair and leaned on the edge of the bed, clutching her palm between both of his and keeping his eyes trained upon hers. He became the anchor for her pain, swallowing it through her agitated gaze and her bone-breaking grasp as she whimpered and grunted.

'Push,' Dr Wolfe ordered and she strained to obey. 'Push,' he said again. And then, 'The legs are free. We are getting there. Your assistance, *Frau* Carey. That is it. *Gut*. Push, *Frau* McGovern!'

Bridget keened like a banshee, her back rising off the bed with the effort. Cormac heard Dr Wolfe's bark of triumph, followed by Derval's sharp intake of breath.

And a newborn cry pervaded the room.

There was a flurry of activity beyond Bridget's bent knees but all Cormac could do was continue to hold her gaze, his pulse racing. Her dark brown eyes brimmed with relief and anxiety and her chest rose and fell with heaving gasps. She was still breathing. She was still alive. Thanks be to God.

He felt a nudge at his elbow.

'Take him,' said Derval.

Cormac managed to tear his gaze away from Bridget's to peer down at the tiny creature Derval was placing into his arms – a boy, coated in some sort of greasy substance and with a cord tied off at his navel. His head was misshapen but he, too, was alive and breathing. In fact, he was bawling loudly enough to wake Mr and Mrs Hill next door.

Miraculous.

Cormac leaned towards Bridget to pass the baby to her. Tears streamed down her cheeks and, as he surrendered their son into her embrace, he realised that they ran down his own as well. Glancing over his shoulder, he saw Derval's eyes swimming and was astonished to perceive that Dr Wolfe was also weeping. How extraordinary and touching. He would have to apologise to the doctor later for accosting him the way he had.

He turned back to Bridget and their boy. Wrapping his arms around them, he thanked God again that they were both here.

Dr Wolfe gave a loud sniff. 'It is not over,' he said gruffly. 'The afterbirth must still be delivered. And then you shall need to be watchful for many days for the possible onset of childbed fever. The danger is not yet past.'

In that moment, Cormac was deaf to the doctor's warning. Pure joy ran through his veins as Bridget showered kisses on their baby's small nose and cheeks.

'We're so glad you're here, Angus,' he murmured.

Bridget looked up at him with a radiant smile. 'How I wish my father could meet him,' she said.

Cormac pictured the child engulfed by the strapping figure of Lord Courcey. 'He has rather big shoes to fill,' he said, stroking the boy's near-bald crown. 'It is a heavy load to carry that honourable name.'

'Then perhaps we should remove some of the load for now,' said Bridget. 'Let's call him Gus for short.'

'Gus,' Cormac repeated, grinning. 'It suits him.'

He held them both close, exhausted and elated.

CHAPTER 23

Bridget shovelled some lumps of coal onto the glowing embers of the fire, used the poker to shift them into a better position, and waited for the flames to revive. Then she scooped Gus out of his basket and nestled on the sofa, cradling him with a blanket wrapped around them both.

It was the dead of night but of course her new baby paid no heed to that, just as he had disregarded it for the first week and a half of his existence. Rather than disturb the sleeping inhabitants upstairs for yet another night, she had brought him down to the lower floor to calm his cries and feed him. Now she was alert while he had begun to doze so she snuggled on the sofa to enjoy the warmth of the fire and count her blessings.

There had been no childbed fever. Dr Wolfe said she had been very lucky. Her stomach churned when she considered how closely she had brushed with death, how she had discussed the very possibility of her life's end with Cormac and compelled him to make that terrible promise. Guilt swelled in her for putting him through that but it had been the right thing to do. He had needed to know that that was what she wanted, should he have been forced to make the choice. Mercifully, no such decision had been necessary. She had since been churched

199

and Gus baptised, and their thanksgiving on both occasions had been wholehearted.

Barnabas squeaked behind her. She glanced over the back of the sofa and saw Cormac descending the stairs; he had donned a pair of trousers under the shirt he had worn to bed but his feet were bare.

When he reached her, he shivered and said, 'Here, let me get under there too.'

She held up the blanket to allow him to slip beneath it. He draped it back around them and she stretched out her legs on his lap, while Gus snoozed against her chest, the blanket reaching up to his neck, his small head above it rounder than it had been upon his birth.

'Couldn't sleep?' she asked. 'I thought bringing him downstairs might make it easier for everyone to nod off again.'

The sleeping arrangements were a little tight at present. After the birth, Emily and Jack had come back to Acorn House to meet their new brother ('But I asked for a sister,' Emily had protested) and Orlaith and Tess had returned with them to help look after the children and the house while Bridget tended her newborn baby. However, with Bridget's health out of peril, Orlaith and Tess were due to go home to Broad Street the next morning, although they would visit again the following week to enjoy a festive dinner together on Christmas Day.

'No, I was wide awake,' said Cormac. He placed a gentle palm on Gus's rump underneath the blanket. 'But not because of you, *a mhic ó*.'

Bridget cocked her head. It was the first time she had heard him use that address.

'It's a bit like "*a mhac*",' he explained, 'but Gus is an even littler lad than Jack.'

She herself had taken to calling their baby boy 'little miracle'; she could think of no more fitting an endearment.

'So is that what kept you awake?' she said. 'Pondering pet names?'

'I wish,' he replied, and the firelight showed the sombreness of his expression.

'Is something the matter?' she asked.

'You could say that.'

Startled, she altered her posture to face him more directly. The movement was not so painful as it would have been a week ago, as her nether regions slowly healed.

'Tell me,' she said.

He didn't say anything at first, only stared towards the hearth as though gathering his thoughts. He took a breath and released it slowly.

'I'm struggling,' he finally said, 'to reconcile myself to the fact that you could have died.'

She started to speak but he cut her off.

'I know what you're going to say. That it didn't happen, that you're fine, that all is well.' A haunted look shadowed his blue irises. 'But the reality is that you could have died. I could just as easily have spent the past week burying you, writing to our friends in Ireland to tell them you were gone, trying to explain to our children why their mother was no longer here.'

His voice fractured. Beneath the blanket, she reached for his hand and clasped it. He gulped back his emotion and carried on steadily.

'I wasn't prepared for the stark truth that childbirth could have led to your death. I mean, I understood the hazards on some level but I never truly entertained the idea that it might happen to you. I can't even fathom how I greeted the news of your pregnancies with such pleasure when I now realise that they brought with them the greatest of risks.'

'But they also brought wonderful joy,' she whispered.

'I know that, and I love our children. I would do anything for them. But I don't want to court that risk again.'

She tried not to smile because he was being so grave. 'We can't quite control that, you know. If a baby results from our activities...'

He levelled his gaze at her. 'Not if we don't engage in those activities.'

Her jaw dropped. 'You don't mean—'

'I do.'

'*Abstinence*?' she said, horrified.

'Yes,' he said with a stubborn set to his jaw.

She pulled her hand back. 'I refuse to even contemplate it.'

His mouth twisted wryly. 'There's not much you can do about it without a cooperating partner.'

'But not every birth would be like Gus's,' she said, desperate to convince him.

'There would still be a danger of it though, and I am willing to go to any lengths to avoid it.'

She gaped at him. He was entirely serious. How could he possibly consider it? To forsake the rapture of joining together in passion and devotion, to endure the rest of their lives without that sweet, glorious release. It was unthinkable.

With all her earnestness, she said, 'I can't live without your touch.'

'I can't live without *you*,' he said simply.

She had no response to that. Gus slumbered in total contentment on her bosom, unaware of the strife he had caused. The fire sparked and Cormac glanced at it sharply but nothing fell out of the grate. Minutes passed in uneasy, unhappy silence.

'What if...' she said haltingly and stopped.

'What if what?' he prodded.

She plucked at the frayed edge of the blanket. 'What if...' she repeated and went on in a rush, '...we don't deny ourselves those activities but we take steps to prevent a baby being conceived in the process?'

Beneath her legs, she felt the muscles in his thighs tighten. 'The Catholic Church says that's a sin.'

'That is true,' she said. 'But how many other transgressions have we committed in the eyes of the church?'

'Too many,' he said despondently.

'Do you believe we are evil people?'

After a beat, he shook his head.

'Do you believe that avoiding conception would make us evil?'

He hesitated again. 'I think there's a certain immorality to it. But not evil, no.'

'Then might you consider it?'

This time the pause was so long that she was convinced he would answer in the negative. But eventually he admitted, 'Maybe,' and she knew he no more wanted to be abstinent than she did. She released a soundless breath of relief.

'Let us speak no further on it for now,' she said. 'My body isn't ready for it yet in any case. I will let you know when it is and we can discuss it again then.'

She gave him a reassuring smile even as she began to ponder the practicalities of what she had proposed. She didn't know the first thing about it.

The answer came to her the next morning. Cormac left for the docks when it was still dark while Orlaith rose at a decent hour and volunteered to bring Emily and Jack to fetch water from the public well. Tess, in contrast, dragged herself from bed only after Orlaith and the children had already departed. She entered the kitchen, where Bridget was nursing Gus at the table, with a sluggish air.

'Morning,' she said, yawning and pushing her tousled red hair out of her face.

'Good morning,' Bridget replied, her brain already working furiously. 'Did you sleep well?'

Tess let out a humourless laugh. 'Are you really asking that?' Orlaith and Tess had been sharing Emily's bed alongside Jack's cot while Emily and her old mattress had been moved temporarily into the box room.

Bridget curbed her desire to retort with a similarly sarcastic remark. 'You must be looking forward to returning to Broad Street.'

'I'm definitely looking forward to having my own bed again.' Tess reflected on her words and snorted. 'Listen how high and mighty I've become. There was a time I would've done almost anything for a blanket, let alone for the chance to share a single bed with just one other person.' Her lip curled. 'You must be rubbing off on me.'

Once again, Bridget stilled her tongue. She glanced down at Gus's assiduous mouth and steeled herself before looking back up. 'May I ask you a question?'

Tess took a seat at the table with a faintly bored expression. 'Sure.'

'It is a rather delicate subject.' Bridget faltered, then ploughed on. 'I was wondering if you could acquaint me with the methods known to prevent a woman from getting with child.'

Tess was scratching her nose; she stopped mid-scratch and gawked.

'And also where I might acquire such items as would be necessary to achieve that purpose,' Bridget finished bravely.

Affronted, Tess demanded, 'What makes you think I'd know?'

Bridget coloured. 'I assumed that, given your previous occupation, you would have some knowledge in these matters. I can't imagine you would have been eager to raise a baby on the streets of Dublin.'

Tess crossed her arms. 'I suppose not.' She offered nothing else.

Bridget pressed her lips together. 'So can you advise me?'

Tess narrowed her eyes. 'Why are you asking? It doesn't make sense. You've got a man and you've already had his babies. Why wouldn't you want another child by him?' Her countenance transformed into one of outraged reproof. 'Are you going behind his back with another fella?'

'Of course not! Cormac is the one pushing for this.'

Tess's eyebrows shot up. 'He doesn't want any more children with you?'

'To put it baldly, yes, that's right.' Bridget was beginning to regret having started this conversation. But who else could she turn to for such unpalatable information? 'I am therefore seeking your help. Do you have the facts and the will to educate me?'

Tess's arms tightened and she hunched in on herself, whether in embarrassment or resentment Bridget could not tell. At last, she muttered, 'Why doesn't he just pull out before...you know.'

That notion had occurred to Bridget but she could only imagine such an approach resulting in a sense of emptiness which would surely defeat the purpose of the pleasure they sought from the act. 'I should prefer to investigate all possible means, including physical barriers which are perhaps more reliable than...what you suggested.'

'I couldn't afford to pay for such things in Dublin,' said Tess. 'I never got with child though so I must've either been barren or lucky.'

'I see,' said Bridget, disappointed. 'So you do not know what items I need or where I might obtain them in Boston?'

Tess's expression turned cagey.

'Or do you?' said Bridget perceptively.

Tess shrugged.

Bridget wanted to shake her for being so contrary. Instead, she took her time to switch Gus to her other breast. As he resumed suckling, she said, 'I am not going to judge you, if that's what you think. Your business is your own.' Nevertheless, her curiosity was roused as to whether there was a man who had engaged Tess's affections, or at least her carnal attentions. If so, she was keeping any such relationship very quiet.

Tess uncrossed her arms and picked at a small indentation in the table's surface, scraping her nail in and out of the little hollow. With a sigh, she sat back in her chair. 'I can tell you a few bits.'

Bridget listened to Tess describe the paraphernalia that could be used by a man or by a woman to stop a child from being conceived as well as where they could be procured and, as both of them tried not to blush, she thought that the pessary, which she would have to insert, sounded like the most practical option.

'Thank you,' she said with genuine gratitude. 'I appreciate your candour.'

Tess gave an indifferent toss of her head. 'It's fine.'

When they heard the sound of the front door opening and the voices of Orlaith, Emily and Jack drifting through, Bridget was supremely relieved that the awkward conversation could come to a swift conclusion.

CHAPTER 24

'Time to put the Baby Jesus in the manger,' Cormac said to Emily.

She eagerly picked up the small wooden infant and placed it with care into the nativity scene, which stood on a stool by the hearth. Cormac had built it from broken bits of barrels and crates at the warehouse; it was just a simple tableau containing carvings of Baby Jesus, Holy Mary and Saint Joseph with an angel perched on top of the stable, but O'Mali had supplied a scrap of blue fabric from his daughter, Tilly, to wrap around the Holy Mary figure.

Emily pressed her palms flat together to whisper a prayer over the scene and then announced, 'I made a Christmas wish that the Baby Jesus will help us find Auntie Bronagh.'

Cormac noted with interest that her speech was developing an unusual blend. While traces of her English accent were still audible, it had softened noticeably and a stronger American twang had come to the fore, with a stray Irish inflection on an odd word here and there.

'That is very thoughtful of you, *a stór*,' he said, even as he felt a pain behind his ribs at the mention of his sister. He had grown convinced that she was lost to the family for good.

They had gone to the Cathedral of the Holy Cross the previous night for midnight Mass and afterwards he had spoken to Father Whitty. Bronagh still had not made an appearance at the cathedral and he was beginning to wonder if he should cease placing sporadic notices in *The Boston Pilot*. Every enquiry he had made at boarding houses for immigrants or lodgings in Irish communities had proved fruitless. He had even searched in areas where homeless people were known to live rough, but there was no sign of her. The situation seemed quite hopeless.

Orlaith wasn't quite as discouraged. 'Please God let this be the year,' she said with a smile at Emily.

She and Tess had joined them for midnight Mass but had returned to Broad Street to sleep in comfort before coming to Acorn House later on Christmas morning. They were intending to go home after dinner to celebrate with the Careys – Brian Mór was on shore leave for the Christmas period so it was more of an act of support for Derval, should his surly nature subdue the festive atmosphere. However, Orlaith now continued, 'I'll only have a small bite to eat here if that suits. I have to leave early.'

'Does Derval want you back sooner?' Bridget asked as she cradled Gus in one elbow and wiped a smudge of dirt from Jack's nose with her other hand, murmuring, 'We must try to stay clean on Christmas Day, my lamb.'

Orlaith flushed. 'No, I—I'm meeting Charlie.'

Cormac frowned. 'Charlie? Today?'

How perplexing. It suggested a familiarity far greater than what he had assumed between the pair of them, given that Orlaith had commenced her involvement with the Ursulines during the past year. Was she misleading Charlie?

She fidgeted with the cuff of her dress. 'His ma burned her fingers on the kitchen stove last week. He asked me to tend her and then she invited me to have tea with the family this afternoon.'

That was equally mystifying. Cormac couldn't see how Orlaith would be welcomed in a Protestant household, unless Charlie's more lenient views towards Irish people had influenced his mother too. If that was the case, then was he courting Orlaith in earnest?

'Have you told Charlie about your intention to become a nun?' Cormac demanded.

'That isn't set in stone,' she said, her gaze darting away.

Before he could respond, Emily – who had run to the front window – piped up in disappointment, 'I also made a Christmas wish for snow but there's none falling yet.' Hardly pausing for breath, she rushed on, 'I have a present for everyone—may I give it now?'

'How lovely,' said Orlaith, looking keen for a distraction.

Emily barrelled up the stairs, shouting, 'Happy Christmas, Barnabas!' as she jumped onto the eighth step.

While she was gone, Orlaith nudged Tess to make room on the sofa and flopped down next to her, avoiding Cormac's eye. Bridget caught it instead and she gave him a slight shake of her head. He didn't pursue the subject of Charlie any further and instead bent over the nativity scene to make unnecessary adjustments to the positions of the figures.

Emily came back downstairs with a sheaf of pages. 'I hope you all like them,' she said, going suddenly shy. She handed the pages to her mother first, one at a time because Bridget was still carrying Gus in the crook of her arm. As Bridget took each sheet, her eyes widened.

'Good gracious, gooseberry. These are wonderful!'

She passed them to Cormac and he looked at them one after another, his jaw dropping. They were portraits of the whole family and he was incredibly impressed to realise that he could identify them all. This one was clearly Bridget grasping Jack's hand and that was Orlaith reading her Bible and here was Tess staring out a window and there was Cormac himself holding up his hammer. The proportions were quite accurate and a degree of shading provided them with a lifelike quality. Emily was only nine but her skill was beyond her years.

'I am very proud of you, *a stór*,' he said and enveloped his daughter in a warm hug.

'I haven't had time to draw any of Gus yet,' she said. 'But I will. I want to keep practising and get better and better.'

Orlaith and Tess both examined the pictures and they, too, praised Emily's talent. She didn't stop beaming for the rest of the day.

They sang carols after that. Tess only mumbled along and Emily's pitch was completely off, but Bridget, Cormac and Orlaith could carry a decent tune. Jack banged two of his wooden blocks together with noisy glee until Gus howled in protest, at which point the carols came to a speedy end in a chorus of hoots and snorts.

Still laughing, they sat down to eat in the kitchen, where the one extravagance of the occasion, a clove-studded roast ham, adorned the centre of the table. Its delectable aroma permeated the air and Emily took several deep breaths of ecstasy, declaring that it was the best smell in the whole wide world.

As Cormac sliced into it, he said to Orlaith in an offhand manner, 'So what are your arrangements for later?'

With the barest lift of her chin, she said, 'I'm meeting Charlie at the Common where we'll go for a stroll before having tea at his parents' house.'

'And following that?'

'He'll walk me back to Broad Street.' She spotted Cormac's raised eyebrows. 'After which he'll return home himself. It's harmless.'

'All the same, I'll accompany you to the Common.'

'That's not necessary,' she said.

'It is,' he insisted. 'You're better off not being alone on the streets today with all the drunken louts bound to be about. Tess will need to come with us for the same reason. I'll escort her to Broad Street from the Common.'

Tess looked gratified to be included in his considerations.

'Fine,' said Orlaith. 'I won't argue.'

Maybe he was being overprotective and meddlesome but Bronagh's absence weighed heavily upon him. With Mary, Margaret and Bronagh all out of his reach, Orlaith was the one sister he could still look out for.

He, Orlaith and Tess departed from Acorn House after dinner, bundled up warmly against the bitter chill. A vast expanse of grey cloud hung low in the sky and the light was already fading, signalling an early arrival of evening. The streets were mostly quiet but every now and then a fellow staggered past, barely upright from intoxication, having caroused a little too freely on his day off from work. One chap slipped on an icy patch and landed on the footpath on his rear end, where he seemed content to remain, singing a bawdy tune as they went by.

When they arrived at Boston Common, Charlie already stood outside the ornamental iron fence, gloved hands tucked under his armpits. Rather than seeming perturbed by Cormac's unexpected appearance, he greeted them all with a jolly 'Merry Christmas!' before turning to Orlaith to add, 'My mother has made her renowned ginger biscuits. They're my favourite so let's keep the walk short, shall we?' He grinned.

Cormac relaxed. There was nothing shady in Charlie's guileless demeanour and, whether or not Orlaith had changed her mind on becoming a nun, choosing between Charlie or the convent wasn't a commitment she was obliged to make in this very moment. Still, as Orlaith and Tess were bidding farewell to each other, Cormac seized the opportunity to take Charlie aside.

'I'd like you to note that unchaperoned walks are not advisable,' he muttered. 'A short stroll would indeed be wise, especially as darkness is beginning to fall. Please keep her safe.'

Abashed, Charlie said quickly, 'Will do.'

Cormac clapped him on the shoulder. Then he said to Orlaith, 'Enjoy your evening. Convey my good wishes to Mr and Mrs Adams.' He had met them very briefly when he had brought Charlie home after the riot; they had been so relieved to see their son that they had not even questioned which side of the brawl Cormac had been on, although he supposed Charlie had filled them in afterwards.

Orlaith cast him a suspicious glance before saying, 'Thanks.'

With a cautious exchange of smiles, she and Charlie entered the park while Cormac and Tess started in the direction of Broad Street.

When they were out of sight of the Common, Tess said, 'Y'know, I think he's a good fella.'

'Yes, I think so too,' said Cormac.

'If you ask me, she'd be mad to join the nuns. The decent ones don't come along too often. There's not many out there like him. Or you.' She elbowed Cormac playfully.

He nudged her back. 'In fairness, she's not yet sixteen. It isn't a decision she needs to settle upon right away.' Having missed so much of Orlaith's childhood, he wasn't ready to see his little sister grow up just yet.

'I guess she should try to stay young as long as she can,' said Tess, echoing his own thoughts. 'She had a hard life before this.'

'It would have been even harder if you hadn't been there for her all those years ago,' he said, a rather raw edge to his emotions.

'You did so much to keep the family together. I'll always be grateful to you for that.'

Even in the waning light, he could see that her cheeks had flamed the same colour as her hair. She stared at her feet and didn't say anything.

They carried on down the next street which the lamplighters had already passed through, the glow of the lit lamps banishing some of the thick gloom around them. Even so, his extremities felt frozen and he considered lingering at Broad Street to warm himself in front of the Careys' fire before returning to Acorn House.

He was about to say this out loud when Tess seized his elbow and exclaimed, 'Look!'

He peered around. Soft, white flakes were wafting down from the sky. Emily was going to be thrilled. Even as they watched, the flurries grew thicker and he wondered if it might be better not to delay getting home after all. He wanted to urge Tess onwards but she had halted to marvel at the arrival of the snow.

'It's beautiful!'

She stretched out her hands and spun about, the snowflakes landing on her bonnet and cloak. Suddenly, she lost her balance on an unseen patch of ice and pitched against him. He caught her and kept her upright as she laughed within the ring of his arms.

Then she put her palms flat on his chest and kissed him.

Shocked, he jerked back. 'What are you doing?'

'Exactly what it looks like,' she said breathlessly and pressed her mouth to his once more. Her lips were warm despite the cold and she parted them, trying to deepen the kiss.

He wrenched away again, this time releasing her and stepping backwards. 'Stop, Tess.'

Her countenance was feverish with excitement. 'Why?'

'*Why*?' he repeated, utterly bewildered by this unexpected turn of events. 'Surely that's obvious?'

She twisted her mouth. 'You mean Bridget, I suppose.'

'Of course I mean Bridget,' he said emphatically.

'But you're not actually married to her,' she said with an air of triumph, like she was defeating his argument with irrefutable logic. 'You're a free man.'

He stared at her with incredulity. 'I don't see it that way.'

'You should. There's no law binding yous together.'

She stepped closer and he retreated further, the wall of the adjacent building now at his back. Carol singing floated from within.

'I made a vow to Bridget,' he said. 'It doesn't matter if it wasn't witnessed by a priest or recorded on any register. It was a solemn oath and I won't break it.'

Tess blinked. 'But...she told me you didn't want any more children by her. I thought that meant you were falling out of love with her, that maybe you'd been disgusted by what you saw in the birthing bed.'

He shook his head. 'It's because I love her so much that I don't want any more children. I'm terrified that having another baby will prove too great a risk to her life.'

A deep flush rose on Tess's cheeks in the lamplight and she looked away, mortified. Then she returned her gaze to him with an obstinate jut of her jaw.

'Are you attracted to me?' she asked.

Discomfited, he said, 'I view you as my sister.'

'What if Bridget wasn't here?' she persisted. 'What if she had died in childbirth?'

He was appalled. 'It's beneath you to wonder such a spiteful thing.'

Her eyes went steely. The snow still drifted down but it had lost its picturesque nature, instead coating their clothes and the footpath like a frosty shroud.

'I've gone and made a fool of myself, haven't I?' she said, her tone clipped.

'You haven't,' he said gently. 'We can forget it ever happened. To preserve the family's contentment, I won't tell anyone what you did.'

'Well, I'm not content,' she retorted and, whirling about, she stormed away into the falling snow.

Instinct told him not to follow her.

'Jesus Christ,' he said under his breath, conscious of his blasphemy on this holy day.

CHAPTER 25

Bridget inhaled and exhaled slowly as she walked along the street beside Orlaith. After seven weeks, it was her first time to be separated from Gus and she was having trouble suppressing her anxiety. Even though she would only be gone from home for a couple of hours, she was missing her baby dreadfully.

She ran through a list in her mind of all the advice she had given Cormac before she left. She had fed Gus at the very last minute so with any luck he would not need feeding again until she got back, but she had expressed some milk into a cup just in case.

'You can dip a clean rag into the milk and let him suck on it,' she had told Cormac, doing her best to keep the fretfulness from her voice.

He had nodded. 'I remember doing that once with Patrick.'

'If he cries and won't stop, rub him firmly between his shoulder blades. He likes that.'

'I know. I was there when you discovered that for the first time.' He had given her a gentle push. 'Off you go.'

Orlaith had invited her to a food shelter which was administered by the Ursuline nuns. Given Bridget's past experience at St Swithun's Workhouse, she was eager to help, even though she wouldn't be able to commit to it on a regular basis. Still, an odd Sunday now and then would be feasible. If only she wasn't pining for her baby so much.

Next to her, Orlaith didn't notice her agitation as she said, 'Thanks for coming today. I don't know why Tess wouldn't. She's been in a sulky mood since Christmas, whatever's wrong with her.'

'Hmm,' said Bridget vaguely.

She had no room in her head for concern about Tess's mysterious woes because another disturbing idea had added itself to her list of worries. She had just realised that this was her first time out on the Boston streets since the day the strange man in the high collar had seemed to be pursuing her and Jack. Fearful, she glanced behind her but there appeared to be nothing or no one suspicious in the vicinity. Neither did she have that prickling sense of alarm that someone was watching her. In fact, she felt entirely safe. Perhaps she really had just been imagining things that day. Some of the tension dissipated from her body as she faced forwards again.

In an effort to prevent her thoughts from reverting back to Gus, she said, 'Speaking of Christmas, how did tea go with Charlie and his parents?'

Orlaith reddened. 'It was grand.'

'Just "grand"?'

Orlaith gave a shrug. 'I suppose it went fine. His ma was nice to me. I'm not so sure about his da though. He asked a lot of questions about me being from Ireland and Catholic and the like.'

'Do you suspect he has an objection to your connection with Charlie?' Bridget asked and added hurriedly, 'Not that I'm making any assumptions about the nature of your relationship.'

'Neither am I,' said Orlaith with a grimace. 'I'd a notion he might try to kiss me when he walked me back to Broad Street that night, but in the end he didn't.' She straightened her shoulders. 'Arrah, it's nothing to be bothered about, at least not for now. I want to concentrate on becoming a better nurse and doing good deeds with the nuns. Here we are.'

They had arrived at a building with a throng of people gathered haphazardly in front of it. A mixture of men, women and children grumbled and jostled towards the door, all gaunt with hunger, their clothing too thin for the winter weather. Judging by their accents, there was a strong concentration of Irish among them. A nun stood in the doorway, a set of rosary beads hanging at the belt of her habit and her hands raised in a placating gesture.

'Please be patient!' she called out. 'Everyone will be fed in due course.'

She caught sight of Orlaith and waved her over. Bridget scuttled after her, avoiding the glares of the unfortunates around them who clearly thought they were skipping ahead.

'Sister Annunciata,' Orlaith greeted the nun. 'This is my sister-in-law, Bridget, who I was telling you about.'

Sister Annunciata bowed her head to Bridget. 'Thank you for coming. You are so generous to give your time to help these poor souls.'

She led them inside the building, where Bridget discovered that the circumstances of this food shelter were not unlike those of St Swithun's old soup kitchen. Benches and stools occupied the large hall within, while two nuns tended boiling pots over a roaring hearth. She experienced a strange tug of homecoming and nostalgia. St Swithun's had played a major role in providing her with a sense of purpose during her lonely years in London.

Sister Annunciata guided them to a table stacked with bowls and spoons as the two nuns at the fireplace carried one of the pots over. It contained a rather watery-looking stew with sparse chunks of vegetables. Orlaith picked up a pair of ladles and handed one to Bridget.

'A single serving per person,' Sister Annunciata directed. 'If there is some spare at the end, the children may have second helpings.'

She went back to the door to admit the waiting crowd. As they streamed inside, it took the admonitions of all three nuns to corral them into straggling rows. They shuffled into line, their hungry eyes focused on the pot of stew, curls of steam rising from it. They approached the table one by one and Bridget and Orlaith took turns to ladle the stew into bowls and pass them to each person.

About half of them had received their portions and were slouching on the surrounding benches and stools, spooning the stew gratefully into their mouths, when a woman with dirt in her dishevelled hair stepped up. She stank powerfully. Her gaze was trained on the floor but she peered up as Orlaith handed her a bowl and her eyes widened.

'What're you doing on that side of the pot?' she said in astonishment. Then she squinted and frowned. 'Oh, never mind. Thought you were someone else.'

Bridget and Orlaith exchanged glances.

'Who did you think I was?' Orlaith asked.

'Another girl who used to come here. You look a lot like her.'

A wave of excitement crossed Orlaith's features. 'What was her name?'

The woman scratched at her dirty hair. 'Don't remember. Something beginning with "buh", I think.'

'Was it "Bronagh" by any chance?' Orlaith said eagerly.

The woman brightened. 'That sounds about right.'

A surge of shock shot through Bridget.

'God Almighty,' said Orlaith. Unmindful of the remaining queue beyond, she entreated the woman, 'Please tell us everything you know.'

***

'*A haon, a dó, a trí,*' said Cormac, stacking Jack's wooden blocks on the floor before the hearth. 'One, two, three.'

Jack clapped his hands together and repeated an approximation of the words in both languages.

'Very good, *a mhac.*' Cormac ruffled his son's hair. '*An-mhaith ar fad.*'

He peeked into Gus's basket next to him and was pleased to see that the boy was still fast asleep.

'Papa?' Emily's voice floated into the front room from the kitchen, where she was painting at the table. 'What is the Irish word for pink?'

'*Bándearg,*' he called back, trying to keep his pitch low enough so as not to wake Gus. 'It's a combination of *bán* for white and *dearg* for red.'

'Oh, that's clever,' came her reply.

He smiled to himself, thoroughly enjoying his Sunday off with his children. Then he suffered a pang of misgiving as he remembered the letter crumpled inside his pocket: further correspondence from Mrs O'Hara seeking more money for Henrietta's medicine. Bridget had been correct that this might indeed turn into a slippery slope. But could he really deny Henrietta his help? What if Mrs O'Hara's next letter conveyed the news that the girl had died because she hadn't been able to pay for a doctor to make her well? He didn't want that guilt on his conscience. She might not be his daughter but she was still a child in need and, so long as he was in a position to assist her, he could not allow himself to do otherwise. He would have to communicate, however, that the money was for an emergency

220

and that he was not a bank Mrs O'Hara could withdraw funds from at will.

Bridget might not be very happy when he imparted the contents of the letter but he wouldn't even contemplate the idea of not telling her about it. Keeping one secret from her was quite enough. His guts stirred uneasily at the memory of that snowy street on Christmas Day. He hadn't seen Tess since. He supposed their next interaction might be a little awkward but he hoped she would be able to overcome her embarrassment in time. He just wanted things to go back to the way they had been.

A whine came from Gus's basket and turned into a bloodcurdling scream faster than Cormac could blink.

'Damn,' he muttered.

Leaving Jack to play with the wooden blocks by himself, he picked Gus up and tried unsuccessfully to calm him down. Nothing worked, not offering him the milky rag to suck on or rubbing him between his shoulder blades or rocking him or changing his clout. To Cormac's chagrin, the boy was still wailing when Bridget and Orlaith came rushing through the front door a while later.

'I can't figure out what's upsetting him,' he confessed, feeling like a terrible parent.

Bridget stretched out greedy arms for Gus and Cormac relinquished him to her. After all his caterwauling, he quieted almost at once in his mother's embrace.

'Ah, he just wanted his ma,' said Cormac, endeavouring to conceal his twinge of jealousy.

Bridget kissed Gus's nose and hugged him tightly but she focused her gaze upon Cormac, her eyes sparkling. 'We have news!'

That was when he spotted the exhilarated glow of Orlaith's cheeks. She was practically bouncing on the spot. 'News of Bronagh!' she added in a triumphant exclamation.

He stared. 'What?' he said uncomprehendingly.

'Bronagh,' Orlaith repeated. 'We met someone who knew her.'

And they proceeded to describe their encounter with a woman at the Ursulines' food shelter who had mistaken Orlaith for another girl. A girl called Bronagh.

'She said the resemblance between the pair of us was uncanny, only that our eyes were a little bit different. But it was clear we must be sisters.'

Cormac could hardly believe it. After all his futile searching and growing doubt, here was proof at last. Bronagh had indeed come to Boston.

'When was the last time this woman saw her?' he asked, hope bursting within him.

Bridget's face fell. 'That's the regrettable part. She couldn't say for sure but thought it must be more than a year at least. Certainly, it was before the Ursulines came back to the city and took over the food shelter. And the woman only ever saw Bronagh at the shelter so she had no information as to where she might have been living at the time or where she is now.'

Cormac refused to be disheartened by this. 'It's still terrific progress. To get confirmation that Bronagh actually did come to these shores is an enormous relief. And in fact,' he continued with increasing optimism, 'I have an idea.' He crossed to the kitchen and stuck his head through the doorway. 'Can you come out here, *a stór*?'

Emily stood her paintbrush carefully into a jar next to her watercolour box and scurried after him into the front room. 'Yes, Papa?'

'Do you remember the pictures you sketched of everyone for Christmas?' he asked.

She nodded, beaming proudly.

'Do you think you could do another one? If I asked you to draw Auntie Orlaith again but this time with her eyes less round? That would make her look more like your Auntie Bronagh.'

'Yes, I'm sure I could do that,' Emily said confidently.

Bridget's face shone with delight and Orlaith let out a thrilled whoop.

'Excellent,' said Cormac. 'In that case, I shall ask you to make several copies.'

He would retrace his steps across the whole city. With a visual representation of Bronagh to show around, he would surely have more luck in his search. He was feeling more positive than he had in months.

CHAPTER 26

Another year and a half slipped by and by the time they reached their third summer in Acorn House, Bridget had ascertained that there wasn't a breath of air to be had anywhere inside once the sun rose on the hottest days. On this Fourth of July, she traipsed from the front of the house to the back, propping each door open wide, including the door separating the front room and the kitchen. She then stood on that threshold and waited for a breeze to waft through. None came. She sighed, knowing all along it would be a vain attempt. It was so unlike the weather she had experienced in Ireland and England where truly sweltering days had been a rarity. Sometimes she found herself longing for the cool, high-ceilinged entrance hall of Oakleigh.

'Still, we wouldn't change you for the world,' she said, patting the doorframe fondly.

'Are you talking to the house?' came Orlaith's voice.

Bridget looked up quickly to see Orlaith and Tess entering through the open front door. 'No,' she said and, to cover her embarrassment, hurried on, 'You're a bit earlier than I expected. I don't have the food ready yet.'

'Not to worry, we can help you,' said Orlaith. Now seventeen, she had developed a lot over the past year and a half, her adolescent body filling out with more womanly curves. She grinned and added, 'Happy Independence Day!'

The family was gathering today to celebrate the special occasion out of loyalty to their adopted home. Needless to say, given the success of American liberty from British rule, they continued to harbour hopes of a similar triumph for the Irish people back in their homeland.

As Bridget reciprocated the felicitations, she glanced at Tess. Always rather prickly, she had been growing steadily more distant for quite a while now, to the point that Bridget had hardly even seen her in recent months. She had a pinched look about her and only muttered a greeting without making eye contact.

'Charlie should be along shortly too,' said Orlaith. She flushed and Bridget didn't think it was on account of the heat.

A loud thumping resounded on the ceiling above. Bridget marched to the bottom of the stairs and shouted up, 'Quieten down, both of you!'

She received two boyish grumbles of compliance in response.

As she returned to the others, Orlaith said shyly, 'Do you have a few moments before we start preparing the food? I'd like to talk about something important.'

'Of course,' said Bridget, intrigued.

She, Orlaith and Tess pulled out chairs to sit around the kitchen table. There were a few letters scattered upon it; Bridget shuffled them into a pile and set them to one side. Tess folded her arms and half faced away towards the window but Orlaith sat up straight, palms flat on the table's surface.

'I spoke with Sister Annunciata yesterday,' she said. 'The Ursulines' attempt to revive the convent and school hasn't worked. They're leaving Boston again.'

'Goodness, that is a shame,' said Bridget. 'Where will they go?'

Orlaith swallowed audibly. 'Quebec, or New Orleans. They've got other convents established there.'

Bridget gaped. 'And...do you plan to go with them?'

'I-I don't know.'

There was a pregnant silence, during which they heard some further bangs from upstairs, but Bridget had no intention of interrupting this conversation to admonish the boys.

'What is swaying your decision?' she asked gently.

Orlaith pressed her fingertips into the table, causing her nails to turn white. 'I've been thinking for such a long time about joining the nuns properly. I feel like I could do some real good with them. And I've plenty to thank God for so it'd be the right thing to serve him. But...but my family's here in Boston.' She stared down at her hands. 'And so's Charlie.'

Yes, so was Charlie. Good-natured and obliging, he had remained in the McGoverns' sphere of acquaintance, on friendly terms with them all while patiently waiting for Orlaith to grow older. And now she was seventeen and attaining an age of true womanhood at last, and she might end up slipping from his grasp just when she was finally within his reach. What cruel timing.

Bridget tilted her head, studying Orlaith's torn expression. 'Do you know what your feelings are for him?'

'I can't put him out of my mind,' Orlaith admitted. 'But I keep thinking my life's purpose should be for God's work.'

'There are other ways to do God's work. Choosing to build your life with a man doesn't prevent you from doing that, nor does it make your life less valuable. So long as the man merits that choice.'

Tess shifted in her seat, eyes heavy-lidded but voice mute. Orlaith compressed her lips, pensively gazing into space.

After a long minute, she looked back at Bridget. 'Is love worth it?'

Bridget smiled. 'I think you have your answer right there. If you believe you are in love, hold onto it with all your might and never let it go.'

Orlaith hesitated and then a smile of her own grew slowly until her whole face lit up with it.

There was a rapping sound of knuckles on wood. 'Hello?' Footsteps crossed the front room and Charlie appeared in the doorway to the kitchen. He pointed behind him. 'The door was open so I just...'

'Of course, come in,' said Bridget, beaming at him. 'You're very welcome.'

He greeted each of them but it was easy to see how his body language gravitated towards Orlaith.

She did not prevaricate. 'Will you come out to the yard with me?' she asked, extending her hand to him.

Brow furrowed, he took it and she led him out the back door, leaving Bridget and Tess alone in the kitchen.

***

Emily perched on the window sill of the box room, the sketches in her lap forgotten as she sought fresh air by pushing open the sash window as far as it could go. A cool breeze still proved elusive. Beads of sweat pooled on her chin and nose and she wiped them away self-consciously, even though she was on her own.

She could hear Jack and Gus thrashing about in the other back bedroom, which had become the boys' room once Gus was old enough to share with his brother. Papa had moved Emily's bed and cupboard into the box room where they just about fit, although it was a rather tight squeeze. Sometimes she missed having company but, at eleven years old, she really was above her brothers' childish antics now. At least possessing a room all to herself meant she could draw in relative peace.

Technically, she was not alone because Mabel still remained in the bottom of the cupboard. However, she had grown used to shutting off her thoughts whenever Mabel intruded and the pain of their separation had eased over time. She had also succeeded in retaining Emmeline as her friend, and school itself had become more bearable after a year when another teacher, young and jolly Miss Green, had taken over from Mr Miller. Emily had never been so relieved to see the back of that man with his horrible hairy growth on his nose. Her second full year of school was now finished for the summer but she hoped Miss Green would still be her teacher when lessons resumed in September.

She heard a noise below her window and peered down to see Auntie Orlaith and Charlie emerging into the yard. They were holding hands but Auntie Orlaith dropped Charlie's as she stepped forwards. Delilah and Jemimah, who had been pecking about in the parched grass, flapped away at the humans' encroachment on their territory. Beulah, wisely, was resting in the shade beneath the hen coop.

Auntie Orlaith's voice drifted up to the window. 'Thanks for coming outside. I wanted to talk with you in private.'

Emily squirmed. Perhaps she ought not to be listening. But, to her shame, she couldn't resist leaning closer to the window to get a better look at the pair. Charlie was tugging nervously on the rim of his maimed ear.

'What about?' he asked.

'The future,' said Auntie Orlaith. 'You know I've been involved in activities with the Ursulines over the past couple of years. They've taught me a lot about nursing. Well, turns out they're leaving Boston. For good.'

Charlie's dismay was blatant in his countenance. 'Are you l-leaving too?' he stuttered.

Auntie Orlaith took a deep breath. 'No,' she said. 'I'm going to stay.'

Charlie glowed so brightly that Emily imagined the temperature in the back yard must have increased tenfold. 'Then does that mean—' He cut himself off.

'What were you going to say?' Auntie Orlaith asked encouragingly.

'I don't want to push...'

'I think I'm ready to be pushed.'

He gulped. 'Are you staying...for me?'

'I am,' she said simply.

Bashful, Charlie reached out and grasped Auntie Orlaith's hand again, and she placed her other one over his. After a tiny hesitation, he leaned in and lightly joined his lips to hers. Emily couldn't rip her gaze away and she had to stop herself from squealing with delight.

When Charlie drew back, he said, 'So...do you think someday you might like to...marry me?'

Auntie Orlaith bit her lower lip. 'What'll your parents say? 'Specially your da?'

'I'm not concerned about him. I only care what *you'll* say. Do you want us to be married?'

Auntie Orlaith nodded vigorously and, thrilled, Emily wondered if she should start calling him Uncle Charlie. Then her auntie said, 'But not right away. I'm still very young.'

'I can wait,' said Charlie with a wide grin. 'It's good enough for now just to know.'

He bowed his head towards Auntie Orlaith's again and this time they kissed with a great deal more passion. He put his free hand at her waist and she wrapped her arm around his neck, leaving their other fingers interlaced. Emily goggled when their lips parted and she caught a glimpse of their tongues in the space between before their mouths locked together again. She ducked away from the window, her pages tumbling to the floor, certain she had seen too much.

She collapsed back on her bed, staring at the ceiling in raptures. Auntie Orlaith and Charlie were going to be married, how wonderful! What would it be like to fall in love? She hoped she would experience it someday.

Meditatively, she lifted her closed fist above her face and curled her thumb across her bent index finger to make the shape of a mouth. Feeling powerfully curious, she brought it to her lips and stuck her tongue into the little hollow she had made. Then, blushing, she withdrew it. She tried to envisage touching her tongue to someone else's tongue. The idea was intimidating and alluring all at once.

Cheeks still burning, she sat up to retrieve her fallen sketches.

***

After Orlaith and Charlie went outside, Bridget and Tess sat at the kitchen table in uncomfortable silence.

'Have you had many injuries to tend to lately?' Bridget asked.

'A few,' said Tess.

'How is old Mrs Kane these days?'

'She's grand.'

More silence.

Bridget was relieved when steps came pounding down the staircase, heralded by the ever-present Barnabas, and Jack galloped into the kitchen. Gus lagged behind as, at nineteen months, he could still only manage the stairs by sliding down one step at a time on his bottom. He toddled in after his brother, arms outstretched to his mother. Bridget jumped from her chair and swung him up with the same unfailing joy she always felt for her littlest boy. Having birthed four children, the youngest at last bore her likeness – Gus had dark brown eyes and a charming mop of chestnut curls.

He submitted patiently to her hug, then looked around the kitchen and said, 'Where Da?' with a worshipful expression.

'He said he'd be a little late today,' said Bridget. 'But after he comes home we're all going to the Common to see the illuminations.'

Jack and Gus both let out hollers of excitement and dashed from the kitchen again, Gus once more straggling after his older brother.

Tess sat back in her chair. 'Late?' she said.

Bridget disliked her tone. 'It's regrettable but unavoidable.'

'Did he say why?'

Bridget didn't respond.

The corner of Tess's mouth curved slyly upwards. In an apparent change of subject, she said, 'Today's so special for the folk in this country with the celebrations and food and illuminations. Lots of people see it as a family day. But I suppose many will want to share the occasion with their American sweethearts.' She threw an idle glance towards the window. 'Ah, looks like that pair have come to a happy arrangement.'

Bridget didn't follow her gaze, instead remaining stony-faced in Tess's direction. Inside, she was boiling with rage. She had grasped what Tess had insinuated and it left her with a strong urge to throttle her.

The problem was that Tess had touched a very sensitive nerve.

Not for one second did Bridget believe that Cormac was being unfaithful to her with an American girl. However, she did suspect that he was hiding *something* from her.

It had been going on for months now, him coming home late in the evenings after work or disappearing for hours on end on Sundays. He usually cited his ongoing search for Bronagh as the reason for his frequent absences and, oftentimes, that was indeed the case. Once Emily had drawn several portraits of Bronagh based on Orlaith's features, Cormac had taken them around the city, revisiting boarding houses, lodgings, locations where homeless people gathered, and anywhere else he could think of, but it had been to no avail. After still finding no trace of her in spite of the visual clue to help trigger people's recollections, he had admitted to Bridget the possibility that, even though they now knew for certain Bronagh had arrived to Boston, she could very well have left it since and settled somewhere else. With that despairing thought in mind, he had started leaving copies of her picture at stagecoach stops and even at the newly built railway stations. He had written the address of Acorn House on the back of each picture, in case anyone should recognise her face and want to get in touch with information.

On the whole, it had once again turned into a fruitless endeavour. Nevertheless, he had persisted in keeping up the search, or so he claimed anyway. What Bridget began to find strange was that he no longer spoke much about his ventures, volunteering very few details and becoming evasive if she pressed him for more. Nowadays, he was gone more often than he was home, and yet when Bridget asked Emily if her papa had requested more drawings she revealed that he hadn't. Which made his secretive behaviour all the more questionable.

Despite this, Bridget could not identify anything lacking in their family life or their own relationship when he was present. He adored the children and they him. He never neglected to tell Bridget how much he loved her. As for encounters of a more amorous nature, these had resumed once her body had healed after Gus's birth and, with the implementation of the pessary, his fears had been assuaged and their passion had been renewed without impairment. There was no evidence of any

232

kind that she could point to as a cause for secrecy, but she still knew something was not quite right. And Tess had picked at her insecurities like a scab.

With an innocent grin, Tess said, 'I think they've had enough time to themselves now.'

She rose from the table and wandered out the back door, flicking her red hair over her shoulder as she went. Bridget stayed seated, glaring at Tess's empty chair, full of loathing and doubt.

To distract herself from her unpleasant ruminations, she reached for the top letter on the pile she had pushed to one side on the tabletop. It was another missive from Laurence Enright and John Corbett, informing her of the latest developments at Oakleigh. While every attempt was being made to rebuild the manor in a style as close as possible to its previous incarnation, they confirmed that it had proved feasible to accommodate the request she had put forth with regard to one specific alteration. She was very pleased to hear it and wished they had an artist as talented as Emily to draw an illustration of the progress made thus far. With a stab of wistfulness, she wondered when they might ever return to see it in the flesh.

She supposed she ought to write to Garrett to keep him abreast of the advancements at Oakleigh and, with that thought, an unwelcome memory intruded. He had been unfaithful to her ever before they had married, conducting a love affair with Cormac's sister Mary for many months while simultaneously courting Bridget. And she hadn't had even the slightest inkling of it at the time.

Something oily settled unwillingly deep in the pit of her stomach.

Chapter 27

'Thank you, Mr Walker,' Cormac said and stepped out of the foreman's office.

'McGovern!'

He turned and saw O'Mali striding towards him across the warehouse floor. 'In trouble again?' the fellow said with a grin and a jerk of his head towards the office.

Cormac smiled at the joke but didn't offer an explanation for his audience with the foreman. He started walking towards the entrance of the warehouse and O'Mali fell into step beside him.

'Did you bring your young ones to the illuminations the other night?' O'Mali asked.

'I did,' said Cormac. 'The noise was a bit much for my smallest boy but the older lad hasn't stopped talking about them since. My daughter loved them too. What about your own?'

'Tilly thought they were spectacular. Her mouth was open so wide she could've caught flies in it.'

They emerged into the summer heat and headed towards the wharf. There was a lot to be said for working on the docks when a cooling breeze came in over the water. It was rather less pleasant down in the stifling holds, however.

O'Mali lifted his hand to shade his eyes against the sun. 'Have you had any luck yet finding your sister?'

He was aware of the protracted search for Bronagh because Cormac had made enquiries along the waterfront and circulated her picture there too, just in case anyone might recognise her from when she had first disembarked upon her arrival to Boston or, God forbid, if she had subsequently taken passage on another ship. He hardly wanted to give credence to the idea that she could have since sailed back to Ireland for some unknown reason.

'No luck at all,' he said heavily. Nearly four years had passed but there hadn't been a trace of her apart from that woman's account at the food shelter, which ultimately had been a clue to nowhere. 'It's like she turned into a ghost almost as soon as she set foot here.'

O'Mali cleared his throat, looking uncomfortable. 'Have you considered the fact that she might have...' He trailed off.

'Come to an unfortunate end?' Cormac finished gloomily. 'I have. That could well be the case, and if so may God rest her soul. It would certainly explain why I haven't been able to find her. But I don't see how I can stop searching for her until I know for sure.'

He feared he could search for decades without success and felt daunted by the prospect of treading a perpetual path of failure with no foreseeable end to it. In contrast to this, while it seemed morbid to even think it, he had gained a certain closure to learn of the demise of his mother and sister Margaret in Dublin, even though the news had been crushing. At least Tess had witnessed their passing, and he had been left in no doubt as to what had happened to them. According to Tess, it had been July when they had departed from this life, which meant that the anniversary of their deaths was some time during this month. He would go to Saint Augustine's on his way home to request the offering of a Mass for their souls.

He had another place to stop by as well which would make him even later, but at least the church was a decent excuse.

***

Bridget bent over the garment in her lap, guiding the needle carefully in and out. She wanted to do an especially good job as she was on a trial of sorts. At the shop where she purchased her spools of thread, she had struck up a conversation with a fellow customer and learned that her name was Madame Roche, a dressmaker with an establishment on Summer Street. The lady had been lamenting the loss of the best seamstress in her employ ('Her father has been seduced by the lure of the west and insists the whole family must go, *c'est terrible!*') and, on a whim, Bridget had expressed her interest in the position, though admitting she would be obliged to do the bulk of the work in her own home as she had two small boys to look after. Madame Roche had appraised her down the long slope of her nose and demanded that she bring a sample of her handiwork to Summer Street within the next week.

Now, as Bridget paid meticulous attention to her labours, Cormac and Orlaith held a serious discussion alongside her at the kitchen table, while through the open back door wafted the raucous sounds of Jack and Gus's boisterous play.

'Hush a little,' came a gentle remonstration from Emily, who was not participating in the boys' frolics but had gone outside to lie on the grass in the sun and sketch, 'or Mr and Mrs Hill will come over again to complain.'

Meanwhile, Orlaith was saying, chin propped in her hands, 'If she left Boston, there's no knowing where she could have gone to next. New York, out west, maybe even north to Canada.

How would we even begin to look for her across the whole continent?'

It was a topic they had debated a dozen times before, and a solution had never presented itself.

Cormac dispiritedly turned the pages of the latest edition of *The Boston Pilot*. 'This has some national circulation. Maybe she'll see one of our notices, even if she's in a different city.'

No one bothered to point out how minuscule the odds of that had to be.

He folded the newspaper with an air of finality. 'I'm going to go out for a little while. I'll visit the cathedral and ask Father Whitty if he's heard anything from Bronagh.'

'I can go with you,' said Orlaith, starting to rise.

'No, no,' he said, waving her back down. 'You stay here. You've already walked all the way from Broad Street in this heat.'

As he went out to the back yard to bid a brief farewell to the children, Orlaith said to Bridget, 'I'm sorry Tess couldn't join me today. She was feeling very under the weather this morning. She didn't go to Mass either, although I'll be the first to admit she'd use any excuse not to go.'

She gave a crooked smile but Bridget did not return it. Her gaze followed Cormac as he re-entered the kitchen, calling back over his shoulder, 'We'll play when I get home, I promise!'

He stooped to kiss Bridget's cheek and, in the space of time it took for him to exit the kitchen and cross the front room to leave the house, she had strengthened her resolve. As soon as she heard the front door close, she said, 'Oh, goodness, I've just remembered an errand I meant to run earlier. Could I ask you to mind the children for a short time while I pop out?'

Orlaith looked a touch surprised but said, 'Of course, happy to do it.' She grinned. 'I'll get them to teach me some Irish words. My own knowledge is woeful.'

Bridget gathered up her sewing and dropped it in a slapdash pile on the table. 'Thank you. I'll be as quick as I can.'

She didn't go out to the back yard to say goodbye to the children but instead hastened straight to the front door, afraid she might not have enough time to catch up to Cormac before he disappeared. However, when she emerged onto the steps she glimpsed his back as he strode down the street. She hurried to follow at a discreet distance.

She knew she was being irrational; the idea of Cormac playing her false couldn't be more preposterous. And yet she also knew that he was concealing something from her, and he had regrettably proved himself capable of lying to her in the past – Thomasina reared her pretty head in Bridget's mind. She shoved her resentfully away. Really, she had nothing to worry about.

Then her heart sank as Cormac crossed the street ahead of her, his steps taking him in the exact opposite direction of the Cathedral of the Holy Cross. Tess's sly insinuations once more slithered beneath Bridget's skin and took poisonous hold.

She shadowed Cormac for several minutes, tailing him into an area of South Boston with which she wasn't familiar. Her feet felt like lead and sweat accumulated at her neck and under her arms, not all of which she could attribute to the temperature of the day. She watched furtively as he walked along another street and entered a building with a blank facade. Frowning, she approached it herself. What sort of establishment didn't advertise its trade with some sort of sign above its door or in its window? It could hardly be a brothel...could it?

She opened the door cautiously and, after a quick glance, slipped inside. She stood in an entirely empty room with a single door set into the back wall. There was still nothing to say what kind of building it was.

The inner door was ajar and through it she heard a grunt. Aghast, she recognised it as the kind of sound Cormac made when he was putting a lot of physical effort into something. She had heard it more than once in their bed.

Horrified, she found herself drawn to the sound against her will. She pulled the door wide and, stomach in knots, stepped across the threshold.

She blinked. 'What?' she said involuntarily.

Cormac looked up, startled, and dropped the heavy wooden object he had just lifted into his arms. It fell on his toes and he swore, hopping back in pain as it landed flat on the floor with a solid thud.

'What are you doing here?' he exclaimed.

She had no words to reply. She stared around. The space they were in was larger than the first room and filled with pieces of wood of all different shapes and sizes. A large bench occupied the centre of the room and an open cabinet on one wall displayed a range of tools. There was nobody else there.

'I—' she said at last. 'I-I followed you to—where *are* we?'

He grimaced. 'It was meant to be a surprise.'

After testing his injured toes gingerly, he bent to lift the heavy object again with another grunt, turning it so she could read what it said. It proclaimed 'McGovern' in proud lettering next to a fine carving of a hammer.

'Welcome to my workshop,' he said. 'Soon to be the location of my full-time employment as a carpenter.'

She gaped.

'I wanted to wait to tell you until I was certain I could achieve it. I only notified my foreman after Independence Day, which was quite fitting when you think about it.'

She swallowed as shame burned her insides. 'Your workshop,' she said, her voice faint.

'I know it might seem like a bit of a risk,' he said quickly. 'Working at the docks brought a reliable wage which has been a blessing while the country is still in the midst of this slump.

But I truly believe I can make this venture a success. Over the past months, I've been gathering my own tools one at a time and scouting for suitable premises. I've built further pieces for Mr Walker and through him I've had commissions from several of his acquaintances, almost more than I can manage.' He coloured as he propped the sign up against the bench. 'Some day I would be very pleased to add "& Sons" to this. In the meantime, if I garner enough business to merit hiring an apprentice in the future, I thought I could take on Rory Carey.' He glanced at her hopefully. 'What do you think?'

Bridget longed for a hole to crack open in the ground so she could jump into it to escape her massive blunder. 'I-it sounds like a marvellous scheme. You've obviously considered it from all angles.'

He relaxed, relieved. 'I was worried you might be upset that I hadn't told you before now.'

'Well, I am rather put out about that,' she said, her indignation rising. 'If you'd been upfront about it, I wouldn't have harboured silly suspicions for no good reason.'

'Suspicions?' he repeated, his brow puckering.

It was her turn to redden. 'Surely you didn't suppose I wouldn't notice your increasing lateness and numerous absences? How could I not wonder what you were up to? It was inevitable that it would cause doubt in my mind. And after what Tess said—'

'Tess?' he said sharply. 'What did she say?'

'It's of no consequence now,' Bridget said with an awkward shrug. 'My fears were clearly baseless.'

'I still want to know,' he insisted.

Unwillingly, she said, 'It happened when she and Orlaith came for the meal on the Fourth of July. I mentioned that you expected to be late that day and she commented that many people preferred to celebrate the occasion with their American sweethearts. I realise now that she was just being her usual contrary self.'

'No,' he said, looking troubled. 'There was more to it than that.' He rubbed his jaw. 'I'm aware that this will appear even worse from your perspective following my other concealment, but it is best for you to know the truth. Tess tried to kiss me, two Christmases ago.'

She reeled, unable to believe her ears.

'Needless to say, I stopped her at once. I had originally decided to keep my silence because I wanted to save her from embarrassment. But I no longer feel she's deserving of that consideration. I've got a strong misgiving that her comment to you was deliberate.' His eyes glittered with anger. 'An attempt, perhaps, to drive a wedge between us.'

A blaze of fury sparked within Bridget, expanding until it scorched every inch of her skin. She supposed she could rage at Cormac for keeping another secret from her but there was a more pertinent target for her ire.

'How dare she!' she spat out. 'What an abominable thing to do.'

His mouth compressed into a thin line. 'It is disheartening to believe her capable of such malice.'

At last Bridget understood why Tess had always been so aloof with her. She had coveted what she could not have and resented Bridget for being the obstacle who stood in her way. Bridget seethed at the injustice and immaturity of Tess's behaviour.

'What shall we do about this?' she demanded. A substantial part of her wanted to cut off their connection with Tess altogether.

'I'm not sure,' he admitted. 'I had judged the issue to be settled, given how much time had passed, but now I see that it is not. However, it's a tricky situation. She is Orlaith's closest friend and they live together. To cease any association with Tess would be difficult without also impairing Orlaith's relationship with her and with us.'

'But this cannot slide by without acknowledgement,' Bridget protested.

'No, it can't,' he agreed with a heavy sigh. 'I'll have to speak to her, make it plain that she has stepped beyond the bounds of what is acceptable. If she heeds the warning, then that will be the end of it.'

'And if not?' said Bridget, her tone clipped.

'Then there will be consequences. For the whole family, I expect.' He ran his hand through his hair. 'I can't imagine you will be happy for me to see her, but do I have your consent to go to Broad Street?'

She gave a jerky nod of acquiescence, still fuming. If she were to confront Tess, she could make no guarantee that she would be able to restrain herself from slapping her.

Cormac took a step closer. 'So when you followed me today, what were you expecting to find?'

The heat in her cheeks turned from wrath to mortification.

'Me locked in the arms of another woman?' he suggested.

'Not truly,' she said, trying to convey how earnestly she meant it. 'I found it impossible to give credit to such a notion. But I did dread discovering evidence of some sort of deceit. And, in a way, there was.' She waved her arm to indicate the workshop. 'But I'm very glad that it was for a worthy reason, no matter how misguided your rationale for withholding it.'

He offered her a lopsided smile. 'Shall we agree to acknowledge that we have both acted foolishly and grant each other unreserved forgiveness?'

The knots in her stomach unravelled with relief. 'Yes, let's do that.'

Bashfully, they both crossed the space between them to meet in the middle. He caressed her hip where the trio of freckles lay hidden and she rose up on her toes to kiss him. When he wrapped his arms tightly around her and his tongue delved deep into her mouth, she got the distinct impression that he wished to bring about a physical resolution to their grievances right then and there. She pulled out of the kiss with great reluctance.

'Later,' she assured him, her voice husky with promise.

Yes, later they would demonstrate how their bodies and souls were bound so closely that the insidious words of a bitter woman could never divide them.

CHAPTER 28

The next evening, Cormac entered the building on Broad Street and dragged his feet up the stairs with little enthusiasm for the conversation ahead. He knocked on the door and Orlaith answered it.

'Cormac?' She laughed. 'You don't need to knock, for God's sake. Come on in.'

He trailed after her into the room. She scuttled over to the fireplace where a pot was simmering over the flames, a wooden spoon sinking into its depths.

'Tess, could you not keep an eye on it for two seconds?' she said in exasperation, rescuing the spoon and stirring it vigorously.

Tess, lounging on the sofa, did not respond. She sat up straight at Cormac's appearance and gave him a small smile.

'You on your way home from the docks?' she asked.

He nodded; he had agreed with Mr Walker to stay for two more weeks. He had yet to tell Orlaith and Tess about his imminent change in occupation but that could wait until another time. There was no use delaying the task at hand.

'May I speak with you in private?' he said formally to Tess.

She raised her eyebrows while Orlaith frowned between them in bewilderment.

'Sure,' said Tess, affecting an air of indifference. 'Orlaith, can we go into your room? There's no window in mine and I guess that pot still needs stirring.'

Orlaith dumbly waved her affirmation with the spoon. Tess hopped up and led the way into the front bedroom. Cormac followed and shut the door behind them; it was against his better judgement but this exchange required discretion. She tossed a suggestive glance at the bed. While not an explicit proposition, he sensed that if he were to tumble her onto the bedcovers right this instant she would not hesitate to reciprocate. He crossed his arms. With a shrug, she wandered over to the window but he remained near the door, leaving as much space as possible between them. The evening sun came slanting through the window panes, highlighting her fiery hair.

'So what's all the fuss?' she said.

'Bridget told me about the remark you made to her on the Fourth of July.'

Tess twisted her mouth. 'Ah, you'll have to be a bit more specific than that. Did I say something memorable?'

He ground his teeth. 'Your comment about American sweethearts? You essentially implied that I had another lover.'

'Come on now,' she said, letting out a scornful snort. 'I was talking in general terms. Is it my fault she read too much into it?'

'I think you did it on purpose.'

'Why on earth would I do that?'

'To cause a rift between Bridget and me.'

She blinked. 'You've a mighty high opinion of yourself. One little kiss a couple of years ago and you assume I've been pining for you ever since?'

Was that just bravado? He couldn't be certain.

'I told Bridget about the kiss,' he said.

Tess's eyes flashed and she turned her head away to gaze out the window. 'Right,' she said in a flat voice. 'Am I banished from the family so, is that it?'

'Not this time. But I fear you are walking on thin ice. If you try anything like this again, it can't possibly be tolerated.' He added gently, 'Nothing will ever happen between us, Tess. Please believe that.'

The rays of the sun had shifted, sinking lower than the rooftops and casting her face in shadow. 'Got it,' she said. 'Loud and clear.'

After a long pause, he went back out to the other room. He lingered for a few minutes to talk to Orlaith, skirting any explanation for his private interview with Tess. By the time he departed for Acorn House, Tess still had not emerged from the bedroom.

***

Bridget stepped across the threshold of the building on Broad Street with a rising wave of resentment which she struggled to push back down. She threw a baleful glare up the stairs without any idea whether Tess was at home or not. Cormac had assured her the previous week that he had made it emphatically clear to Tess their objections to her spiteful conduct, but Bridget was still tempted to give her a piece of her own mind. Nonetheless, she supposed it was best to be the mature party in this situation, no matter how satisfying it might be to vent her animosity.

'Come along,' she said to Emily and Jack behind her, keeping a maternal grip on Gus's hand as she knocked on the Careys' door.

A short time later, Derval and her four children were ready to go and the group set off with their baskets for Quincy Market.

'I'm astonished at the height of you, Rory,' Bridget remarked as they walked along. 'You must have shot up at least a foot since I saw you last. What age are you now?'

'Fourteen,' he mumbled. His voice had deepened too, although he didn't look like he needed to start shaving just yet.

Emily scowled. Her reaction might simply have been a manifestation of her longstanding feud with Rory but Bridget had noticed recently that any mention of height appeared to rankle her daughter. She had grown comparatively little over the past couple of years and it was quite likely that the other girls at school were developing faster than her. Even ten-year-old Una was a year younger but two or three inches taller. Bridget would make sure to remind Emily later that she had nothing to worry about; she would doubtless catch up eventually.

They carried on and reached Quincy Market, its long, rectangular hall bustling with patrons visiting a variety of food stalls.

'Don't wander off,' Bridget warned her children. Even as Derval gave the same order to her own, a look of devilment glinted in Brian Carey's eyes.

They browsed the stalls, examining the produce on display. Bridget purchased a block of cheese and placed it in her basket, observing with surprise that Derval did not do likewise.

At her questioning look, Derval explained, 'Brian Mór wrote to say he's due to be back this week. He hates the smell of cheese.'

'I can't wait for Da to come home!' said Sorcha and little Brian also beamed with excitement, but the glum expression on Una's face told Bridget that the girl took a different view on her father's imminent arrival. Maybe she was old enough now to sense the friction that existed between her parents.

Rory, too, looked sullen. 'He should just stay away,' he muttered.

'Rory Carey, you'll get a hiding if you're not careful,' Derval snapped. 'Take your sisters and brother over to that bread stall and get a loaf, and let there be no more cheek from you.'

She gave him a coin and a brief clip around the ear. He trudged off with his siblings in tow. Bridget urged her own three after them, cautioning Emily and Jack, 'Don't let go of Gus's hands.'

Once the children were out of earshot, Derval said, 'Sorry about that.'

'There's nothing to apologise for,' Bridget assured her. She hesitated. 'Do you want to talk about it?'

Derval's green eyes filled with pain and, to Bridget's alarm, tears. 'Yes,' she whispered. 'I'm tired of keeping it to myself.'

Glancing around, Bridget coaxed Derval into a gap next to the cheese stall. The other customers and vendors paid them no mind and she could still see the children a little further up the concourse queuing for the bread.

'I don't know why I'm getting upset now,' Derval said, rubbing a knuckle in one eye. 'I made my peace with it a long time ago.'

'With his prolonged absences?' said Bridget gently.

'And the reason for them.' Derval's voice was clogged with emotion as she continued, 'He's got another woman at another port.'

Bridget's jaw dropped. She quickly closed it again.

'I don't know where and I don't know her name,' said Derval. 'I never wanted to know, 'specially not when he told me he loved her more than he ever loved me or our children.'

'Oh, Derval,' Bridget breathed, appalled. 'I'm so sorry.'

Her estimation of Brian Mór – never very high to begin with – plummeted. How unspeakably callous of him to treat his wife in such a manner.

Derval's shoulders curved inwards, wretchedness outlining her hunched posture. 'He admitted it not long before little Brian was born. He'd already been with her two years at that stage. Said he didn't want to pretend with me any longer. But he promised he wouldn't let us go hungry and that he would keep supporting us. And, in fairness to him, he's kept that promise. He sends money even if he doesn't make it home himself very often. I'm grateful for that at least.'

Bridget bit her tongue so as not to spew a stream of invective targeted at that odious man. 'You deserve so much more than that.'

A tear escaped Derval's brimming eyes and she wiped it away. 'I'm not so hurt on my account anymore. But I wish he'd be a better father to the children. The older they get, the more they recognise how he's failing them. As you can tell from Rory's attitude.' She shook her head. 'It became more obvious after you and your family moved in, watching Cormac with Emily and then Jack when he came along. Mine could see what they were missing out on. Rory wouldn't say it out loud but he's come to idolise Cormac.'

Bridget glanced over at the group of children again, reflecting upon how lucky her three were. They had moved on from the bread stall and were gathered in front of a butchery table, gawking in awe as the butcher deftly chopped up the carcass of a pig. When she looked back, Derval had dropped her gaze and was chafing her palm along the handle of her basket.

'I think what hit me hardest,' she confessed, 'was that New Year's Day when you went into labour with Jack. We'd just got back from Mass and Brian Mór told me he was leaving us again so soon and he passed a remark about wishing he hadn't stayed away from home for Christmas. That was when I realised we were no longer his home. We were only a duty to be endured once in a while, and less often if he could manage it. I'm afraid the day will come when the *Integrity* will dock in Boston and he won't even bother to come ashore.'

With no words to offer that could bring solace, Bridget simply reached out and embraced her, her own basket knocking awkwardly against Derval's hip. Stroking her free hand down her friend's back, she thought that now would be an ideal time to tell her about Cormac's future plan to take on Rory as an apprentice in his workshop. That would cheer up Rory and Derval both, she was sure.

But as they separated, Derval said in a tone of panic, 'I can't see Brian or Gus.'

Bridget whirled back to the cluster of their children at the butcher's stall. She gasped; the two youngest were indeed nowhere in sight. She dashed up the concourse, Derval on her heels. When they reached the butcher's stall, the expressions of alarm on the older children's faces communicated that they, too, had become aware that their younger siblings were missing.

'I only let go of him for a minute, Mama!' Emily burst out in distress. 'I'm sorry!'

'They can't have got too far,' said Rory with a look of extreme guilt. 'I'm the eldest here—'tis my fault for not keeping a closer eye on them.'

While this could have been viewed as a chivalrous attempt to take the blame, Emily seemed to perceive it as an arrogant claim of superiority. '*I'm* the eldest in *my* family,' she asserted. 'I am just as responsible.'

'We don't have time for bickering,' said Bridget, fear climbing into her throat. 'Let's start searching for them at once.'

'Found them!' Jack announced.

Everyone spun in his direction. He was back at the bread stall, holding up the edge of the cloth that covered the table spread with loaves. Brian and Gus were huddled beneath it, cramming fistfuls of bread into their mouths. Two women stood behind the table; when they noticed the commotion, one of them lifted the tablecloth from the other side.

'Get outta there!' she barked at the two small boys.

They scuttled out, but not before Brian had snatched another handful of bread from what appeared to be a box of burnt loaves stashed underneath the table. The second woman rapped him smartly on the wrist as he emerged and he dropped the bread with a yowl.

Bridget tugged Gus to her and hugged him with relief, then gave him a fleeting smack on his bottom. She and Derval uttered profuse apologies to the two women and offered to pay for the pilfered bread.

The first woman shrugged their offers away. 'It was already burnt anyway,' she said.

Her companion pursed her lips. 'There'll be less now for Bronagh Mac's people though.'

'Pardon?' said Bridget, taken aback. 'Who did you say?'

'Just this woman who buys the spoilt produce for a cheaper price. She doles it out to the poorer folk in her neighbourhood.'

Bridget's heart thumped. 'Do you know her full name?'

The second woman frowned. 'No, she's just known as Bronagh Mac. Why?'

'My husband is searching for his sister, Bronagh McGovern.' Hardly daring to hope, she added, 'I wonder if this Bronagh Mac could possibly be her.'

'Has he tried putting a notice in *The Pilot*?'

'He has, but with no luck unfortunately. Could you please describe what this woman looks like?'

If only she had one of Emily's drawings or Orlaith had come with them to the market today. Bridget felt an irrational annoyance towards Tess for being the reason she hadn't gone upstairs at Broad Street.

The first woman made a humming sound. 'Hard to say. Nothing striking about her anyway.'

'Did she have dark hair?'

'Dark enough, I suppose.'

Bridget tried not to get impatient. 'Can you tell me where I might find Bronagh Mac?'

'Oh, that's easy. She lives on Charter Street up in the North End. That's where we drop by at the end of the day if we have burnt loaves.'

A thrill of excitement obliterated the fear that had coursed through Bridget just a short time earlier. 'Thank you very much for your help,' she said. 'We shall seek her there. Please do take this to cover what the boys ate.'

She held out a couple of coins again and the second woman grabbed them eagerly.

'Just be careful,' said the first woman. 'The North End can be a shady sort of area.'

CHAPTER 29

Cormac approached the North End district, his insides jittery with nerves. Orlaith walked beside him, arms swinging as she tapped her fingertips against each other in a repetitive motion. They spoke little, each occupied with their own thoughts. Bridget had imparted the news of what she had discovered earlier at Quincy Market and now they were heading to the North End of Boston, wondering if this would be the day when they would finally be reunited with their sister.

They found Charter Street, where Cormac stopped a passing urchin who had a chunk of blackened bread in her scrawny fist and an oozing scab on her knee.

'Do you know where Bronagh Mac lives?' he asked.

She thrust the whole chunk of bread into her mouth, as though afraid they might thieve it from her. 'What's in it for me if I tell you?' she said as she chewed, crumbs spraying from her lips.

He held out a shiny penny and her eyes went as round as it.

'She lives there,' she said, pointing at a house two doors down from them. 'But right now she's up the street that way. There's a crowd gathered 'round—you won't miss her.'

He flicked the penny and the girl caught it gleefully. As she ran off, he and Orlaith continued along the street in the direction

253

the urchin had indicated. Further ahead, they glimpsed a swarm of people thronging around a stationary wagon. Most looked severely malnourished and wore stained, ragged clothing. A woman crouched in the wagon bed, passing out portions of burnt bread to eager, outstretched hands.

As they neared the wagon, a familiar sting of disappointment punctured Cormac's hopefulness.

'Damn,' said Orlaith softly.

Their Bronagh would be twenty-four by now but this woman was in her forties at least. And although her hair was dark, it did not resemble the shade that his mother and three of his four sisters had shared. Another dead end.

'Damn indeed,' he said, speculating dully how many more punches to the gut he could take. They seemed to be sailing an ocean of defeat where cresting each tiny wave of optimism only plunged them into a deeper trough of frustration.

'That's all there is for today,' Bronagh Mac called out and a groan rumbled through the crowd. They dispersed, some squabbling among themselves over the scraps they had obtained. When she shuffled to the edge of the wagon bed, Cormac hurried forwards and offered his arm to help her. She took it and clambered down to the street.

'Thanks,' she said. 'Sorry ye didn't get any bread.'

'Not a problem,' he replied. 'We weren't here for the bread.'

'What were ye here for?'

'You,' he said and added with a regretful shrug, 'until we realised you weren't the person we were seeking.'

She slipped out of his grasp, looking mistrustful. 'Who're ye looking for?'

'Our sister,' said Orlaith. 'Her name's Bronagh too, but she's a bit younger than yourself. Our surname is McGovern.'

'Ah,' said Bronagh Mac, her expression clearing. 'I'm a MacDonald myself.' She blinked. 'There was another Bronagh on this street before.'

After so many previous disappointments, Cormac didn't quite have enough energy to feel encouraged by this, until the woman nodded at Orlaith and said, 'She looked a lot like you.'

Orlaith perked up. 'Did she?'

'Same hair, for sure, and similar face. Different eyes though.'

'And she lived on this street?' said Cormac, hope rising despite himself.

'Right across the way there,' said Bronagh Mac, pointing with her chin at a shabby two-storey building on the opposite side of the street. 'She didn't show her face much but we got to talking once and realised we had the same name. Not such a common one so that's why I remember her.'

'How long did she live there?' Cormac asked with more urgency now. 'Do you know when she left?'

Bronagh Mac squinted as she tried to recall. 'Hmm, must be three years since I last seen her. And she might've been there for a couple of years before that, hard to say for sure. They didn't let her out too often.'

'They?' Orlaith repeated. 'Who did she live with?'

Bronagh Mac's lips pinched together. She scratched the back of her hand, drawing their attention to a poorly wrapped bandage around her wrist, patches of inflamed skin visible beneath it.

'That looks sore,' said Orlaith. 'D'you want me to take a look at it? I'm a nurse.'

Bronagh Mac tucked her hand behind her back. 'No, 'tis fine. I'd best be on my way.'

'Wait,' said Cormac before she could leave. 'What is it you're not telling us? Who else lived in that house?'

Her gaze darted to the side. 'Folk I'd rather didn't catch wind of the fact that I'd been talking about them.'

Cormac experienced a rush of misgiving. Who had Bronagh become involved with?

'I don't want to put you in a difficult position,' he said carefully, 'but can you tell us anything at all about these people? What their names were or where they might have gone when they left here? We would be grateful for any piece of information that might lead us to our sister's whereabouts.'

Bronagh Mac drew her hand back out and scratched it again, nails scraping agitatedly across her skin. 'There were three fellas,' she muttered. 'And at least one other girl besides Bronagh. One of the fellas was known as Bully Billy. Never knew the names of the others.'

'I see,' said Cormac, his unease growing with every passing second. 'Did they have any sort of occupation?'

She shot him a derisive glance. 'If they did, it was nothing honest. I've no idea what went on behind that door, nor do I want to.' Her voice lowered even further in pitch. 'All I know is that they scarpered, leaving a dead body behind.'

'God Almighty,' said Orlaith, her face full of shock.

'It was days before anyone discovered it—not until the folk next door went in to investigate 'cause the place had started to stink to high heaven. The body turned out to be none other than Bully Billy himself.'

'Does anyone know how it happened?' asked Cormac.

She shook her head.

'Or where they went next?'

Another shake.

'There's no chance they stayed in Boston if they're mixed up in something that awful,' said Orlaith weakly. 'They'd need to get as far away as possible. And do their level best to keep out of sight.' She turned her distraught countenance to Cormac. 'She won't ever want to be found.'

Then she did something that was very unlike Orlaith – her chin trembled and she began to cry. He pulled her to his chest and let her weep, the same grief choking his own throat. No wonder they could scarcely discover a trace of Bronagh in the city. She was long gone, and probably lost to them forever.

Bronagh Mac looked uncomfortable. 'Sorry to be the bearer of bad news.'

'No, thank you for telling us,' said Cormac over the top of Orlaith's head. 'It is better to learn the truth. We appreciate your time.'

'Wish I could've done a bit more,' she said. 'Look after yourselves.'

With a compassionate pat on Orlaith's back, she turned and walked away.

Orlaith continued to sob against Cormac, her shoulders shaking. 'She's as good as dead to us,' she blubbered.

He didn't refute it. Not only was Bronagh's ultimate destination unknown to them, but she and her companions would have taken careful steps to prevent anyone from tracking them, if they were implicated in a murder. They had disappeared, and so too had any realistic hope of finding their sister. It was a devastating realisation. A black cloud of despair seemed to descend upon them, in contrast to the balmy summer's evening.

At length, Orlaith's tears subsided. Withdrawing from Cormac's embrace, she wiped her nose on her sleeve and stared at the shabby building across the way.

'I hope you're safe and well, wherever you are,' she whispered.

Footsteps came tapping along the street and the urchin they met earlier skipped into view. Her face lit up. 'Did you find Bronagh Mac, mister?'

'We did. Thanks for your help.'

She lingered, perhaps hoping he might have another question she could answer and earn a second penny. She bent to pick at the scab on her knee which was leaking yellow pus.

Orlaith sniffed. 'You should leave that alone. It'll get worse if you keep at it like that.'

The girl gave a dismissive shrug and, with no further pennies forthcoming, scampered away again. Orlaith's pensive gaze followed her.

'Y'know…' she said slowly, 'maybe some good can come out of this.'

'What do you mean?' said Cormac.

She chewed on her lip. 'This is the kind of place the Ursulines should visit to help the needy, only they can't 'cause they're leaving the city. But I could still come.' She gestured after the urchin and then motioned in the direction Bronagh Mac had gone. 'I could nurse wounds, maybe bring some food if I can. I know they wouldn't be able to pay me anything but I could do my bit to make life a little easier for them.'

He didn't question her motivation but he thought he could guess it. Bronagh had formed a connection with this place, albeit a tenuous one with an extremely disturbing outcome. Giving back to this community that had claimed her as an inhabitant, even for a brief time, was a way for Orlaith to both remember their sister and mourn her to a limited degree.

He also didn't allude to Orlaith's apparent assumption that she would continue to live in Boston, despite the fact that their search for Bronagh was very likely at an end. As for him and the rest of his family, he would need to have a serious discussion with Bridget about that.

He walked Orlaith back to Broad Street and elected not to go upstairs in case Tess might be there. Instead, he made for home with a heaviness in his steps. As he entered Acorn House, Emily bounded over to him.

'Papa, I found out that Miss Green will still be my teacher this September!' she exclaimed.

She galloped away again without waiting for a reply and raced up the stairs, making her customary greeting to Barnabas along the way. A distant clanging noise from the floor above sounded like Jack and Gus were banging spoons on upturned pots in their bedroom.

Bridget emerged from the kitchen. One glance at Cormac's face was enough to tell her that his and Orlaith's visit to the North End had ended in failure. With a sorrowful sigh, she beckoned him out to the yard where they sat on the back step and he related the details of the encounter with Bronagh Mac.

When he had finished, she put a consoling hand on his knee. 'What dreadful news,' she murmured. 'After all these years of searching.'

He blew out his breath in a long exhalation of despondency. 'It is a crippling blow. And it effectively means we came to this country for a hopeless cause.' He gazed across the back yard; Beulah's head was poking out of the hen coop but her companions were already within, ready to roost for the night. 'I suppose now we must make a decision.'

'What decision is that?' Bridget asked.

'Whether we stay here or go back to Ireland.'

Silence billowed between them. The window of the box room above was open and Emily's voice drifted down, humming tunelessly over her brothers' sporadic clinking.

'Do you know which you would prefer to do?' Bridget said at last.

'No,' he answered honestly. 'Do you?'

She traced her fingertip meditatively over his knee. It tickled and his leg jerked in reflex. She let out a breathy noise, almost a laugh but not quite.

'I'm torn,' she admitted. 'I do miss Ireland dearly. But we have built a life for ourselves and our family here. It would be unfortunate to leave just as you are about to open your new workshop. Furthermore, I visited Madame Roche's after returning from Quincy Market—she has reviewed my work and is so satisfied with it that she intends to take me on with immediate effect. Emily is settled in school and the boys are happy here too.' She paused. 'This could continue to be our home if we wish it, at least for a while longer.'

He pondered her words. Although a part of him always ached for their homeland, Boston had come to feel very much like home too. And she was right; a new chapter of their lives was just beginning with his carpentry business and her employment as a seamstress. What reason did they have to leave right now?

'I agree,' he said. A certain contentment settled in his bones, despite the rawness of his grief. 'Let's stay.'

Her sad smile showed that she, too, was trying to contend with a similar jumble of contradictory emotions. 'In any case,' she said with cheerful pragmatism, 'while they have made great progress on the rebuilding of Oakleigh, it is not ready for habitation yet.'

She seemed to take it for granted that they would reside at Oakleigh whenever they returned to Ireland but there was no guarantee that Garrett would sanction this. Moreover, Cormac found it difficult to envisage them living in the manor house. Was their family really grand enough for such opulence? However, he only said, 'That's a fair point too.'

As though in concurrence, Beulah clucked and ducked her head inside the coop. Bridget gazed past their fence to the darkening sky.

'There is much hardship in this city,' she said, 'but we are in a better position than most. We have a good life here.'

He lifted her hand from his knee and kissed her knuckles. 'Long may it remain so,' he said.

A week later, they stood on the footpath outside his workshop, beholding the sign above the door that said 'McGovern' and the other one in the window that said 'Open'.

'Your father would be so proud of you,' Bridget breathed, linking her arm through his.

Even as Cormac yearned for the pride and approval of the senior Jack McGovern, his heart constricted with regret for the loss of his father's treasured tool chest, taken from him so long ago on the Willowmere Estate back in Ireland. The incensed Lord Strathroy had commanded for it and the rest of Cormac's belongings to be burned after the gentleman had received Garrett's damning letter which had blackened Cormac's character beyond salvage. Even now, Cormac lamented the demise of that tool chest and the precious implements it had contained, which had known the skilful touch of his father's hands so well. All he could do was hope that his own set of tools, so newly acquired, would in time pass on to *his* sons.

A pair of figures came striding up the street towards them, one round-shouldered and the other tall. They halted in front of the workshop.

'We came to wish you all the best,' said Mr Walker as O'Mali stuck out his hand. Cormac freed his arm from Bridget to shake it and to make introductions – O'Mali had been to Acorn House on more than one occasion but Bridget and Mr Walker had never met before. After they had exchanged greetings, the foreman turned to Cormac.

'While I hope this new venture proves to be a success for you,' he said, 'I'd like to add that you'd be welcome back at Robert Smith & Company any time, so long as it's in business.'

'Thank you, that's reassuring to know,' said Cormac, glad that he had made a positive impression during his employment at the docks.

'And I'll probably call by again in the next week or so,' said Mr Walker. 'Mr Smith made a rare appearance at the warehouse yesterday and, when I told him where one of his finest workers had gone, he expressed an interest in commissioning a piece from you.'

Bridget beamed proudly at this and O'Mali clapped Cormac on the shoulder.

'Stay in touch, won't you?' he said with a wink.

After the two men departed, Cormac and Bridget entered the workshop. He had attached a small bell to the door which would alert him to the presence of a visitor if he was occupied in the back room; it rang merrily as they crossed the threshold. The front room now boasted a table with a chair on either side. Emily was sitting behind the table, pretending to take orders from a customer, while Jack and Gus chased each other around the room under Orlaith's watchful eye. She smiled when Cormac and Bridget came in.

'Big day for you,' she said to Cormac. 'Congratulations.'

'Thanks very much,' he replied, buoyant with anticipation at embarking upon this new path he had forged for him and his family. 'Could we ask you to mind these three for a few moments longer? I have something in the back to give to Bridget but don't want the children to get near the tools.'

'Of course,' she said and, with a nod of gratitude, he led Bridget into the back room. A partially built cot rested on top of the bench, a job he had been working on for one of Mr Walker's acquaintances before he had even officially opened the workshop. Bridget looked at him with puzzled expectation. He went over to his cabinet of tools and extracted the object he had placed within it the previous day. Returning to Bridget's side, he presented it to her.

'Oh!' she uttered softly.

He had spent a great deal of time trying to get this new carving just right. The five figures stood in a row on a wooden base, their clothing grooved and their faces and limbs polished to a smooth finish. In the centre was a male and female couple, the man's arm draped around the woman's shoulder and her arm wrapped about his waist. The man's free hand clutched that of a curly-haired girl by his hip while on the woman's side a pair of boys, the second one slightly shorter than the first, also joined hands with each other and with her.

Bridget took the carving and caressed every figure, touching the hem of the girl's dress, the foot of the taller boy, the mop of curls on the smallest child.

'It is simply splendid,' she murmured. 'I am in awe.'

He turned it over in her hands to display the bottom of the base, where he had etched the outline of a bird – a reminder of this carving's predecessor. A little sob escaped her but she quickly smothered it.

'I resolve to only be joyful,' she said, her eyes glistening. 'For this truly is a day of joy.'

CHAPTER 30

Cormac was measuring a length of wood for a bookcase shelf when the bell tinkled on the door of the workshop. After nine months, its chime had become a welcoming sound synonymous with his thriving business. Setting down his ruler, he hurried into the front room where he found Charlie Adams hovering by the table. The young man was tugging self-consciously on his ear.

'What can I do for you, Charlie?' Cormac asked pleasantly.

He thought he could guess the reason for his appearance. Orlaith had turned eighteen a few months ago so it was probable that, after their long and patient courtship, Charlie at last wanted to tie the knot. Without Orlaith's father around, Cormac was the most appropriate person Charlie could approach to ask for her hand in marriage. He would certainly be happy to give his blessing, so long as Orlaith felt she was ready to marry.

His conjecture strengthened when Charlie said, 'I need to talk to you about something.' However, then he carried on with a worried expression, 'Something very troubling.'

Cormac's eyebrows shot up. 'What is it?'

Charlie shifted his weight from one foot to the other. 'I don't—it's hard to find the words...'

Cormac waited calmly. Charlie stared down at the floor, where a layer of sawdust always accumulated, no matter how thorough Cormac's efforts were to keep it swept.

'The other evening,' Charlie began hoarsely and stopped. Clearing his throat, he tried again. 'The other evening, I was on Ann Street—'

Cormac's calmness vanished at once. 'Ann Street?' he barked. 'What the hell were you doing there?' Maybe he wouldn't be so quick to give his blessing after all, if that was the kind of district the pup frequented.

'One of the firemen was getting married the next day,' Charlie hastened to clarify. 'The whole company went for drinks to celebrate.' A wave of relief washed over his face. 'I'm glad you already know it so I don't have to explain what goes on there.'

Indeed, no explanation was necessary. Ann Street was a notorious neighbourhood for brothels and other establishments of an unsavoury nature. It was also the area, Cormac had subsequently discovered, into which he had unwittingly strayed after his first day of work at the docks when he had been invited into a nondescript building by a woman with rouge on her cheeks and lips.

'Can I assume that your conduct there was above suspicion?' he demanded.

Charlie nodded vigorously. 'Yes, sir. I only had two beers and intended to go home before the situation grew too rowdy.'

'So what's troubling you?'

Charlie's throat bobbed. 'The men started making noise about bringing the groom to—uh—to a house of—'

Given his struggle to even speak it out loud, it became clear that he was entirely unacquainted with such places. Cormac relaxed a little.

'A brothel,' he supplied. 'Go on.'

'I decided to just accompany them as far as...their destination, and then leave them to it. As we walked along, women stood in the doorways of different establishments and called out to us, claiming that their services were the best. The men were enjoying the banter but I didn't pay much attention myself until...' He faltered. 'Until I recognised one of them.'

Startled, Cormac hardly dared to ask, 'Who?'

Charlie's gaze dropped. 'Miss O'Leary.'

Cormac rocked back on his heels in shock. 'Tess? You're sure?'

'I am,' said Charlie miserably. 'I'd know the colour of her hair anywhere.'

'Jesus Christ,' said Cormac. 'Did she see you?'

Charlie shook his head. 'I hung back at the rear of the group. I wouldn't have had a clue what to say to her if she'd spotted me.'

'And was she—' Cormac winced. 'Was she offering her services herself? Or is there any possibility she was just helping to bring in customers?' It sounded like a feeble excuse even to his own ears, but maybe she and Orlaith were struggling to pay for the rooms at Broad Street and this was Tess's daft way of earning some additional money.

'I can't say for certain, but judging from what she was wearing...'

Cormac's stomach sank. 'Have you told Orlaith?'

'No.' Charlie shrugged. 'I didn't know how. I mean, Miss O'Leary is her closest friend. How could I reveal this to her?'

'Do you think there's a chance Orlaith might already be aware of it?'

'I'd be very surprised if she was but there was no way I wanted to risk telling her in case she wasn't. All things considered, I thought you were the best person to bring this news to.'

Cormac rubbed his jaw, wishing his initial guess at the purpose for Charlie's visit had been correct. It would have been far easier to grant his blessing for Orlaith and Charlie to wed than to contend with this unwelcome information.

'Was there anything to distinguish the outside of the establishment?' he asked with a weary sigh. 'How would I recognise it?'

Charlie's eyes widened. 'You plan to go there?'

Cormac could think of nothing he would like to do less. But, despite Tess's past dubious actions, he still regarded her as his sister. And he could not tolerate the idea of such dreadful circumstances befalling any member of the McGovern family.

'I have to try to help her,' he said. 'She's in critical need of it. Could you describe the place?'

Charlie pondered for a moment. 'It was just past The Black Bridle tavern—I remember because one of the other men stopped to get sick on the stoop and the tavern owner came out to roar at him. I saw Miss O'Leary only a couple of buildings further on from there. I think it had three windows across the upper floor, and there were red ribbons tied around the handle of the front door. Do you think you'll be able to find it?'

'Yes, that will be enough to go on. I'll head there as soon as I close the workshop for the day.'

There was no guarantee Tess would be there. After all, if she was concealing her disreputable activities from everyone, she could not make it a nightly endeavour or Orlaith would notice that she was never at home. But he supposed it was where he ought to start. If he could not find Tess on Ann Street – and he sincerely hoped that would be the case – he would follow up with a visit to Broad Street.

Charlie left shortly after that and no further visitors came in, leaving Cormac with only his perturbed thoughts for company until the evening drew in and he could close up the workshop.

He would be late returning to Acorn House but that couldn't be helped. He made for Ann Street, dreading what he might find when he reached it.

The district was growing busy as night fell. Drunkards already stumbled along the footpaths, laughter and fiddle music drifted from the taverns, and female voices glided on the air, enticing potential customers into their domains. He located The Black Bridle easily enough, noting the foul stain on its stoop which hadn't been washed away properly. Two doors down, he came upon the building Charlie had described, curtains drawn tightly across its three upper windows and gaudy red ribbons fluttering from its door handle. Two women loitered on the threshold; thankfully, neither of them was Tess.

When he approached the doorstep, the plumper of the pair said, 'I think it's my lucky night.'

Her companion, a much bonier girl, countered, 'No chance. I spotted him first.' She hurried up to Cormac. 'I'd be delighted to please you this evening, sir. If you'll come with me...'

She tried to hook her arm through his but the plump girl jerked her back. 'It's my turn,' she growled and added with a simper, 'You just follow me, sir, and I'll take right good care of you.'

'Thank you, ladies, but I'm not here to engage your services,' he said hastily. 'I'm looking for my sister. I heard a rumour she might be in this establishment.'

Disappointment and suspicion shadowed their faces. 'Are you going to cause trouble?' the bony girl asked warily.

'I'm not,' he said, even though he couldn't imagine that a confrontation with Tess would occur without strife of some kind. 'I just want to speak to her. Can you tell me if she's within? Her name is Tess O'Leary.'

The plump girl's forehead crinkled. 'Don't know her.'

This gave him a spark of hope that perhaps Charlie had been mistaken. Still, to be thorough, he added, 'She has red hair and an Irish accent.'

The plump girl's expression cleared. 'Oh, *Vixen*,' she said. 'Yes, she's here.'

Even as her response extinguished his hope like a fire doused in cold water, the bony girl nudged her stouter companion. 'I don't reckon she'd want us spreading that around. You know how secretive she is.'

The other girl bit her lip. 'Maybe she's not here after all,' she said to Cormac unconvincingly.

He kept his features and demeanour as unthreatening as possible as he said, 'I mean her no harm, I assure you. But it's vital that I speak to her without delay.'

The bony one's eyes narrowed but the plump one tossed her head. 'Come on in then.'

Leaving the other girl on the step, she led him through the doorway and into an antechamber off a narrow hall. An assortment of chairs filled the room, some occupied by men in various stages of intoxication, seemingly waiting for their turn to be brought further into the depths of the building. A scantily-clad young woman roamed among them, distributing drinks, and the scent of incense pervaded the air, poorly masking the odour of the men's sweat.

'Wait here,' the plump girl said and disappeared.

He glanced around the antechamber with discomfort. Even though he had a legitimate purpose for being here, he didn't like to think what Bridget would say if she could see him now. As the young woman with the drinks bent over suggestively to hand a glass to one of the other men, Cormac sidled back out of the room and into the hall.

He was just in time to catch a glimpse of a stout form climbing the stairs out of sight. He followed, treading lightly on the discoloured carpet. His uneasiness increased as sounds from the upper floor wafted down the stairwell – grunts, gasps, and a rather theatrical 'oh, *yes*'.

The top of the stairs led out onto a corridor, its floor covered in the same carpet as below and threadbare in several places. It was lined with closed doors; the plump girl had her ear pressed to one halfway down. She shook her head and stepped away, then looked up in alarm as Cormac drew near.

'You can't be up here,' she objected.

He pointed at the door. 'Is that where she is?'

'They're not finished yet,' she said in a shrill whisper. 'You have to wait.'

It appalled him to even contemplate standing in the corridor and waiting for the deed to conclude. He sidestepped the girl and reached for the door handle.

'No!' she protested. 'There are rules—'

The door wasn't locked. He pushed it open and strode inside with more audacity than he felt. He did not want to witness this, but Tess's welfare was more important to him than his own embarrassment.

It was a small room, lit only by a three-branched candle holder sitting on a table in front of the drawn curtains. The bed was occupied by two bucking bodies, the sounds of male panting interspersed with female moans of encouragement. Cormac's view was mainly of a hairy back and buttocks cradled by white thighs, but a spill of familiar red hair across the pillow removed all doubt. The room smelled of the act of intercourse and he wondered bleakly how many customers she had already entertained that evening.

At the creak of the opening door, Tess's face peered over the man's shoulder. Her jaw dropped in sheer horror and she struggled to push the man away. Too far gone to stop, he gave one final almighty thrust and crumpled upon her with a sated bleat. She shoved against him again but he didn't budge.

'Get off me!' she snapped, smacking at him.

Cormac started to move forwards to assist but then the man rolled away onto his back and Cormac instead averted his gaze to avoid seeing either naked body.

'What's the matter?' the man slurred. 'You didn't squeal at the end.'

Tess didn't respond. Cormac heard her slither off the bed and pad a few quick steps across the carpet. After a brief rummage through whispering folds of clothing, she muttered, 'You can turn around now.'

He swivelled cautiously. She had draped a robe around herself and tossed the rumpled bedcovers over her customer's exposed lower half.

'What're you doing here?' she seethed.

The plump girl stuck her head in the door. 'He barged right in. I couldn't stop him.' She glanced over at the man on the bed. 'No refunds.'

'What about a discount?' he tried.

'Not a blooming chance.'

Tess ignored their exchange. 'Get out,' she said to Cormac, hands on her hips. Her hair clouded around her angry face in fiery disarray.

Now that he had got this far, he wasn't quite sure how to proceed next. 'Tess,' he began.

Her customer, who was striving to reach for his own clothes abandoned on the floor while still keeping himself covered up, pivoted back towards her. 'Tess? I thought you said your name was Vixen,' he said in an accusatory tone.

She shot him a withering glare. 'D'you really think that's what my mother christened me?' She returned her attention to Cormac. 'How dare you come in here? Leave right now.'

'I will, if you come with me.'

She jutted out her chin. 'What d'you care if I go or not? This is none of your concern.'

'Exactly,' said her customer, who inadvertently revealed a great deal more of himself than Cormac wanted to see when the bedcovers slipped off him as he endeavoured to pull on his trousers. 'So piss off.'

'I will not,' Cormac threw back at him. 'She's my sister.'

The man cast him a disparaging look. 'Well, you didn't take very good care of her, now did you?'

'No,' Cormac agreed. 'I didn't. And I'm heartily ashamed of that fact.'

Tess crossed her arms. 'I don't need taking care of. I'm a grown woman. I make my own choices.'

'Why did you make this one?' he asked her, flinging his arm out to indicate the room.

She said nothing.

He turned to the plump girl, who was still hovering in the doorway and watching the scene with avid fascination. 'Can you get him out of here? I need to speak with Tess alone.'

She glanced at Tess who jerked her head crossly. With a dubious expression, the plump girl approached the man – he had managed to put his trousers on backwards and was staring down at himself in some confusion.

'Come on,' she said. Gathering up the rest of his clothes in one hand, she took his elbow with the other and guided him from the room. A reek of strong spirits drifted out with him. Cormac shut the door after them.

When he looked back at Tess, she was making an effort to wrap her robe more tightly around herself. If she was trying to spare her modesty, she might as well give up the attempt for the fabric was so thin that he could distinguish the curve of her breasts beneath it and even the faint shadow of her navel. He refused to let his gaze drop any lower than that.

'Are you going to tell me how this happened?' he said gently.

She avoided his eye. 'The madam will expect money off you if you stay any longer. You're keeping me from earning—the next fella will be waiting.'

'Tess—'

'It's not your job to save me,' she interrupted loudly. 'So just leave me be.'

'It *is* my job,' he contradicted her. 'You became a part of my family when you sailed across the Atlantic with us. Since then, you have always had my protection and my friendship.'

'I don't want any of it.'

He stared at her in disbelief. 'You'd prefer this?'

She turned her back on him, bending to pick up a few garments which she must have been wearing before she disrobed for her customer. She laid them out on the bed and, surveying them, plucked a clump of dirty fluff from a sleeve.

'This is what I'm good at,' she said at last.

A burst of pity splintered inside him. 'How can you even think that?'

''Cause it's the truth.' She fingered the tatty heel of one stocking. 'I haven't got any other talents worth speaking of. I couldn't get the knack of reading. Orlaith's far better than me at nursing. I don't have enough kindness to be a midwife like Derval. And never in a hundred years would I be able to sew as well as Bridget. I'm not cut out for anything except lying on my back.'

She said it in such a matter-of-fact way, like she was commenting on the weather.

'Please tell me you don't really believe what you're saying,' he said weakly.

''Course I do. There's no evidence to prove otherwise.' She shrugged. 'It's not so bad. At least it's an improvement on how it was in Dublin—I've got a room and a bed instead of an alley and a wall.'

He was speechless. Had she so little faith in herself? She ordinarily exhibited such bravado and nonchalance that he found it difficult to comprehend this blatant decline in her self-esteem. When had this happened? He gulped as the most likely answer struck him. But he could not fathom how his rejection could send her so far down this egregious path.

He took a step closer to her. 'You're better than this. You don't have to be here.'

'I do. I need the money.'

'But the nursing—'

'I've been lying about that for ages.' She pushed the garments to one side and began moving around the bed, straightening the covers. 'Orlaith had the skills, she built up a reputation, folk knew to call for her if they had an injury or illness. I couldn't match that. I was nowhere near as good as her. But I still had to bring in my share of the rent.'

'How many times did we tell you both to ask us for help if you needed it?' he demanded. 'We would have come to your aid in an instant.'

The scathing look she gave him conveyed that she would rather have walked over hot coals. 'At first, I only did it on the odd occasion, just to fill a gap when funds were particularly low. I thought that Bridget had found me out when she asked me for advice on ways to stop from getting with child. But then I realised she was only thinking of herself.' She fluffed up a pillow. 'Sometime after that I started relying on it more.' She sighed. 'And more.'

In the stark silence that ensued, they heard heavy footfalls out in the corridor and a thump.

'Lord, you're so drunk you won't be able to get it up at all,' came a female voice, followed by a tinkling giggle. 'Makes my job easier, I suppose. Maybe we'll just take a nap.'

In the garbled response she received, Cormac could only make out the word 'darling'. The rest was an unintelligible mess of stuttering syllables.

'That's right,' the female voice said soothingly. 'It's gonna be the best night of my life. On your feet now, come on.'

A few stumbling steps later, a door shut further down the corridor.

Cormac stared hard at Tess. She still would not meet his eyes.

'This is no place for you,' he said. 'You left all this behind in Ireland.'

'Once a whore, always a whore.' It was the kind of remark she would have typically delivered with flippancy, but this time her voice was laden with misery. 'And I can pretend here.'

'Pretend what?'

'That I'm loved.'

Her gaze finally rose to his. All of a sudden, he was jolted back in time to that warehouse in Dublin where he had first met her. This moment in the brothel felt like an echo of that day for she seemed once again green and vulnerable, squandering her precious body in an act of desperation.

'Tess—*Teresa*, you are loved,' he said, willing her to believe it.

'Not the way I want to be. Not the way it is between Orlaith and Charlie. Or you and Bridget.' She barely veiled the bitterness in her tone when she uttered Bridget's name. 'Not the way it matters.'

'Other types of love matter. You have people around you who are as good as family to you, brothers, sisters, nieces, nephews. That has to count for something.'

'It's not enough. I want what everyone else has.'

'What about Derval?' he said, desperate to convince Tess even though he was reluctant to allude to their friend's woes. In strict confidence, Bridget had imparted to him the shocking truth Derval had revealed at Quincy Market, but he would only make an oblique reference now to corroborate his point. 'Her husband is largely absent and he doesn't bring much joy when he is around. Although she can't claim to possess the sort of love you speak of, she is still relatively happy.'

'At least she had it once,' Tess shot back. 'And she has her children, which seems to be something else I'll never have either.'

He found himself wordless again. He had had no inkling that Tess desired children. Was it possible she was engaging in these activities at the brothel in an effort to produce a baby by the only means within her grasp? He rubbed the back of his neck awkwardly.

She sat down on the edge of the bed. 'Please,' she said. 'I want you to go.'

He had shown up here to liberate her but perhaps all he was doing was hurting her even more. If he couldn't persuade her to depart with him, then he supposed he could only wait for her to come to the right conclusion by herself.

'Very well,' he said. 'I'll leave if that's what you wish.'

He took an unenthusiastic step towards the door. If only she hadn't tried to kiss him before, he would have had no compunction in striding over to the bed and wrapping his arms around her, offering her whatever platonic solace he could. But a physical barrier had risen between them that Christmas Day and he could not cross it.

He reached the threshold and looked back at her. 'Does Orlaith know?'

She shook her head. 'Are you going to tell her?' she asked.

He chewed the inside of his cheek. 'Do you want me to?'

'Might as well. The cat's out of the bag now.' She gave an artificial laugh and continued laughing as he left the room.

By the time he set foot on the top step of the stairs, her laugh had turned into a sob.

CHAPTER 31

'God Almighty,' said Orlaith.

She dropped onto the sofa at Broad Street, her countenance aghast. Opposite her, the fire crackled. Cormac stood near it but its heat couldn't warm up his bones. He cast a wary eye at the flames before switching his attention back to his sister.

'So you didn't suspect anything?' he asked.

She pressed her fingertips to her mouth. 'Not this,' she said through them. 'Nothing so dreadful as this.'

'But you had noticed something amiss?'

She nodded. 'Now and again, she came home at odd times or made excuses to go out on her own. But I do be out at all hours myself sometimes, usually up in the North End, so it didn't strike me as that peculiar. Except...she talks about wounds she's treated, only she never seems to need to restock her bandages as often as I do.' Orlaith let her hand fall. 'I've been a blind fool.'

'Don't say that. She was doing her best to hide it from you, from everyone.'

'Poor Tess,' she said with a sigh. 'Too proud to ask for help so she goes and does this to herself instead. And here I thought we were two independent women actually able to support ourselves.' She clicked her tongue. 'So stupid.'

'You're not—'

'Not me, her! Why on earth couldn't she just own up that she was struggling? You always said you'd lend a hand if we needed it.'

He cleared his throat. 'Well, that's complicated by another matter unfortunately.' And, in as few words as possible, he related what had occurred between him and Tess that Christmas after Gus was born.

Orlaith looked incredulous. 'I can't believe she did that. It's as plain as day there's no one for you but Bridget and that you'd be too damn honourable to play her false anyway. Tess must've been really smitten not to recognise that.' She blew out her cheeks. 'I feel bad for her though. How hard it must be to love someone who can't love you back the same way. Makes me realise how lucky I am to have found Charlie.'

'I greatly sympathise with her predicament too,' Cormac said, 'though I expect she wouldn't thank either of us for feeling sorry for her.'

'But what happens now? She refused to come away with you so does that mean she's just going to carry on with this even though we now know what she's doing? I don't think I could stomach that.'

He glanced at the fire again, picked up the poker and nudged a lump of coal in from the edge of the grate. As he set the poker back down, he said, 'I hope she'll have a good think about it and reassess this path she's chosen. We have to get through to her that she doesn't need to live like that now. She has a whole family willing to help her.' He supposed Bridget's support might be somewhat tepid but surely even with their chequered past she would not wish to see Tess fall so low. 'When she comes back to Broad Street, will you speak with her? Maybe she will be more disposed to listen to you than to me.'

'I'll try my best,' said Orlaith doubtfully. 'But when have you ever seen Tess do something she doesn't want to do?'

***

Emily sat on the steps of Acorn House, chewing on her pencil and clutching her sheaf of loose pages securely to prevent them from getting swept away by the late spring breeze. She had told her mama that she wished to sketch the sycamore tree growing in Mr and Mrs Hill's well-tended front garden, but in truth she wanted to ogle the three young men gathered on the porch of the boarding house next door. They looked to be perhaps twenty, which was significantly older than her almost-twelve years, but they were very handsome and pleasing to her eye. Though all three had snagged her attention, one in particular stood out, a muscular fellow with charming dimples in his cheeks. She threw sidelong glances in their direction while idly drawing the branches of the sycamore and its leaves which were just beginning to bud.

After a while, her legs became stiff from being in one position for too long and she stretched them out onto the lower steps. She was relieved that she had finally started to grow a bit taller over the past few months and, although still smaller than most of the other girls in her age group at school, she no longer felt quite as diminutive next to them. The hem of her skirt still only dropped as far as her shins but she eagerly looked forward to the day when it would be let down to cover her ankles and she could be considered a woman.

As she peered once more towards the group of men conversing genially on the porch next door, she glimpsed a familiar figure walking along the street in front of the boarding house.

'Miss Green?' she called.

Her youthful teacher's head swivelled around. Emily waved from the front steps.

'Miss McGovern!' Miss Green said with pleasure.

Emily set down her pencil on the step, tucked her pages under her arm and ran down to the footpath. 'How nice to see you,' she said, beaming. 'I have already learned my spellings off by heart for Monday.'

'I would expect no less from one of my best pupils! What is that you're holding there?' When Emily showed her the sketches, Miss Green exclaimed in admiration. 'This is fine work. Your attention to detail on the sprouting leaves is superb. You'll become a very accomplished artist if you keep practising.'

'Thank you, I will!'

'And is this where you live? What a pretty house.'

Emily thought the grey shutters and brown door made the house appear rather drab but it was just like Miss Green to offer praise wherever she could. 'What are you doing here?'

'Oh, I—' Miss Green blushed and peeked under her eyelashes at the group of three men. They were watching with interest and, unexpectedly, the muscular fellow started striding down the steps of the boarding house towards them. Emily almost fainted. Had he noticed her peeping at them before?

When he reached the footpath, he gave Miss Green a smile, displaying his delightful dimples, and said, 'Do you know this little girl?'

Emily bristled. She might be somewhat short but she was by no means a *little girl* anymore.

'She is a pupil of mine at Hawes,' said Miss Green warmly.

'Miss Green is an excellent teacher,' said Emily in a dignified manner, wanting to convey that she could partake in a conversation among adults.

'How nice,' said the young man amiably. 'I suppose you will miss her very much after she is gone.'

Emily gaped at him. 'Gone?'

Miss Green shifted uncomfortably. 'I hadn't yet informed my pupils, Ronald.'

He looked abashed. 'I'm sorry, dearest, I didn't realise.'

Emily transferred her shocked gaze to her teacher. 'You're leaving the school?'

'Yes, at the end of this term.' The colour heightened further in Miss Green's cheeks as she gesticulated shyly to Ronald. 'I am getting married to Mr Kendrick.'

Perhaps Emily wasn't quite so grown up as she had believed because, instead of offering her hearty congratulations at the happy news, she blurted, 'But who will be my teacher next September?'

Miss Green's brow puckered. 'I can't say for certain but I suppose Mr Miller might be the most likely candidate. He has been taking some of the older classes these past couple of years.'

Emily's bones suddenly felt like lead. 'Oh,' she said, trying to conceal her despair. 'Thank you for telling me. I hope you will have a beautiful wedding.'

'That is sweet of you,' said Miss Green, although she still wore a slight frown. 'And I hope you will continue to develop your artistic skills. You do have a special gift.'

'Thank you, I will.' It was the same response she had made to Miss Green's previous compliment, but this time she spoke it without inflection. 'I've got to go now. See you on Monday.'

She bade Mr Kendrick a polite farewell too, though she could not muster even a scrap of pleasure at being upon the receiving end of his dimples. Heels dragging, she walked back to the front steps of Acorn House. She had hardly resumed her spot and reached for her pencil again when she heard footsteps approaching. She looked up; Auntie Tess stood on the path. It had been quite some time since she had last seen her and she found herself taken aback by her gaunt frame, lacklustre hair and hollow eyes.

Auntie Tess advanced towards the steps, cracking a weak smile. 'Still making impressive works of art?'

Even her voice sounded subdued, lacking the liveliness that usually accompanied the whip of her witty tongue.

'I'm just drawing a tree,' said Emily, showing the page where she had focused on the sprouting leaves.

'Nice.' Auntie Tess's gaze flicked to the house. 'Is your da home?'

'No, he's at his workshop. But Mama is here, sewing a skirt for Madame Roche. Shall I call her?'

'Don't,' Auntie Tess said quickly. 'How do I get to the workshop?'

As Emily gave her the directions, she thought it strange that Auntie Tess had never been to the workshop before now – after all, Papa had opened it the previous summer.

'Thanks for that,' said Auntie Tess. She turned and walked back to the street, her shoulders slouched. While they had been talking, Miss Green and Mr Kendrick had been joined at the front of the boarding house by the other two young men from the porch. After some light-hearted chatter, the couple now departed in one direction and the two men in another, heading towards Auntie Tess. Emily expected her to throw them a flirtatious wink or a teasing comment as they passed but, to her surprise, Auntie Tess kept her head down and paid them no heed.

As she vanished out of sight around the corner, the door of Acorn House opened behind Emily.

'Did I hear you speaking with somebody, gooseberry?' said Mama.

283

Emily was no longer particularly fond of that childish nickname but she just said, 'It was Auntie Tess. She's gone to visit Papa at his workshop.'

When she glanced up, Mama was frowning but she didn't say anything.

***

The noise of the saw's blade cutting into the timber was so loud that Cormac didn't realise he had a visitor until the inner door to his workshop swung open. Startled, he squinted through a cloud of sawdust and saw Tess framed in the doorway.

'Can we talk?' she said.

He put the saw down on the bench and gestured for her to come in. She stepped through but he remained where he was next to the bench. She looked like she hadn't eaten or slept in the few days since he had last seen her at the brothel.

She clasped her hands before her in a demure gesture that was very unlike her. 'You've got into quite the habit of saving me, haven't you?' she said with a wry twist of her lips.

He surveyed her uncertainly. 'Have I saved you this time?'

'I think so.'

They stared at each other across the workshop floor. She dropped her gaze first.

'I was ruining myself,' she muttered, ''cause I didn't think I had anything to lose. The first few times, I really did just resort to it for the money. But after that awful Christmas I was full of spite and disappointment and I wanted to do something reckless. It felt like nothing had changed since Dublin, not really. Whoring was all I was good for.'

Painful guilt scratched at his insides. How had none of them realised how lost she had become?

'When I went back to Broad Street the other night, I had a row with Orlaith but then she managed to knock some sense into me. Said I could wind up losing yous all, and reminded me how Margaret died from a disease she caught working on the streets. Except the difference between me and Margaret is that I've a choice about what I'm doing and there's no need for me to end up the same way. Orlaith said I've got to believe I'm worth more than that.' Tess gave a rather helpless shrug. 'It's hard to see it but I'm going to try.'

'I'm glad to hear that,' he said, relieved. 'We all only want what's best for you.'

'What's best for me...' she repeated. Her pale eyebrows bunched together. 'I thought the love of a man was what I wanted most. But I understand now that the love of a family can mean as much to me. More, maybe. And I need to earn it back 'cause I've let yous down.'

'You haven't,' he said. 'You may have strayed a little but you're back with us now and we can consign these unhappy events to the past.' He wasn't sure how amenable Bridget would be to giving Tess a warm welcome but he hoped she, too, could let bygones be bygones.

Tess grimaced. 'It won't be as easy as that.'

'What do you mean?'

'I made a promise to Orlaith. By her request, I've agreed to spend some time at...the Penitent Females' Refuge.' At his frown, she carried on, 'We heard about them back when we did work with the Ursulines. They take in fallen women and help them rebuild their lives. I think they're quite religious,' she added with a wince.

Doing his utmost to hide his astonishment, he said, 'And you're willing to go there?'

She looked resigned. 'It's what I've got to do to regain Orlaith's trust. I'll do it for her.'

He was impressed that she placed such value upon preserving her friendship with Orlaith. 'How long will you spend there?'

'As long as it takes. But I've something to ask you.' She wrung her clasped hands. 'While I'm gone, Orlaith won't be able to cover the rent for the rooms at Broad Street by herself. Will you help her?'

It would perhaps stretch his funds a little thin, given the lease he had taken on the workshop premises, but he said, 'Yes, of course.'

Her fidgeting hands relaxed. 'Thanks. I know she might well end up living with Charlie if she marries him in the meantime but I didn't want her to feel forced into it sooner than she wanted to just 'cause of me. Not when his da's still not keen on the match.'

Cormac had heard of Mr Adams's reservations about his son's choice of bride. He doubted it would make a difference to Orlaith and Charlie's plans in the long run but he concurred with Tess that Orlaith shouldn't have to make that commitment before she was ready.

'That's very considerate of you,' he said. 'Rest assured, I will look out for her.'

She gave him a brief smile which partially diminished the haggard quality of her features. She started to turn towards the door but halted and faced him again. 'I meant to tell you, I did make some use of my sinful time on Ann Street. I took the opportunity to ask around about Bronagh, even showed the other women one of Emily's drawings. No one recognised her name or her face. So, whatever she got up to, at least there's no evidence she became involved in anything of that nature.'

He experienced the same tightening around his heart that he always did when he thought of his missing sister. 'That is good to know. Thank you for making those enquiries.'

She looked like she was about to leave again but hesitated once more. Her hands resumed their restless twisting. 'I've got one more thing to say, and then I swear I'll never mention it again.'

Against his better judgement, he said, 'What is it?'

She took a slow breath. 'I've often imagined what might've happened if things had gone differently in that warehouse back in Dublin,' she said softly. 'What if, rather than just giving me that money, you'd taken it upon yourself to look after me instead? Maybe brought me back to your lodgings and given me food and shelter for a couple of days. We might've formed a bond. Who knows, maybe we would've fallen in love. In my wilder daydreams, I even fancied that you could've married me and I could've borne your children.' She sighed. 'Did you ever wonder?'

He didn't want to hurt her feelings by saying he had never contemplated such a scenario. So, for her sake, he allowed himself to envisage it.

'It's difficult to say,' he said cautiously. 'When I picture what you describe, I comprehend that the inevitable outcome of any prolonged acquaintance between us would have been my discovery of your connection with my family. So all I can see in that version of events is my mother and sister still living and breathing and me doing all I could to make a better life for them and for Bronagh, Orlaith and Patrick as well.' He paused as a shard of remorse pierced him. 'Of course, had things happened that way, I would never have got on the ship to England, which means I would not have reunited with Bridget nor learned of Emily's existence. It is agony to me that both of those realities could never coexist.'

An expression of sad acceptance came over her face. 'Your thoughts always return to Bridget, don't they?' She made for the door, shaking her head. 'I could never compete with that, in real or imaginary worlds.'

CHAPTER 32

Emily gazed out of the schoolroom window. A spider had built its web in the nook where the sill met the wall and she watched, fascinated, as a fly became caught in the web's silken strands. Almost of their own volition, her fingers reached for her chalk and slate and began drawing the scene of imminent slaughter.

She grasped the piece of cloth attached to her slate by a string and wiped away one of her arithmetic calculations to make more space for the corner of the web where the spider lurked. She didn't care; she probably hadn't calculated the sum correctly anyway. Not much about school held her interest anymore. After Miss Green had left, she had been forced to endure another two years under the instruction of the odious Mr Miller. But soon the final term of this year would end and both her fourteenth birthday and the summer holidays beckoned.

'Miss McGovern!'

She jumped. Mr Miller glared at her from the top of the classroom, the hairs in the growth on the side of his nose quivering.

'Do you have a final figure for the second equation?' he said testily.

She looked down at her slate. Of course it was the one she had wiped away. 'No,' she answered.

'Nothing at all? Then what is on your slate?'

'A drawing.' Feeling reckless, she held it up for him to see.

His eyes bulged. 'Get rid of those silly scribbles at once and return your attention to this lesson!'

'They're not silly.' The words had popped out of her mouth before she could stop them but she realised they were true. It was, in fact, a very realistic depiction of the carnage beyond her window and she was proud of it. 'This is a good drawing.'

Emmeline's bushy hair bobbed about her head as she swivelled towards Emily, her jaw gaping in horror. The rest of the girls in the class also stared at her as though she had gone mad.

Mr Miller plainly thought the same. 'Don't be absurd. Stop wasting time.'

She understood that he meant his time but she deliberately misinterpreted him. 'I'm not wasting time. I practise every day and each drawing makes me better. I'm going to be a great artist.'

He snorted. 'I've never heard such nonsense.'

She ought to have stayed quiet and just let it be. But she said defiantly, 'Miss Green said I have a special gift.'

'Did she?' he sneered. 'And do you believe that Miss Green's opinion matters, or did you forget that she is a female? As are you, I might add, and only a half-grown one at that.'

She flinched. Every night, she lay in bed and stretched out her arms and legs as far as she could reach, but she still remained a touch shorter than all of her classmates.

'No woman could ever be a great artist,' the schoolmaster went on derisively. 'What an outrageous notion. The best you can hope for is to leave this establishment with adequate faculties so that a man will deem you competent enough to mind his house and bear his brats. A woman cannot be anything but mediocre.'

He turned back to the rest of the class, dismissing her and the subject entirely. She waited for the tears to come but all she felt was a boiling rage, and a desire to prove him wrong.

She licked her cloth to dampen it and wiped the slate clean again, removing both the spider's web and her other arithmetic calculations. Once its surface was clear, she seized her chalk and began to draw with sharp, angry strokes. The square-shaped face quickly took form, with close-set eyes and a vile growth on the side of the nose, bristles of hair sticking out from it at all angles.

She was so engrossed in her creation that she didn't notice the heavy footsteps until they stopped right at her desk.

'Miss McGovern, I will not tell you again—'

Mr Miller's voice choked off as he caught sight of what she had drawn on the slate. She knew he could not fail to recognise himself, nor the quality of the artistry. He gawked for several seconds of silence. Then he dragged his fingertips down the centre of the drawing, smudging the chalk marks.

'To the top of the room, Miss McGovern,' he said, his tone dangerously soft.

She got out of her chair and stalked between the desks up to the schoolmaster's blackboard. She still held her stick of chalk. 'What should I write, sir?'

'Nothing at all,' he said, striding to the front of the classroom too. 'Put the chalk down.'

Confused, she placed it on the dusty ledge that jutted out from the bottom of the blackboard as Mr Miller reached for his satchel which lay upon his desk. From it, he withdrew a rolled leather strap which he unfurled with a flourish. A chorus of gasps rose from the other girls. Emily's eyes widened in terror.

'Hold out your hands,' said Mr Miller.

All of her audacity leaked out of her. She tucked her hands under her arms and mumbled, 'I'm sorry for doing the drawing, sir.'

'It's too late for apologies,' he said. 'Hold them out or I shall double the number of strokes.'

With a whimper, she let her arms fall to her sides. She would have much preferred to receive the beating on her backside rather than her precious hands, but they had been the perpetrators of the act. Ever so slowly, she presented them to Mr Miller, palms up. His eyes glittered in anticipation.

The first blow was so hard that she cried out in pain. Her skin turned red after the second. She closed her eyes for the third.

By the sixth stroke, she and the whole class were weeping.

***

'Ma?' said Jack, running into the kitchen from the back yard.

'Yes, my lamb?' Bridget responded as she snipped a length of thread on her latest assignment for Madame Roche, a lace shawl with a rip in its hem.

'When will I go to school like Emily?'

'Hmm, let's see. You turned six in January so I expect you will start school this coming autumn. Would you like that?'

He considered his answer seriously before replying, 'Yes.'

'What about me?' demanded Gus, appearing behind Jack.

She spread the shawl out on the kitchen table, examining the hem closely. 'Well, you are two years younger so you will have to wait another couple of years.'

In her peripheral vision, she glimpsed his lower lip protruding. 'Not fair.'

'Just think of all the extra hugs you'll get when it's only the two of us here,' she said, shooting him a conspiratorial wink.

He brightened.

'I thought that might cheer you up, little miracle,' she said.

Her pet name for him had proved just how apt it was the day she had found him next to her upturned sewing basket, patches of fabric scattered about and spools of thread rolling in all directions. It was an absolute miracle that he had not pricked himself on a needle or cut himself with the scissors.

He, however, didn't yet understand the word so, upon her addressing him with it on that occasion when he knew he had been naughty, he had mistaken it for an admonition. Hence, he now said indignantly, 'I amn't a miracle!'

She chuckled. 'You most certainly are. And remember, it's "I'm not".'

There was a distant bang as the front door opened.

'There's your sister now,' she said and both boys beamed.

In the next instant, she heard Emily's wail of distress and, leaping up from the kitchen table, dashed into the front room to find her daughter in floods of tears. Emily dropped her pail on the floor and held out her shaking hands. Big red welts crossed both of her palms.

'Who did this to you?' cried Bridget, horrified.

'M-Mr Miller,' Emily wept and fell into Bridget's embrace.

Aghast, Bridget drew her into the kitchen. Jack and Gus watched with large eyes as she set a basin of water on the table and directed Emily to soak her hands in it. Emily cringed when she submerged her tender skin in the water.

'Tell me exactly what happened,' Bridget commanded.

She was better able to control her fury than Cormac who, when he came home from the workshop later that evening, exploded with outrage.

'That sadistic *bastard*,' he said savagely, not seeming to care that his daughter was within earshot of his invective; at least

Bridget had already put the two boys to bed. 'How dare he touch her!'

Emily, who was now curled up on the sofa with a blanket wrapped around her, sniffed as she stared down at her wounds. 'I'll never be able to draw or paint again,' she said pitifully.

'Of course you will,' said Bridget in bracing tones. She had had some time to absorb the shock of Emily's traumatic experience and was striving to be level-headed. 'They're just going to take a little while to heal.'

Cormac paced in front of the hearth. 'I want to wring his damn neck.'

Bridget bit the tip of her tongue. She couldn't help thinking that Emily would never have been punished in such a manner if they had retained a governess for her instead of sending her to school. But their decision to abscond from London, and its subsequent ramifications, had ensured that such a prospect had become a permanent impossibility, in both financial and practical terms.

Perhaps unsurprisingly, Emily's own thoughts seemed to be running along a similar vein. 'Miss Davison would never have struck me,' she bemoaned. 'How I miss her. I wish she could have come to America with us. I hate Mr Miller!'

Cormac's face showed that he shared the sentiment, but Bridget said pragmatically, 'While I do not defend his actions, you must acknowledge some blame in this affair, Emily. You should never have drawn a caricature of the schoolmaster. It was quite disrespectful.'

Emily's blue eyes were eloquent with betrayal. 'Do you mean to say you think I deserved this?'

'Emphatically not. Although you ought to have received some form of chastisement, his behaviour was revolting and cannot be condoned. Has he ever taken the strap to you prior to this?'

Emily sniffed. 'No, but he has a cruel tongue. He made me cry on my very first day. He has brought every single girl in the class to tears at one stage or another.'

It was all Bridget could do not to weep herself at the idea of her little gooseberry being subjected to such humiliation – and that neither she nor Cormac had had an inkling of it.

Cormac curled his hands into fists. 'He's nothing but a bully. You should have told us long before now.' He looked directly at Bridget. 'We must take her out of that school.'

'I agree,' she said. 'She cannot spend a further second in the domain of that detestable man. I do believe there is another schoolhouse on Broadway.'

Emily glanced between them. 'Must I still go to school at all?' she said plaintively. 'I would rather just focus on my art.'

'You are not yet fourteen,' said Bridget. 'You ought to spend at least one more year gaining an education. Perhaps, once you turn fifteen, you may consider leaving then.'

'And at that point, *a stór*,' said Cormac, gentling his voice, 'you'll have to think about making your own advancement in the world.'

Emily's forehead creased. 'You mean...employment of some kind?'

He nodded. 'It's a big step, so staying in school will give you more time to contemplate it.'

She reflected upon this for a few moments. Touching a fingertip tentatively to one of the red welts, she withdrew it with a hiss. 'In that case,' she said, raising her chin, 'I'd like to stay at Hawes.'

'Surely you don't mean that,' Cormac protested.

'I do,' she insisted. She sat up straight and the blanket slipped off her shoulders. 'I want to prove to Mr Miller that he knows nothing about what females are capable of. I'll work hard to be the best pupil and I'll work even harder to become a great artist, and I'll show him that he's an ignorant, nasty sod.'

Though it was remarkably salty language to hear coming from their daughter's sweet mouth, Bridget supposed she should be glad that Emily hadn't emulated her father's earlier, fouler expletive.

'Are you certain?' she said.

Emily's lips pressed together into a thin line of determination. 'I am.'

Cormac rubbed his jaw. 'Then I'm going to the school first thing tomorrow to warn that man not to lay a finger on you again.'

'No, Papa,' she said quickly. 'He will see it as a sign of weakness. I have to stand up to him by myself.'

Cormac looked unconvinced but he gave a reluctant nod of acquiescence. 'If he so much as breathes in your direction with that leather strap in his hand, you must tell us right away.'

'I will, I promise.'

Although Bridget felt full of apprehension, she nonetheless smiled. 'This is very brave of you, gooseberry.'

Even as she said it, she wondered if the term of endearment had become too infantile for the young woman blossoming before her.

CHAPTER 33

It took every ounce of Cormac's willpower not to march to Hawes School and beat the schoolmaster to a pulp. His blood boiled when he imagined the brutal strap striking his little treasure's soft palms. However, his pride in her soared as she departed for school the next morning, a bandage wrapped across each of her hands and her spine as straight as a ramrod. It reminded him of another spirited young girl he had once known.

Giving Bridget an affectionate kiss on her cheek, he left Acorn House to head for his workshop. With all the turmoil of Emily's ordeal the previous evening, he had had little opportunity to reflect upon the other significant event that had happened yesterday. The day had marked the end of Tess's two-year habitation at the Penitent Females' Refuge.

He had not seen her in all that time. Despite its proximity in the South End of Boston, visitors were not permitted at the Refuge apart from exceptional circumstances where written permission had to be granted in advance, so Orlaith had taken precedence on those rare occasions. She had reported back that Tess had seemed to be in decent spirits, in spite of the unrelenting piety of the institution. Orlaith had exchanged some letters with her over the two years as well – Tess's initial scrawls had been nearly illegible but her writing had gradually improved as time went on. Cormac had written twice and received short notes in return which had been polite but distant in tone.

He had to admire her fortitude for she had essentially enrolled herself into a prison – the women admitted were even referred to as inmates. They toiled in a laundry, received religious instruction, learned needlework and songs, and attended weekly Mass. It must have been a gruelling time, but he hoped it had helped Tess to find some peace within herself. He wondered how her homecoming to Broad Street had gone last night and resolved to wait a few days before visiting to allow her and Orlaith a chance to reconnect.

He had scarcely reached the corner at the end of the street when a burly figure came around it from the opposite direction and barrelled into him.

'Rory!' he exclaimed in surprise. 'What are you doing here?'

It had been quite a while since he had last happened upon Rory at Broad Street and he was astonished to realise that he was able to meet the lad's green gaze straight on; he had developed so much that he now matched Cormac in height. His body had filled out too, his shoulders broadening and his limbs becoming muscular rather than gangling. His ears still protruded rather prominently but he had let his brown hair grow shaggy which somewhat concealed them. Cormac did a quick calculation in his head – Rory must be seventeen now. He wasn't a boy anymore.

'Mr McGovern,' he panted. 'You need to come to Broad Street.'

Alarmed, Cormac said, 'What's happened? Is it Tess?' All sorts of scenarios ran through his head. Had the Refuge refused to let her leave? Had she and Orlaith had some sort of argument

297

upon her return? God forbid, surely she hadn't gone back to Ann Street already?

Rory shook his head. 'No, 'tis your sister. She's really sick.'

'Tell me on the way,' said Cormac and he started striding in the direction from which Rory had come. The workshop would have to remain closed.

Rory hastened to keep up, admitting that he didn't know much beyond what his mother had told him. Tess had banged on the Careys' door very early that morning and, after a swift discussion, Rory had been instructed to fetch Cormac.

'What about Charlie?'

Rory frowned. 'Ma just said to get you.'

When they reached Broad Street, Cormac ran up the stairs and barged in without knocking. Tess and Derval were gathered near the doorway to the front bedroom, heads close together as they muttered to each other. The bedroom door was ajar and a fetid odour pervaded the air.

'What's going on?' he asked, fearful.

They both turned. Tess's stay at the Refuge had brought flesh back to her bones and colour to her cheeks; she looked healthier than he had ever seen her. Her expression lifted at his appearance but quickly turned sombre.

'Thanks for coming,' she said. 'She's not good.'

'She said not to send for you,' Derval added. 'But we thought it best to.'

'What's wrong with her?' he demanded.

'Can't say for sure,' said Derval, 'but she's got a fever, stomach cramps, and...' She winced.

Tess finished for her. 'And everything's coming out of both ends.'

Cormac winced too. 'Jesus. Is it very severe?'

They exchanged a glance.

'She's not good,' Tess repeated.

His insides clenched. 'Can I see her?'

'Go ahead,' she said, swinging her arm towards the door. 'She's going to hate us for letting you in but we'll deal with that later.'

He sidled into the bedroom. Even though the window was open, the smell became instantly worse and he breathed shallowly through his mouth. Orlaith was curled in a ball on top of the bed, clad only in her shift. She cracked her eyelids apart and let out a groan.

'I told them not to fetch you, for God's sake.'

He crossed the room and sat gingerly on the edge of the bed, avoiding an indeterminate brown smear on the covers. 'I'm glad they ignored you. I'm your family—it's important for me to know.'

Sudden panic rippled across her face. 'They didn't send for Charlie too, did they?'

'Not yet. Do you have any idea how this came about?'

She grimaced. 'Not for certain. But I was up in the North End yesterday—' She broke off with a moan and uncurled her body a little to massage her abdomen. 'I visited Bronagh Mac,' she went on hoarsely, 'with a salve for her itchy skin. She invited me to stay and eat with her, so I did.'

'Was Bronagh Mac well herself?' he asked.

'She was grand when I saw her. She did mention calling on some sick neighbours earlier in the day but I didn't meet them myself.' Orlaith bowed her body again in pain and then her countenance filled with dawning horror. 'Can you please get Tess?'

He surveyed her with concern. 'Can't I help?'

'No,' she said shrilly. 'I need Tess. You've got to leave.'

She tried to push him away, though there was no strength at all in her hand. He rose and made for the door. 'Tess?' he called.

She rushed in. Seeming to read Orlaith's expression with a single glance, she told Cormac, 'Out you go, quick.'

Peering over his shoulder as he exited, he glimpsed her extracting a chamber pot from beneath the bed. He hurriedly shut the bedroom door.

'Poor craythur,' said Derval and he jerked involuntarily at the familiar phrase his mother had so often used. 'I've got a fresh set of sheets to go on the bed after this next bout and I've sent Una and Sorcha to fetch more water.'

'Do you think Dr Wolfe could be of any assistance?' he asked.

She gave an emphatic shake of her head. 'Unless there's a baby inside of her, he wouldn't want to know.'

She and Cormac shared a look.

'No,' he said.

'Unlikely,' she agreed.

'In any case, Charlie should be made aware that she is so ill,' he said firmly. 'Why wouldn't she want him here?'

Derval arched an eyebrow. 'If you were her, would you like your fiancé to see you in that state?'

A faint spurting noise issued from the bedroom.

'I guess not,' said Cormac, flinching. 'He should still be informed though—it would be unfair to keep him in the dark. I'll go to his parents' house.'

'On your head be it,' said Derval.

What Cormac didn't bank on was Charlie insisting upon returning to Broad Street with him, even when he stressed how much it was against Orlaith's wishes.

'This is so typical of her!' Charlie burst out. 'Keeping me at arm's length for no good reason.'

He stormed along the street, worry etched in the lines of his face, and marched into the building in high dudgeon, but he quietened his steps before climbing the stairs. Cormac hung back, for the sake of discretion and not a little cowardice.

Rory dallied in the doorway to the Careys' rooms. Cormac approached him and said, 'Thanks for coming to get me earlier. I appreciate it, even if Orlaith might be somewhat less enthused.' He leaned his forearm against the door jamb. 'Tell me, have you started working anywhere yet?'

Rory shrugged. 'I've been doing a few bits for Donie Kane now and then. A couple of his friends are bricklayers and sometimes they need extra hands to carry the bricks.'

'I think I'm ready to take on an apprentice at the workshop,' said Cormac. 'Are you interested?'

Rory's eyes widened. 'Yes!'

Cormac grinned.

They were in the middle of discussing which skills he might start teaching Rory first when Charlie reappeared at the top of the stairs. He stamped down the steps, looking equal parts annoyed and anxious.

'Tess wouldn't let me in to see her, no matter what I said. I only wanted to find out how she was. I honestly don't care about the smell!' He folded his arms. 'It's inappropriate how possessive Tess is being. I'm going to marry Orlaith. I should be the one looking after her.'

Cormac clapped a hand on Charlie's shoulder. 'Maybe let Tess have her way this time. She's been gone from the family for two years—she might just need to feel needed. What do you think?'

Charlie tugged on his ear and then gave a grudging nod. 'I suppose that's fair. And the most important thing anyway is for Orlaith to get better.'

Cormac was glad that his advice had appeased Charlie, but he himself was beginning to question Orlaith's persistence in keeping her betrothed at a distance. It was understandable in her current unpleasant circumstances, needless to say, but not quite so much in general terms. After all, nearly three years had passed since she had agreed to marry him – why were they still not wed?

***

Bridget left Jack and Gus in the gleeful company of little Brian Carey (who was not so little anymore – at nine years old, he was already showing signs of following his older brother's growth spurt) and ascended the stairs at Broad Street, her basket over her arm and her heart beating in her throat. After five harrowing days, Orlaith had finally begun to recover from her illness and was more disposed to receive visitors. Charlie had taken precedence, of course, but Bridget also wished to call by. However, there was another person whom she would have to face first.

'Hello, Tess,' she said, when the other woman answered her knock.

Tess's face was unreadable as she stood back to let her in. When Bridget entered, she took a quick breath and was glad to note that the air smelled fresh. The bench and stool had been placed in front of the lit hearth and a wet sheet was draped over them to dry.

'I brought some soup,' she said, lifting the cloth on her basket to reveal a fat, corked bottle. 'It just needs heating up over the fire.'

'I know how to make soup,' said Tess, her tone touchy. Then she added, 'I mean, thanks.'

Bridget nodded neutrally. 'How is Orlaith today?'

Cormac had visited his sister the previous evening and reported afterwards that she had been able to keep down a morsel of bread. She might even have managed to walk downstairs to the privy at the back of the building, had Tess not quashed the suggestion outright.

'She's fine,' said Tess. 'She got a good night's sleep.'

'That's positive to hear.' Bridget paused. 'And how are you?'

Tess squinted at her, as though trying to ascertain if she was being genuine or not. 'Grand.'

'It can't have been easy,' said Bridget, 'being thrown into such a stressful situation immediately upon your return to the outside world.'

Tess tossed her head. 'I'd do anything for Orlaith's sake.'

'I know you would,' said Bridget quietly. That fiercely protective loyalty was Tess's finest quality, and it went a long way towards compensating for her other less attractive attributes. 'The whole family is very grateful for your attentive care of her.'

Tess blinked but didn't say anything.

Bridget cleared her throat. 'Once she is well again, you must start thinking of yourself. What is your plan? Do you intend to resume nursing?'

With a shake of her head, Tess said, 'I did a lot of laundry over the past couple of years and it turns out I've got strong arms. The Refuge helped secure a position for me as a washerwoman at Tremont House. I'm due to start next week.'

'That's terrific,' said Bridget. 'I'm very glad for you.'

Tess looked away uncomfortably. 'Right. You want to go in and see her? She's awake.'

'Yes, I'd like to do that.' Relieved to accept this exit from the conversation, Bridget set her basket down on the table, crossed to the front bedroom and knocked on the door. Orlaith responded and she went in.

She was pleasantly surprised to find Orlaith sitting up in bed, though her pleasure was tempered when she observed her waxen skin and the sharp angles of her collarbones and elbows. Her

303

round eyes stood out even more prominently than usual in her drawn face but she managed a weak smile.

'Good to see you,' she said.

'And you,' said Bridget, perching on the edge of the bed. 'You gave us all quite a scare.'

'I gave myself a scare too,' Orlaith admitted. 'I never want to feel that ill again.'

Bridget gave her a sympathetic pat on her bony hand.

'To tell the truth, I thought I wasn't far off meeting my maker. But I was lucky.' Orlaith swallowed. 'Turns out Bronagh Mac and those neighbours she'd been visiting all got it too. And the neighbours' daughter...died.'

'Gracious, that's awful,' said Bridget, only just beginning to grasp how close Cormac had come to losing yet another sister.

'I feel bad that I couldn't help them 'cause there's nobody else looking out for the people up in the North End. But sure I was in no fit state to nurse anyone.' She grimaced. 'God Almighty, it was disgusting. Poor Tess was a saint to put up with it.'

Bridget never thought she'd hear Tess and sainthood being mentioned in the same sentence. 'By all accounts, she has made every effort to ensure your recovery. It was fortunate timing that she had just returned from the Refuge.'

'It sure was. I don't know what I'd have done without her.'

'Well, you would have still had Derval, Cormac and me, so you wouldn't have been abandoned.' Bridget hesitated. 'And Charlie too, naturally.'

Orlaith gave her a swift glance. 'Did Cormac tell you I wouldn't let Charlie in to see me when I was going through the worst of it?'

'He did. I'm sure you had your reasons.'

Bridget let the silence swell between them, until Orlaith sighed.

'I guess it seemed harsh,' she said. 'But I was just too embarrassed. I mean, I'm going to marry him! I couldn't let him see or hear *that*.' She cringed.

Bridget tilted her head. 'Did you believe it would have lessened his regard for you?'

'How could it not? He wouldn't have ever wanted to kiss me again, let alone do...other things after we are wed.'

'You know,' said Bridget delicately, 'those other things can be embarrassing too. You will still be exposing your body, and there may be smells or tastes or touches that are unwelcome or uncomfortable. The splendid part is being able to wholly share that primitive experience with another and not feel self-conscious about it at all.'

Colour bloomed in Orlaith's pale cheeks. 'Oh. I didn't realise...' She trailed away, then spoke again in a small voice. 'It's hard to imagine being so open with a man about something so private.'

Thinking she had stumbled upon the truth, Bridget said, 'Is that why you've pressed for such a lengthy engagement? Are you anxious about the physical aspect of your union? That would be perfectly understandable,' she hastened to add, 'as it requires the ultimate degree of vulnerability. But let me reassure you that the pleasures of it would outweigh any discomfort, particularly as you both develop more, shall we say, proficiency.'

She blushed as well, given that the man with whom she herself engaged in such intimate relations was Orlaith's own brother. Orlaith shifted her weight in the bed, her skinny frame hardly stirring the covers.

'Maybe that's part of it,' she mumbled. 'Although I've got to admit I'm curious to try it too.' She lifted one shoulder in a shrug. 'I guess there's more than one reason for putting it off for so long.' At Bridget's enquiring expression, she said, 'Mr Adams, for instance. He's barely polite to my face and he's made it clear to Charlie that he doesn't want me as a daughter-in-law. I think he's hoping Charlie will lose interest in me. Charlie said his da even advised him to bed me just to scratch that itch and move on.'

Bridget clicked her tongue. 'That's very disappointing to hear. But Charlie's far too respectful to stoop to such ungallant conduct.'

'He is, thank God. He's never even tried to cross the line of what's acceptable.'

'And are you persuaded that he will ignore his father's wishes, even if they remain contrary to his own?'

Orlaith smiled shyly. 'Yes, I think so.'

'Then how is that an impediment to your marrying him?'

Orlaith glanced away. 'I suppose it isn't.' Her fingertips tapped lightly on the bedcovers. When she looked back, her round grey eyes were troubled. 'Right, here's the root of it. When I marry, I'll become a man's property. By law, Charlie and I will be one person and I'm afraid I'll lose *me* in the process.'

Bridget's gut clenched. How well she understood that fear. How miserably she had endured it when she and Garrett had dwelled under the same roof. Even now, though she had travelled to a different continent and resided with another man, Garrett legally held an unutterable power over her, and she lived in dread of the day he might choose to exert it again.

Orlaith appeared capable of reading her thoughts. 'You know exactly what I'm talking about,' she said glumly. 'I'm right to be fearful, aren't I?' She slumped back against her pillow. 'Tess's past behaviour, no matter how foolish it was, shows that there's great freedom in spinsterhood. She's made awful mistakes but they were hers alone and no one could've changed her mind if she didn't want to change it. I can't bear the idea of letting go of that kind of independence. Not after what I've been through before.'

That certainly was justification for her reluctance. For a significant portion of her life, Orlaith had had no control over the events that had impacted the course of her existence, from Lady Courcey's ruthless eviction of the McGoverns from their cottage, to the endless circle of poverty which she and her family had endured in Dublin, to her brutal time as a virtual slave in the scullery at Anner House. Not until Cormac had rescued her from the influence of Lady Anner and the nasty housekeeper, Mrs Twomey, had Orlaith gained any semblance of autonomy. Even then, she had remained reliant on her brother for quite a while before she had forged her own path for herself as a nurse. In her view, marriage would cut that path short and terminate her hard-won liberty.

'I comprehend your concerns,' said Bridget, 'but I believe they're unfounded.'

Taken aback, Orlaith said, 'You do?'

Bridget nodded firmly. 'You're worried that, by marrying, you'll be giving your husband the entitlement to oppress you, to take away your choices, to decide who you are and what you can or cannot do. And you're correct. He will have that legal right.'

Orlaith's face fell.

Bridget reached out and squeezed her hand. 'But that would only be cause for unease if you had chosen the wrong man.'

Orlaith blinked. She stared. And then she laughed. 'You're right. God Almighty, you're right! What a clod I've been.' Another burst of mirth bubbled out of her. 'I need to get a message to Charlie. I want to marry him right away!'

Chapter 34

Emily stood outside the closed kitchen door and took a nervous breath. She could hear the muffled sound of her parents talking beyond the door, although she could not make out what they were saying. Gathering her courage, she opened the door and entered the kitchen.

A comforting wave of heat from the stove wafted across her face. Strangely, Mama was sitting on the tabletop instead of one of the chairs. Papa was standing in front of her but he spun around at Emily's entrance.

'We thought you'd already gone to bed,' he said lightly as Mama slid off the table to the floor.

'Not yet,' she said. Worms writhed in her stomach; they had become her almost-constant companions. 'I wanted to speak with you both.'

'Sounds serious,' her father said with a grin.

'It is,' she said solemnly and his grin disappeared. She gestured towards the table. 'May we sit down?'

Wearing identical frowns of puzzlement, her parents sat on one side of it and she seated herself opposite them.

'What's the matter, gooseberry?' asked her mother.

Emily suppressed her flinch at the pet name. 'Mother, Father,' she began formally and ignored their raised eyebrows.

'As you may or may not be aware, it has been ten months and thirteen days since Mr Miller struck me.'

'Has he done it again?' her father said sharply.

'No,' she replied, even though every venomous look the schoolmaster had given her from that day to this had stung as acutely as a stroke from his leather strap. 'But I have never forgotten it or the words he said to me. And I am at last ready to prove him wrong.'

She drew a folded letter from her pocket, a precious piece of paper which she had carried around with her for the past week. Unfolding it, she laid it flat on the tabletop. Her mother squinted at it from her upside down viewpoint.

'What is that?'

'It's a letter of acceptance,' said Emily. She straightened her shoulders. 'From the Brubaker Art Academy in New York.'

Her mother's mouth opened in astonishment.

'Come again?' said her father.

Her pulse pounded in her ears. 'I wrote to them and sent samples of my work. They were very impressed and are willing to take me on as a student.'

'Good gracious,' said her mother. 'I have so many questions that I hardly know where to begin.'

Her father, not at quite as much of a loss, said, 'How did you communicate with them? You've never asked me to post or collect any letters for you.'

Of course his thoughts would alight upon the one element of subterfuge in the whole affair.

'Uncle Charlie helped me,' she confessed. She had taken to calling him that since he and Auntie Orlaith had married six months ago. 'He forwarded my correspondence and loaned me the money for the postage. I've promised to pay him back.'

'Why didn't you ask us?' Her father looked perplexed and not a little hurt.

'I wanted to keep it a secret until I was certain it could become a real possibility. If it all came to nothing, then only I would be disappointed.' In fact, she had a much more valid reason for concealing it up to now, but that would come to light very shortly.

Her mother leaned forwards. 'Tell us how this transpired.'

'It was actually Miss Green who instigated it, although she is Mrs Kendrick now.' The worms inside Emily relaxed a little as she recollected the pleasure of seeing her former teacher again. 'She called by the school before Christmas to visit her old pupils and took me aside afterwards to speak to me especially. Her husband has a sister living in New York who is very talented at sculpture, and last autumn she enrolled in the Brubaker Art Academy which caters exclusively for female students. When Miss Green—I mean, Mrs Kendrick—heard this, she immediately thought of me.'

'And she suggested that you apply to this academy?' said her father, his expression guarded.

Emily nodded, trying to keep her enthusiasm in check. This was an occasion to be sober and mature. Still, she couldn't help some of her excitement shining through as she said, 'Mr and Mrs Brubaker are both artists and they run it together. When they replied to my enquiry, they said they were struck by the advanced standard of my skills. And they even accept Irish Catholics. Most important of all, they can make a recommendation at the end of each year for their best students to be considered as candidates for the National Academy of Design!'

'And where is that?'

'New York as well.'

She didn't miss the glance her parents exchanged with each other, and she wasn't so naive as to not recognise that the geographical distance of the academy might present a significant obstacle to their granting their permission for her to attend it. How she wished it was the only impediment.

It was time to recite the speech she had prepared.

She cleared her throat. 'Mother, Father. Ever since I was a small girl, I have gained satisfaction from painting and drawing, from rendering the things I can see in front of me or in my head onto the page. The older I've become, the more that joy has grown and the more my ability has improved. You have praised me time and again, and Mrs Kendrick believes I have a special gift. I wish to make the most of it.' She pressed her palm reverently on top of the open letter. 'Ten months and thirteen days ago, Mr Miller said that women cannot be great artists, that they cannot be anything but mediocre.' Her ire still burned at the humiliating memory. 'I want to show him that he hasn't the first notion what women are capable of. I want to learn from the best and develop my skills as much as I can and distinguish myself in the field of art.'

Her mother and father looked staggered by her impassioned words but she didn't give them a chance to respond just yet.

'I know the academy is far away and I would be distraught to be separated from you and my brothers for quite some time. But an enormous opportunity has presented itself and I don't want to miss it. In two months from now, I shall turn fifteen. I am ready to take this leap.' She inhaled to fortify her courage and carried on, 'There is, of course, the matter of the money it would cost.'

She eyed them and discerned from the way her father's throat bobbed that he in particular had already been conjecturing about that aspect of her proposal.

'I understand that it would be expensive,' she said, hastening to show that she could be pragmatic as well as passionate. 'There would be tuition fees and board and travel. Which is why I wished to speak with you this evening. I have been pondering it at great length and believe I have a solution. We live in modest circumstances here in America but, Mother, you are still a titled lady. You are the Lady Courcey. Before we left Ireland, you arranged for Oakleigh to be managed and rebuilt in your absence, which means the estate still has money. Could I please borrow some of it to fund my studies? I promise to repay it all as soon as I am in a position to do so.'

The squirming of the worms intensified again as she finished speaking. She gazed anxiously across the table at them both.

Her mother gave her a strained smile. 'You have clearly put a great deal of thought into this. I can't tell you how much I admire your fervour and your determination.'

Her father looked proud too, though a trace of worry lurked in his blue eyes.

'So do you think it might be possible?' Emily dared to say hopefully.

Her parents glanced sideways at each other again, seeming to communicate with just their eyes in that extraordinary way they often did.

'Let's consider it from every angle,' her father said, his tone calm. 'Firstly, I will say with absolute sincerity that our desire is to do everything we can to help you pursue your artistic dreams. You have an exceptional talent and you are right to want to make the most of it.' He hesitated. 'Then there are the practical details to take into account. Have they indicated how much it would cost?'

Wordlessly, Emily slid the letter across to him. He turned it around to face him and her mother leaned in to read it as well. A tiny squeak slipped from her mother's throat before she stifled it. Emily's heart sank.

'Can Oakleigh not spare that much?' she asked. 'I thought it was a large estate.'

Her mother bit the tip of her tongue which Emily recognised as a bad sign. 'It's rather more complicated than that, I'm afraid. Do you recall when we visited Oakleigh all those years ago? You were just six at the time. I'm not sure how much of the situation you might have grasped back then, but it was a most appalling state of affairs. My mother—your grandmama—treated the tenants very harshly and many of them were left without homes or employment. A couple of them were so angry that they set fire to the manor house.'

'I remember the burned ruins,' said Emily. 'Isn't that how my grandmama died?'

Her father shifted in his chair, while her mother nodded sombrely. 'Afterwards, I appointed the land agent, Mr Enright, and the stable master, Mr Corbett, to set things to rights. They were to oversee the reconstruction of the manor and the revival of its lands, and ensure that the tenants returned to their positions with fair rents and wages. In addition, the payment of the Church of Ireland tithes, an unfair obligation upon the Catholic tenants, was to be once again undertaken by the estate.'

Emily frowned. 'Are you saying that Oakleigh has too many financial burdens? Is it running out of funds?'

'Not exactly.' Her mother blew out her breath. 'Oakleigh has always had the potential to be a prosperous estate so long as it is managed well. I'm glad to say that the regular reports I receive from Mr Enright and Mr Corbett suggest that it is slowly recovering from the damage my mother inflicted upon it. However, the more it begins to thrive again, the more it becomes an appealing prospect to another party who has a legitimate concern in its wealth.'

'Who?' said Emily.

'Garrett,' replied her mother.

Emily chewed on her lip, thinking back to the man she had come to refer to as her 'first papa' once she learned who her true father was. She had a few hazy memories of him but she couldn't seem to summon any sense of affection from them.

Her mother continued, 'I possess the Courcey title but, because I am still married to Garrett in the eyes of the law, he remains the legal owner of Oakleigh. Anticipating that his interest would increase in tandem with Oakleigh's renewed prosperity, your father and I therefore took steps to thwart any interference from him should he attempt to exploit the estate in the future.'

'What did you do?'

'When we had the new contract drawn up by Webb & Brereton Solicitors, we made certain it included a clause stating that the entirety of Oakleigh's income and expenditure must pertain to the estate itself. This would prevent Garrett from funnelling wealth away from it for his own purposes.' Her mother winced. 'Unfortunately, that very clause prevents us from doing the same.'

Emily swallowed, disappointment flooding through her. 'So there are funds there, but they cannot be touched?'

'Alas, not for the intention you have in mind.'

Emily sat back in her chair. 'What about here then? Do we have enough money in America?'

'We have some,' her father said cautiously. 'The carpentry business is doing quite well and Madame Roche is giving your mother fair pay for her seamstress work. But we have many expenses too—the lease on the workshop premises for one, and Rory's apprenticeship wage for another. Until Charlie moved into Broad Street, we were assisting with the rent on those rooms too. All in all, while we've managed to build a reasonably comfortable life, there hasn't been much opportunity to set savings aside for a large outlay like these tuition fees.' Whatever he read in Emily's face caused him to add hastily, 'But that's not to say that it's impossible. We can make some economies here

314

and there, and I can seek out more commissions. It just might take a period of time to accumulate such a figure.'

Equally tentative, her mother said, 'Or is there perhaps an alternative art academy closer to home which might appeal to you? If you applied to one here in Boston, we wouldn't need to be concerned with the costs of board or travel as you could continue to live here.'

Emily did her best to keep the whine out of her voice as she replied, 'But attending Brubaker is a substantial stepping stone towards getting into the National Academy of Design. According to Mrs Kendrick's sister-in-law, that is the ultimate ambition as it is extremely prestigious. Moreover, it is the highest mark of accomplishment for a female to be accepted there.'

'Well then,' said her father, 'that will be our objective. We shall just have to exercise some patience before we reach it.'

She slumped, disheartened. How long might she have to wait? She had hoped for a much more positive outcome from this conversation, not maybes and ifs and buts.

'What's the point of being the daughter of an heiress if there's no benefit to be had from it?' she grumbled.

Yet again, her parents shared a look between them. After a long pause, her father gave an infinitesimal nod and they both faced her again.

'Emily,' her mother began.

Noting the lack of 'gooseberry' this time, Emily expected that a grave declaration must be imminent and she made an effort to dampen her frustration and listen.

'I think it might be hard for you to hear this,' said her mother, 'and it is hard for us to say, knowing that we are the ones culpable. But the fact of the matter is that there is little benefit to that status now. We turned away from that life a long time ago and there can be no going back to it.'

'I don't understand,' said Emily. 'I know we don't live in a fancy house anymore, but are you not still a lady?'

'In name, yes. I am the Lady Courcey, and I am legally the Lady Wyndham too. They are my titles by virtue of my birth and my marriage. But society would say that I no longer deserve them after my disgraceful conduct.'

'You mean...' Emily glanced at her father.

'Yes,' said her mother without a trace of a blush. 'These are unpalatable matters to speak of and yet we must acknowledge them, for you are old enough to appreciate the truth. The bald reality is that I committed adultery and abandoned my husband to be with your father and I do not regret it for a single moment. Garrett was unkind in many ways, both to you and to me, and he and I were ill-matched to each other. Your father, on the other hand, I had loved ever since I was a girl and, at an age not many years beyond your own, I had come to realise that there was no one in the world for me but him.'

Even her father did not redden at these thoroughly intimate words. How comfortable her parents were speaking of such private things.

'We ran away to be together for the sake of our love and we don't excuse our actions. If you ever have the good fortune to feel that depth of emotion, and I pray that you do someday, then you'll comprehend the impossibility of letting it go.' Her mother's features shone, before a ripple of guilt washed over them. 'However, other people would call my behaviour selfish and shameful. They would assert that I took a vow and I ought to have adhered to it, no matter the consequences. They would maintain that I debased myself by associating with a man so far beneath my station. There is a vast chasm between the upper and lower classes which most people cannot even conceive of crossing.'

Her father leaned his forearms on the table. 'And that chasm is where you exist, *a stór*,' he said with clear regret in his voice. 'You have your mother's pedigree but my lowborn blood runs through your veins. And this will always cast a shadow over your position in society.'

She was so taken aback by the conversation's unforeseen change of direction that she couldn't even exert herself to get annoyed at the pet name.

'The same could be said for your brothers,' her father went on, 'but arguably their situation is even poorer than yours. Your birth is legitimised by your mother's marriage to Garrett, regardless of the fact that he is not your natural father. In contrast, Jack and Gus were both born out of wedlock, although we have not made that known to our acquaintances here in Boston. Still, they are undeniably illegitimate and would be spurned if they ever attempted to enter polite society back in Ireland or England.'

'Even though they're male?' said Emily doubtfully. She found it difficult to believe that boys could have a more challenging time than girls under any circumstances, if Mr Miller's judgements of the world were anything to go by.

'Indeed,' said her mother. 'In the normal course of events, your brothers would have had every advantage. They may be younger than you but they would have superseded you in the line of inheritance had they been born within a lawful union. However, you are my only surviving legitimate issue and thus, if I were to die tomorrow, the Courcey title would pass to you. At least Oakleigh itself ought to remain a safe haven from high society's accusing eyes.'

Emily suppressed a shiver. She didn't want to think about her mother dying. 'Who inherits Oakleigh doesn't matter to me. I am only interested in my art.'

'And we commend you for your drive to succeed at it.' Her father's gaze held hers. 'But it is our duty to make you aware that the scandal connected to our family means that some doors may always be closed to you.'

She gulped. 'Could it prevent me from accepting my place at the academy once we can afford it?'

'I don't believe so. But, should the truth ever get out, you could be shunned by your peers or your tutors, depending on how intolerant they are of such impropriety. At any stage of your life, you might encounter prejudice or contempt. And it will be our fault for exposing you to it.'

'We are so very sorry,' her mother said, her voice thick. 'It is an unfair burden we have placed upon your shoulders. Your path will never be easy.'

Observing their remorseful expressions, Emily summoned a bright smile to her own. 'Don't be sorry,' she said earnestly. 'What you did is the most romantic thing I've ever heard of. I hope one day I shall be lucky enough to fall in love with someone who is willing to sacrifice everything to run away with me.'

Reaching for the letter, she slid it back across the table to her. She fingered the corner of it pensively.

'You acted upon an impulse you couldn't deny,' she said slowly, 'and you didn't care what other people thought.' Blinking, she raised her chin as a fire kindled in her belly, burning away the worms and replacing them with red-hot conviction. 'So I shall adopt the same approach. I know in my very soul that art needs to be in my future, and I'll do whatever it takes to achieve that goal.' She squared her shoulders. 'I will earn my way until I have gathered enough money to accept my place at Brubaker.'

Her father tilted his head, looking impressed. 'What do you intend to do?'

'I'm not sure,' she said. 'Am I too young to be a governess?'

'A little,' said her mother.

She brooded for a moment, sucking on her lower lip. 'Then I'll enter service,' she declared. 'Auntie Orlaith was younger than me when she first became a maid.'

'That is an arduous job,' her mother cautioned.

'It also doesn't tend to pay very well,' her father added. 'It may take a long time to accumulate sufficient funds.'

She refused to feel discouraged. 'I shall persevere nonetheless,' she said obstinately.

Her father beamed at her. 'Between the three of us, we will accomplish it.'

'And if I get a position close to home,' she said, 'I can continue to live here as you suggested, Mother, and save every penny I make. Where do you think I might seek out employment?'

Her father tapped his jaw, musing. 'I remember O'Mali—the fellow I used to work with at the docks—sent his daughter, Tilly, out to find maid's work several years ago. She got a place over on Beacon Hill. I could speak to O'Mali, see if Tilly knows whether there might be any positions available in the households around that area.'

'Oh, thank you, Father,' said Emily, the fire inside her blazing with determination. She fully believed she could realise this dream; she was prepared to do anything for it.

Chapter 35

The next morning, Cormac noted the bounce in Emily's step as she departed for school, taking Jack along with her by the hand. He was glad their discussion around the kitchen table the previous night had brought her some cheer, even though there would be many challenges ahead.

'I'll go to the waterfront this evening,' he said to Bridget, who was trying to convince Gus to slow down while eating his porridge – the lad did love his food. 'I might get Rory to close up the workshop by himself so I can catch O'Mali before he leaves the docks.'

He had stayed in contact with both O'Mali and Mr Walker over the past few years and had even gone for pints with the dockworkers on several occasions. Robert Smith & Co. had weathered the economic uncertainty that had permeated the country for so long and, happily, was still in operation.

Bridget cast him a worried look. 'Are you sure this is a good idea? You don't think the toil of a maid's life might be too much for Emily? She's only a slip of a thing, after all.'

'I think it's going to be difficult for her at first,' he admitted. 'Still, she's a capable girl, even if she is somewhat petite. She'll manage fine.'

Bridget placed an admonishing palm on top of Gus's mop of curls. 'What did I say about swallowing one mouthful before starting the next?' As their son grumbled and complied, she glanced back at Cormac. 'It just seems a little…jarring, I suppose. At her age, I was a mere year away from being presented as a debutante at Dublin Castle. And here she is, preparing to become a servant.'

While part of him did wish they could give their daughter the comforts of that upper class world, another part of him was heartily glad that she was free from its constraints. 'Entering service is a far cry from choosing the fabric of her dress for her coming-out ball, but it should serve her much better in the long run. It will build her character and teach her a great deal about working hard to achieve her ambitions.'

Just as Bridget opened her mouth to respond, a knock sounded on the front door. 'Who could be calling this early?' she said instead, baffled.

He went to answer it. When he pulled the door open, a boy around Emily's age stood on the top step.

'I'm looking for Cormac McGovern,' he said, puffing out his chest importantly.

'You've got him,' said Cormac. 'How can I help you?'

The boy held out a sheet of paper. 'I have some information.'

Cormac stared down at the page. It was one of Emily's drawings of Bronagh. 'Christ above,' he said.

Some time later – after he had gleaned the essential facts from the boy, hurriedly informed Bridget what was happening, and dashed to the workshop to ask Rory to mind the place for the morning – he found himself gazing up at the facade of The Bucking Deer Inn. It was a bustling stagecoach stop; men and women milled around outside the inn or passed through its open doors, while a pair of ostlers harnessed a fresh set of horses to a stationary coach standing in front of it.

The boy who had visited Acorn House stood in the doorway. 'He's in here,' he called, beckoning to Cormac.

Hastening forwards, Cormac entered the smoky interior of The Bucking Deer. The smells of sweat and stale beer permeated the air and several tables filled the space, a number of them occupied by weary travellers waiting for the coach outside to be ready for the next stage of their journey. The boy pointed towards a man sitting alone at a table by the window, digging into a plate of meat and bread with gusto.

'There's Mr Todd,' he said.

'Thanks, lad.'

Cormac slipped him a coin, then wove his way among the tables and approached the man at the window, who was now drinking deeply from a pewter tankard. He had a bushy black beard which glistened with droplets as he set the tankard down with a satisfying exhalation of breath.

'Mr Todd?' said Cormac. 'You are the driver of the stagecoach?'

'That's me,' said the man, wiping the back of his hand across his beard. 'We're full up for the next stage, no spaces left.'

'I'm not seeking to be a passenger. My name is Cormac McGovern. I understand you have some news about my sister, the girl in this picture.' He withdrew Emily's drawing from his pocket and held it out.

Mr Todd squinted up at him. 'You're her brother? You don't look much alike.'

'She always resembled our mother more, while I took after my father. Please, may I sit with you for a moment? If you have any tidings of Bronagh, I would be very grateful to hear them.'

Mr Todd jerked his chin at the empty chair opposite him and Cormac slid into it, laying the drawing on the tabletop between them. Through the smoke-stained window, he spotted one of the ostlers trying to calm a horse that was tossing its head before he returned his attention to Mr Todd.

'Can you tell me what you know, sir?'

Mr Todd stuffed a slice of gristly meat into his mouth. 'I'm not one to interfere in other folk's affairs,' he said as he chewed loudly. 'Their business is their own, and it's no concern of mine. But I respect women and it gets my back up when I see a thug mistreating one.'

A chill ran down Cormac's spine. 'What do you mean? What mistreatment?'

'Brutish behaviour towards the weaker sex. There's just no call for it.' Mr Todd swallowed the meat and then swallowed again, looking uncomfortable. 'I felt bad that I didn't do anything for her at the time. And I don't even know what good it'll do to tell you now, given how long ago it was.'

Every word out of the man's mouth increased Cormac's apprehension. 'Tell me anyway,' he entreated. 'It's been more than a decade since my family last saw Bronagh. We need to know what happened to her.'

Mr Todd heaved a sigh. 'That's understandable.' He picked up a chunk of bread, took a bite and said, 'I've been a stagecoach driver for nigh on twenty years, although I can't say how much longer I'll have the job with these railways getting so popular. The days of having a full coach like today are getting fewer and further between.' He shook his head and went on, 'I covered this route for years, until I met my wife and took a post down in Virginia so she could be near her parents. It was only after they both passed this year that we decided to come back to Massachusetts and, just by luck, I got assigned to my old route again.' He jabbed a finger at the picture of Bronagh. 'When I walked into The Bucking Deer and saw this nailed to the wall, I recognised her right away. The innkeeper said you'd left your name and address on the back of it and let me send a message to you with his son, as I'm on a rather tight schedule. As soon as the horses are ready, we'll be off again.'

Cormac glanced out the window and caught sight of the ostler pulling roughly on the bridle of the agitated horse. He pressed his lips into a thin line before saying, 'I left drawings of her in all sorts of places—boarding houses, stagecoach stops, railway stations. But I'd long since given up hope that they would prove fruitful.'

'It's a good likeness, I have to say. No mistaking that's her.' Mr Todd scratched at his bushy beard, dislodging a few crumbs which drifted down into his lap. 'Although it doesn't quite capture the measure of her grit.'

Cormac felt an unexpected lump come to his throat. 'How did you meet her?' he managed to ask. 'Did she travel on your coach?'

'She arrived at this inn one day, just as I was about to set off with fresh horses. She said she was making enquiries about the price of fares for five people but, when she realised I was hitting the road right there and then, a sort of desperation came into her eyes and she begged me to let her on. She had no money but she offered' – Mr Todd gave Cormac a fleeting, discomfited look – 'sexual favours in exchange for a space on the coach. Like I said, I have respect for women. So I told her no.'

This time, Cormac couldn't manage to get any words out at all. He gestured mutely for Mr Todd to carry on.

Mr Todd grasped another chunk of bread, eyed it dispiritedly, and put it back down untouched. 'A few days later, I had completed a round trip on my route and was back at The Bucking Deer with a new group of passengers. Your sister appeared again...with a black eye and a cut lip. There were three others with her, two men and a woman. I don't know what happened to the fifth person who was supposed to travel with them.'

Cormac thought of the corpse of Bully Billy abandoned in the house on Charter Street in the North End.

'They had the money for their fares and I had enough space so I let them on. They kept to themselves and I thought they weren't going to cause any trouble, until the rumpus at one stop along the way.' Mr Todd twisted his lips, which were barely visible within the growth of his beard. 'I'd been grabbing a bite to eat inside the inn when I heard a scuffle and angry shouts outside. I went out to see what was going on and spotted the two fellows in your sister's company a short way down the road clutching her and the other woman in iron grips and dragging them back towards the coach. Your sister was holding her arm at an awkward angle, like it was sprained or broken. I can't say for certain what actually happened, but my guess is the women tried to run away while we were stopped.'

With a low groan, Cormac dropped his head into his palms and stared at the scuffed surface of the table as he listened to the remainder of Mr Todd's tale.

'Although we travelled on from there without any further commotion, the other passengers were wary after that. The two men realised they were under scrutiny and didn't manhandle the women again but they never let them out of their sight either.' There was a noisy slurp and the knock of pewter against wood. 'When they got off at our destination, I tried to take your sister aside to ask if she needed help. She just shrugged out of my grasp and walked away with her companions, chin in the air like she could defy the world.'

Cormac let his hands fall and gave the man a weak smile. 'No doubt it's Bronagh then. She hasn't changed a bit.'

Mr Todd did not smile back. 'I'm sorry I didn't do more to aid her. It preyed on my mind for a long time afterwards.'

'She wasn't your responsibility,' Cormac said with a rueful shrug. 'Can you remember approximately when this happened?'

'I can remember exactly, because it was one of my last drives before my wife and I moved to Virginia. It'll be seven years ago next month.'

He absorbed this with grim resignation; Bronagh had left Boston a mere eight months after he, Bridget and their family had arrived in the city. Such wretched luck.

'And what was your destination on that trip?' he asked.

'This route goes all the way down to New York City,' said Mr Todd. 'They stayed on the coach to the end of the journey.'

'New York City,' Cormac repeated, his thoughts too jumbled to consider the enormity of that just yet. 'Do you know where they intended to go next?'

Mr Todd shook his head. 'I'm afraid that's the last I ever saw of her.'

'What about the people she was with? Could you describe their features?'

Frowning, Mr Todd said, 'Not really. The fellows kept their caps down low over their heads, almost like they didn't want to be recognised. They were mid-twenties maybe, and one of them had longish, greasy hair. I got a better look at the other woman. She was quite tall and' – his cheeks went red – 'extremely well endowed in the bust area. I can't think of anything else helpful.'

'Thank you,' said Cormac. 'I'm most obliged to you for this information.'

'It's not much,' said Mr Todd. 'I wish I had more to tell.'

'It's been enlightening, and I'm grateful for that.' Cormac took another quick glimpse through the murky window, where a small crowd had begun to gather around the coach. 'I shouldn't use up any more of your time. Your passengers are waiting for you.' He stood, pocketing the drawing of Bronagh as he did so. 'You might want to go easy on your right-hand lead horse—it'll be a bit skittish after the way the ostler treated it. Thank you very much again.'

He shook Mr Todd's hand and, winding his way once more between the inn's tables, emerged out onto the street. Head roaring as he attempted to process all that he had learned, he sidestepped the waiting passengers and made for home. Rory could mind the workshop on his own for a little longer.

When he reached Acorn House, he found Bridget by the window in the front room sewing at the desk he had built for her. It was specially designed to cater for her needlework, a workload which kept increasing in proportion to Madame Roche's effusive praise, and contained several compartments to accommodate an assortment of pins, scissors, spools of thread, and pieces of fabric. He had also created a cupboard space under the stairs where she could hang items of clothing when she wasn't working on them.

Gus was sitting on the sofa in front of the hearth, poring over a book in which his mother had written out the letters of the alphabet as well as lists of words and short sentences. He sounded them out while Bridget corrected his pronunciation. When Cormac came in, Gus's face lit up. 'Da!'

He dropped the book onto the sofa and ran to him. Cormac swept him into his arms and flipped him upside down so he was hanging by his ankles. Gus giggled, while out of the corner of his eye Cormac caught Bridget wincing. He set their son back on his feet.

'Again!' cried Gus.

'Not just now, *a mhic ó*. You go practise your reading some more. I need to talk to your ma.'

Gus scampered back to the sofa and Bridget laid her sewing in her lap as Cormac approached her and leaned against the desk.

'How did it go?' she asked tentatively.

He told her what had transpired at The Bucking Deer Inn, keeping his voice low so that Gus wouldn't overhear.

Horror flooded Bridget's countenance. 'Dear God, poor Bronagh. She has suffered terrible abuse at the hands of these men, whoever they are.'

Rage churned inside him at the image of a cruel, faceless man beating his sister and giving her a black eye and a broken arm. 'It doesn't bear thinking about,' he said hollowly.

'What do you want to do next?'

He didn't miss a beat. 'I want to save her, if it's within my power to do that.'

Bridget nodded, like she was expecting that answer. 'Seven years is a very long time. Do you think she might still be al—I mean, in New York?'

Her clumsy amendment wasn't enough to banish her obvious misgiving, and he recognised it because he shared it. What were the odds that Bronagh was still alive, given the beastly devils in her company?

'I have no idea,' he said. 'But it's my duty as her brother to do everything I can to find her, if she can be found.' He sighed. 'It won't be easy. If she and her companions still intended to keep themselves concealed even in a different city to the one where they left a dead body behind, then discovering her whereabouts will be a colossal challenge and far more complicated than what we had anticipated when we first came to Boston.'

'Do you...' Bridget hesitated. 'Will you want us to move to New York?'

'I don't know. It would certainly suit Emily, wouldn't it? She would be able to attend Brubaker sooner than she had hoped, if distance and accommodation costs were removed from the equation.' He picked up a spool resting on the sewing desk and began idly winding the thread around his thumb. 'On the other hand, the prospect of uprooting ourselves from Boston after we have gone to so much effort to build our home and livelihoods here...it's daunting to contemplate.'

'It is,' she said faintly. 'We would be very sad to bid farewell to the friends and the life we have made here. Your workshop is flourishing, and I personally relish the small independence I have gained from being in Madame Roche's employ.' She fingered the fabric in her lap with a wistful expression.

He looped the thread tighter and tighter, the skin on his thumb turning white. 'Furthermore, Jack has only started at Hawes this past year so it would be unsettling to remove him at this juncture. He seems happy there and thanks be to God Mr Miller does not teach the younger classes.'

'We must also think of Orlaith and Tess,' she added. 'Would we consider wholly separating from them or asking them to come with us? Bear in mind your sister may not wish for such upheaval so soon into her married life.'

Cormac chewed the inside of his cheek. 'It does seem unwise to disrupt all of that for so tenuous a cause. It might be prudent to see what I can initially achieve from here. I'll send out letters of enquiry first and, if it comes to it, I can travel down there myself to search in person.'

She looked anxious but admitted, 'That sounds like a sensible approach to begin with.'

He slowly unwound the thread from his thumb, one coil at a time. 'It occurs to me that I should retrace my steps across the city and gather up any drawings of Bronagh which might still linger about. Now that we know she has left Boston, it would be undesirable to continue to draw attention to her image in this vicinity, not if the authorities might still be looking for the perpetrators of the crime on Charter Street.'

But first, he would tell Orlaith the news that they had a fresh lead on their lost sister. And then his desperate search would resume.

Chapter 36

Emily examined herself in the narrow mirror, tugging nervously at her white cap. Standing on tiptoe, she craned her neck to get a better view of her figure. The hem of her skirt was lower than it had been on the dresses of her girlhood but it still did not cover her ankles because a maid needed to move around freely in her work. She had just about scraped past five feet in height and today, on the occasion of her fifteenth birthday, she had finally resigned herself to the fact that she could not hope for more. What she found depressing was that no part of her body had appeared willing to burgeon. Turning sideways, she eyed her chest where two small mounds budded beneath her dress and wrinkled her nose.

As she angled her head, she spotted a golden curl escaping at the nape of her neck. Taking a pin out of her pocket, she snagged the wayward loop of hair and tucked it underneath her cap just as the door to the tiny servants' room swung open.

'Are you ready?' said Tilly cheerfully, dangling an empty wicker basket from one hand and a pail from the other. A couple of years older than Emily, she wore a cap too and had striking cheekbones.

Emily took a last glance in the mirror, smoothed down her pristine white apron and said, 'Yes, I think so,' before following Tilly out into the corridor.

Her father's connection to Mr O'Mali had borne fruit; not only had Tilly confirmed that there was an opening for a housemaid in Marlowe House – the very household where she worked on Beacon Hill – but she had also somehow convinced the housekeeper, Mrs Coleman, to put Emily at the top of her list of potential new maids. When Auntie Orlaith heard that Emily had managed to skip the lowly position of scullery maid even though she was only starting out in service, she had said darkly that she was very lucky.

At the end of the corridor, Mrs Coleman was standing at the door that led out onto the paved courtyard at the back of Marlowe House. She barked an order at a chimney sweep's climbing boy who was dallying on the step and he saluted her and scurried away, his brush balanced jauntily on his shoulder.

The housekeeper turned and crooked a finger at Tilly and Emily, who both hastened towards her. She wasn't an especially large woman but she had a pair of thick eyebrows which arched at them in an intimidating way.

'Now, Emily,' she began in a stern voice, prompting Emily to clasp her hands tightly behind her back to prevent herself from fidgeting. 'You come to us with no experience but I expect you to be a quick learner. Tilly will guide you through your first few days here, show you around, explain your routines and tasks. Here at Marlowe House we do not abide substandard work so make sure you listen carefully to everything she says. Do you have any questions?'

'No, Mrs Coleman.'

'Very well. You will take your midday meals here but, as per your request, we shall not provide your evening meals or accommodation. If you should change your mind on that, there is a maid's bed available in the servants' quarters at the top of the house.'

'Thank you, Mrs Coleman.'

The housekeeper nodded at Tilly with an expression of unmistakable fondness. 'Take her upstairs. The family are at breakfast so now's the time to show her the bedchambers.'

'Yes, Mrs Coleman,' Tilly chirped with a reciprocal look of affection and handed Emily the pail. Then, swinging her basket, she led the way towards the servants' staircase at the far end of the corridor. As they climbed the steps up through the belly of the house, she talked nineteen to the dozen and Emily endeavoured to absorb everything she said.

'I'm an upper housemaid and you're a lower housemaid, but don't worry—I won't go lording that over you. We start at six o'clock in the summer, and seven in the winter, so I guess you're gonna have to rise early to make it here on time.'

Emily had been instructed to arrive a little later on her first day so that her induction into her new role would not interfere with the smooth running of the household's morning activities; she tried not to imagine how gruelling that early start was going to be from tomorrow. For a brief moment, she considered taking up Mrs Coleman's offer of staying in the servants' quarters, given that it seemed to be included in her position and would not eat into the money she was trying to save, but then she felt a small tug behind her ribs at the prospect of no longer living at Acorn House. She didn't think she was quite ready for that yet.

Tilly barrelled on, 'Our first duty is to see to the lower rooms like the breakfast room, the drawing room, the morning room and the library. We open the shutters, sweep the floors, clean the grates, lay the fires—it's cold enough for May so we'll keep doing those last bits until the summer heat sets in proper. After that, we dust and polish the breakfast room so it's ready to receive the family. Do you sneeze badly on account of dust?'

Emily shook her head.

'That's good. One of the girls here before used to have awful sneezing fits. You could hear her the whole way through the house.' There was a tinge of awe in Tilly's tone. 'Anyways, once breakfast is served, we can go up to the bedchambers to make the beds and empty the slops.'

They reached the top of the second flight of stairs and Tilly led Emily through a discreet doorway and out onto a landing where she stopped in front of a closed door. Despite the confirmed knowledge that the family was breakfasting, she still knocked and paused to listen for silence before opening it.

'Mistress Marlowe's bedchamber,' she announced.

It had been a very long time since Emily had been in a room as grand as this. No expense had been spared in the furnishing of it, from the thick hangings which framed the windows to the decorative bedside tables. The windows were open and a refreshing breeze blew in, rippling a silk dressing gown dangling over the back of a wingback chair. She tried to remember the feel of silk but she could not recall it and she was too afraid to touch.

'Time for you to start earning your wage!' said Tilly, gesturing towards the enormous four-poster bed with its covers in disarray and its pillows askew. She put down her basket, pulled open the bottom drawer of a large wardrobe and drew out fresh linen. 'Today we're changing the sheets, not just fixing them.'

After stripping the bedclothes, she proceeded to educate Emily on the art of bed-making, from beating the feather mattress and laying down the under blanket to draping the counterpane in elegant folds and neatly arranging the four-poster's curtains. Tilly remained dissatisfied with the job until every corner was tucked in just so and the pillows were positioned to perfection.

Standing back with a critical eye, she said, 'Nice. Now the slops.'

Prior to arriving at Marlowe House, Emily had not given too much consideration to what being a maid actually entailed. By the time she and Tilly had exited Mistress Marlowe's bedchamber, she understood a great deal more, having become closely acquainted with the contents of that lady's chamber pot.

They moved from there to Mr Marlowe's adjoining bedchamber. She thought it rather odd for a married couple to sleep in separate beds, but then she had a vague recollection of her mother keeping her own chamber at the townhouse back in London. Perhaps it was something wealthy people did because they had so many rooms to spare. She had a strong hunch, however, that even if her mother and father had that much space they would still prefer to share one bed.

Once the last corner of the counterpane had been twitched into place and the slop-pail's load had increased further, Tilly said, 'We'll do the young master's room next.'

In a chamber further along the landing, they found a third bed in a similar state of disorder. The sash window was open here too and Emily was grateful for the fresh air which diminished the odour from her pail. She did not require as much coaching on the bed-making this time so Tilly chattered more about the house and its inhabitants.

'Mr Marlowe's grandfather owned it first. It's one of the oldest and biggest in the neighbourhood.' Her words were full of pride. Emily wondered whether a time would ever come when she would be prouder to be a servant in the Marlowe household than a daughter in the McGovern home. 'The master and mistress are fine people. They have a huge fortune and just a single son who turned sixteen this year. Young Master Samuel is gonna be one of the richest men in the city whenever his poppa, you know...' Tilly couldn't seem to articulate that bleak future out loud and instead hastened on, 'So how long have you been living in Boston?'

'Almost eight years,' said Emily.

'My poppa said you're Irish but your name sounds English to me. Which are you?'

'Sort of both. My parents are Irish but I was born in London.'

'To be honest, I was half expecting you to be called Bridie or Bridget or Biddy. That's what most of the Irish girls are known as around these parts. Don't be surprised if folk start calling you that anyways.'

As Tilly rolled up the third set of dirty sheets, Emily did her best not to feel rankled by the unintended slight on her mother's pretty name.

Oblivious, Tilly said brightly, 'I think I'm gonna call you Em. Come on, let's get these down to the laundry room.'

She tossed the sheets into the wicker basket and hefted it up onto her hip.

'Ought I to help you?' said Emily anxiously. 'It looks heavy.'

Tilly raised an eyebrow. 'Ought? You talk very posh for a maid.'

Embarrassed, Emily tried to pass off the remark with a casual shrug. 'Must be just a bit of the English coming out in me. Do you need help carrying the basket?'

'I've lifted heavier than this. You'll have muscles like me soon! Anyways, you have to bring the slop-pail.'

Tilly led Emily towards the door of the bedchamber, peeping back at her with a wink. In the next moment, she let out a shriek as her gaze caught on something behind Emily. Emily whirled, almost spilling the contents of the slop-pail, and saw a pigeon fluttering through the open window. Its wings beat wildly, grazing the hangings, and it shot towards the ceiling, coming to land on the canopy of the four-poster bed.

Tilly's jaw went slack with horror. 'We need to get it out!'

She dropped her basket to the floor with a thump, while Emily set down her pail with a little more care. They approached the bed cautiously and stared up at the canopy where the pigeon perched, stock-still and alert.

Tilly moaned. 'How do we even reach it?'

Emily scanned the bedchamber for a stool but there was only one fancy wingback chair which she wouldn't dream of standing on. 'Maybe we could wave a pillow at it to encourage it to come down?'

She took a step closer to the bed which was enough to launch the alarmed pigeon back into flight. It wheeled about the room and Tilly threw her arms over her head.

'I don't like birds,' she whimpered.

To make matters worse, the pigeon defecated, leaving a splotch of white droppings on the rug at the foot of the bed.

And then the bedchamber door opened and a young man walked in.

'Shut the door!' Emily cried at him, terrified to imagine what would happen if the bird escaped to the rest of the house.

His astonishment quickly changed to comprehension when he spotted the agitated pigeon flapping above their heads and he swiftly stepped into the room, closing the door behind him.

'We have to get it down to the floor,' he said in a firm, calm voice. Glancing around, his gaze landed upon Tilly's abandoned basket and he drew a sheet from it, shaking it out. He eyed the pigeon's erratic movements as it flew near the top of the wardrobe on the far side of the bedchamber. 'Both of you, go over there and clap or wag your hands. We want to drive it to this side of the room where there is no high furniture.'

This instruction did not fill Emily with fear thanks to her experience caring for her hens, but Tilly looked like she would rather run in the opposite direction. Still, they both obeyed, advancing towards the wardrobe and flailing their arms about.

Emily smacked her hands together and the pigeon fluttered away from the noise, flitting into the centre of the room. She followed it, clapping loudly to discourage it from alighting on the bed's canopy again. It retreated further from her, soaring downwards to land on the floor near the door, narrowly avoiding the slop-pail.

The young man flung the sheet and it billowed out and settled over the pigeon. He bent to wrap his hands around the bird-shaped mound and, with complete composure, he lifted the bird, still wrapped in the sheet, and carried it over to the window. Emily hurried to push the sash open even wider. Offering her a brief smile of thanks, he manoeuvred the sheet until he found the edge of it and exposed the pigeon to the air, holding the sheet up against the window frame to prevent the bird from flying back inside again. It took wing at once, ascending above the city street and disappearing beyond the nearest rooftops. The young man let the sheet fall.

Tilly released a shaky breath. 'Oh, Master Samuel, how brave you were.'

He grinned. 'It was nothing. Are you both all right?'

'Yes, sir, thank you,' said Tilly, while Emily could only nod, finding herself wordless.

Now that the panic had passed, she could take a proper look at him – and she had never seen a face so handsome. Her mother sometimes talked about how her father's good looks had swept her away back at Oakleigh but of course he was older now and Emily had not witnessed him in the prime of his youth. Here before her was undeniable proof that perfection in human features was possible.

The young man was, quite simply, beautiful. He had a head of wavy, bronze-coloured hair, which looked so soft that her fingers itched to stroke it. Striking, dark eyelashes framed his eyes and, although she was too shy to gaze directly into them, she was sure that if she did they would be captivating and soulful. Who knew a nose could be so straight, so noble? And his pronounced jaw struck her as all the more masculine because of the attractive cleft in the middle of his chin. Her legs became wobbly and she braced one hand against the window frame to steady herself. She covered it up by pushing down on the sash, as though sealing off access to any more winged intruders.

'We'll come right back to clean that up, sir,' said Tilly, motioning towards the pigeon's filth on the rug.

'I shall get out of your way then,' he replied. 'I only came in to retrieve a new verse I wrote last night.'

He was a poet too? Emily's heart fluttered as madly as the bird's wings as Samuel crossed to his bedside table and withdrew a page from its drawer. Then he gave them a gracious wave and exited the bedchamber.

Tilly seized the fallen sheet, returned it to the basket and, picking the whole lot up, exclaimed, 'Come on!'

Shaking herself out of her daze, Emily reached for the slop-pail. They emerged onto the landing, where Samuel was approaching an elegant woman who had to be Mistress Marlowe; at the sound of his voice, she halted in the process of entering her bedchamber. Keeping their faces averted, Tilly and Emily hurried discreetly to the servants' door and slipped through it.

Emily turned back to ease the door closed but she left it open a sliver to retain a slim view of the landing. She told herself that she was merely curious to catch a proper glimpse of the mistress whom she must now serve with deepest loyalty. Except she angled her head so that Samuel was in her line of vision.

With a charming blush, he handed his mother the page he had taken from his bedside table and she beamed with delight. He held her elbow gently and placed a tender kiss on her cheek, the picture of filial devotion, before he surrendered her to the privacy of her bedchamber.

The desolation Emily felt as he moved away down the landing and out of her sight told her all she needed to know.

'I am in love,' she whispered.

'What did you say?' asked Tilly behind her.

'Nothing,' she murmured.

But it was certainly not nothing. It was both the most wonderful and most tragic thing that had ever happened to her.

***

Cormac rested the plane against the length of timber, bent down to study it at eye level, and pushed the tool forwards. Thin shavings fluttered upwards from the surface of the wood and he blew them off onto the floor. He repeated the process along the full span of the plank, then ran his fingers across it. Satisfyingly smooth.

When he stood back, Rory hurried forwards to sweep up the shavings. Cormac let him brush them into a pile before gesturing for him to look closely at the wood.

'Do you see the even finish? That comes from planing with the grain. Always try to plane with the grain, not against.' Casting around for a discarded piece of timber, he secured it to the bench with a vice. 'Here, practise on this.' He held the plane out to Rory.

Setting aside his broom, Rory gripped the plane rather nervously and lowered his shaggy head over the wood, his nose almost touching it as he examined the grain. Then he positioned the plane and pushed it. He produced splinters on the first go but his second attempt was smoother.

'Good job, keep at it,' Cormac said and left him to it. The lad would work better without him watching over his shoulder.

He crossed the workshop to a desk in the corner which had contracts, ledgers and designs scattered across it. Rifling through them, he unearthed the drawing of the sideboard he was constructing and scrutinised it. He had gained this commission while retracing his steps around Boston gathering up the portraits of Bronagh – Mr and Mrs Rosemount, who owned a boarding house friendly to Irish immigrants, had struck up a conversation with him and learned about his carpentry business. The outcome of this casual chat had been their order of a new sideboard for their dining room which they were refurnishing. He had already returned to the boarding house to measure the space and now pored over the drawing, meticulously confirming the dimensions for the next stage of the project.

The sound of swearing came to him from the vicinity of the bench but he kept his gaze focused downwards, guessing that Rory would look in his direction to check if he had heard. Only when he reckoned the lad had turned back to his work did he glance over to make sure that he had not done any damage to himself or the tool. He was planing again so it couldn't have been anything too serious.

Cormac sought out a pencil beneath the papers on his desk and made some calculations in the margin of his drawing. As always, he experienced a surge of gratitude towards Bridget for teaching him to read and write at the age of seven when he had been just a stable hand's son with no prospect of ever needing such talents. Her kind act had in the past kept him alive and in the present enabled him to support his family more securely than he could ever have dreamed.

When he had completed his calculations, he returned to Rory's side to inspect his progress.

'Well done,' he said, sliding his hand along the wood. 'That's fine work.'

Rory swelled with pride.

'Just remember that there's no swearing in my workshop,' Cormac added and found it hard to conceal his amusement at how far Rory's face fell.

'Sorry, Mr McGovern,' he mumbled.

Cormac clapped him on the shoulder. 'It's fine,' he said. 'Tell me, will you come to Acorn House later? We're having a surprise birthday supper for Emily. Your mother might have already mentioned it to you.'

Rory stared at the floor. 'She did.'

'So you'll come?'

'I don't think Emily would want me there,' Rory muttered.

Cormac regarded him with a wry grin. 'If only you hadn't abducted Mabel all those years ago.'

Rory glanced up quickly and looked away again, but not before Cormac caught the wounded expression in his green eyes.

'Hmm,' he said, with dawning perception. 'Could it be that you weren't in fact Mabel's kidnapper after all?'

Rory reached for his broom and began sweeping up the shavings he had accumulated around the bench.

'Who took her?' asked Cormac.

Rory bent to flick away a clump of shavings that had snagged in the bristles of the broom. 'Una,' he said at last when he straightened. 'She was sad for weeks after our da left that New Year's and she thought the doll's hugs would make her feel better. But she knew Emily wouldn't let her keep it. So...' He shrugged.

'How did you figure out it was her?'

'I just guessed. My sisters were the most likely ones to want the doll but Sorcha wouldn't have had the gumption to steal it.' He swept his pile over to the mound he had created earlier. 'When I saw how upset Emily was, I told Una she had to give it back. She didn't want to be found out though so I said I'd bring it upstairs for her. I thought I could just slip it into the room when no one was looking but then Emily spotted me on the stairs.'

'I see,' said Cormac, recalling Bridget's account afterwards of the loud racket Emily had made when she levelled her accusations at Rory. 'Why didn't you tell her the truth?'

Rory's manner turned mulish. 'She wasn't interested in hearing it. She made a snap judgement and that was that.'

Cormac shook his head, marvelling at the enduring feud that had erupted from Emily's misinterpretation of the situation and Rory's obstinate refusal to set things to rights.

'Come along to the supper anyway,' he said. 'Maybe there will be an opportunity to make amends between the two of you.'

'I'll just end up on Una's bad side then,' said Rory. 'I can't win.'

He said it without glumness, only an air of matter-of-fact acceptance.

***

'We do a deep polish on the furniture three or four times a year,' said Tilly, gaily rubbing her cloth over the surface of the dining room table. 'The polish is equal parts linseed oil, turpentine, vinegar and spirits of wine. Always give it a good shake first. Careful, Em,' she added in a cautioning tone. 'Rub, don't smear.'

Emily adjusted her technique as best she could, although her elbow and her heart ached.

'That's better,' said Tilly. 'We don't want Mrs Coleman telling us off for shoddy work.' A mischievous glint came into her eye. 'Well, she'd probably tell you off. I might get away with it if she's in a decent mood.' She peeked over her shoulder at the closed dining room door, then said conspiratorially, 'She has a soft spot for me.'

Emily offered an inviting look of enquiry and Tilly needed no further encouragement.

'I came here when I was only ten,' she said eagerly, 'so Mrs Coleman practically raised me herself. I was homesick for my poppa at the start but she was so kind to me. She used to give me the biscuits that the cook sent to her room from the kitchens and she let me explore the attic on my afternoons off—I found an old chest of the mistress's clothes from when she was a younger girl and I loved trying on her gloves and things, although I didn't tell Mrs Coleman that. She also explained what was happening to me when I first got my courses.'

Emily nodded sagely at this but she had nothing to contribute as, even though several years ago her mother had made her aware of what to expect, her own courses had not yet come.

'She even threw out the previous chimney sweep when he joked that he nearly mixed me up with his sooty climbing boy. To tell the truth, I think I'm her favourite out of all the girls who've ever worked for her. Watch out, Em, I said don't smear!'

Tilly clicked her tongue and reached over to wipe at the mess Emily had made. 'Is your head in the clouds? You picked things up a lot quicker when we were making the beds.'

'I'm sorry,' said Emily miserably. 'I can't seem to concentrate on anything.'

'Is there a particular reason?' asked Tilly. Emily gave a mute nod and the other maid's face lit up with intrigue. 'What is it?'

'You'll think I'm being silly...'

'Tell me anyways!'

Emily scrunched her eyes shut. 'I've fallen in love.'

'With who?'

'The Marlowes' son.'

Tilly's intake of breath was loud enough to make Emily snap her eyes open again. 'Young Master Samuel? You mean it?'

'Yes, of course I do!'

'But you only saw him for the first time today.' Tilly sounded doubtful.

'Once would be enough for any girl to fall in love with him. Don't you think he is the handsomest boy on this earth? And the most gallant?'

Tilly gave a snort of laughter. 'I've never met all the boys on this earth so I don't know.'

Emily poked her in the arm. 'Please don't tease me. I feel absolutely wretched.'

'I thought love was supposed to make you happy.'

'How can I be happy when I am only a maid in this house?' Emily said plaintively. 'I am beneath him.'

In any case, what would happen even if he disregarded that fact and by some marvellous miracle developed an attachment to her as deeply as she had to him? There could be no favourable outcome, for his parents would surely object to the connection. Even though she would become a baroness someday, it was just an empty title because she would not gain access to Oakleigh's wealth. Without a fortune, she could never be viewed in good standing by Mr and Mistress Marlowe. And no doubt she would also be perceived as an ineligible match on account of the scandal associated with her own parents, just as they had warned her.

'It's quite hopeless,' she said dully.

Tilly blinked. 'Is this your first time to fall in love?'

Emily did not even have to think before responding. She knew she had never experienced such feelings before.

'Well, then! Don't be too forlorn. It'll happen to you again. Just try not to set your sights so high next time!'

Emily could not share her companion's optimism, not when her head and heart were full of Samuel Marlowe. Instead, she fantasised about the possibility of someone rich falling in love with someone below their station – after all, it had happened before, hadn't it?

CHAPTER 37

Bridget considered the spread on the kitchen table with an appraising eye – she wanted everything to be perfect for the special occasion. She had prepared a fine feast with a roast chicken as its centrepiece, to be followed by a rhubarb tart which was currently resting on a high shelf next to the stove. Her final challenge was to ensure that the boys did not succeed in their attempt to take a sneaky bite out of it.

'I can see you staring at it,' she said to Gus, who hovered in the doorway to the front room with Jack just behind him.

'I amn't!'

'Just remember, I'm watching you.' She knew that Gus was the ringleader of the mission, and that Jack would simply follow the example of his domineering younger brother.

A rapping on the door heralded the arrival of the supper guests and Acorn House soon filled with laughter and chatter. Orlaith and Charlie had passed the initial honeymoon period of their marriage but they still held hands at every opportunity, sharing secretive smiles with each other, and their palpable joy was infectious. From time to time, Tess raised her eyes to heaven at their behaviour, but then she was exposed to it more constantly than the rest of them as she continued to keep her room at Broad Street, an arrangement to which Charlie seemingly had no objection.

In contrast, Derval stole frequent, covert glances at the affectionate pair, her longing evident in her sad eyes. Bridget couldn't even recall the last time Brian Mór had come back on shore leave, and she wondered if Derval might never hear from him again.

At fourteen and twelve, Una and Sorcha now deemed themselves grown up enough to sit with the adults but ten-year-old Brian disappeared off upstairs with Jack and Gus. Bridget didn't mind too much where they went, so long as the rhubarb tart remained safe.

The door opened again and Cormac and Rory appeared, both covered in sawdust. Bridget pointedly invited them to get cleaned up before sitting down to supper. As Cormac shrugged out of his coat, he removed two letters from his pocket and placed them on top of the mantelpiece. She caught his eye.

'Later,' he murmured, and that was enough to tell her that they did not contain good news.

***

Emily trudged home from Marlowe House, exhausted to her very bones. She didn't think she had ever been more tired in her whole life. At least her route took her through Boston Common, which cheered her to a degree when she beheld the delightful growth around the park.

She had made the right decision, she tried to convince herself as she plodded along. This position would provide her with the means to achieve her artistic dreams and that was her most important goal above all else. Samuel Marlowe was nothing but an unnecessary distraction.

And yet, the thrill she felt when she recalled his heroic act, and the joy that hiccupped inside her at the memory of his kind smile...never before had she quite so clearly understood why her mother had sacrificed so much in the name of love.

Unbidden, an image of Mr Miller sidled into her head, his hairy growth bristling on his nose. She supposed he would describe her as a weak-willed female, too feeble to stay the course once it became challenging, easily swayed by the paltry notion of love, desperate for the admiration of a man to feel a sense of value. She picked up her pace until she was striding boldly along the park's path. School and Mr Miller might be in her past, but she would never give that man the satisfaction of proving him right.

Emmeline, too, had left Hawes but she and Emily had made no promises to stay in contact. As Emily wondered what lay in her capricious friend's future, she felt the hairs on her neck and arms rise. Her gut twisted and, without knowing how, she was sure she was being watched.

Pace faltering, she glanced fearfully over her shoulder. There was nobody on the path behind her. She looked all around the vicinity but could not perceive anything out of the ordinary. Maybe she had imagined it – she might just be even more fatigued than she had thought. Exhaling, she carried on, although she made a concentrated effort to remain alert and not let her mind wander off to a fantasy realm inhabited by a young man with bronze-coloured hair and an alluring cleft in his chin who held out his hand and asked her to dance—

She walked right into a man crossing her path and emitted a squeal of fright.

'Oh, gracious, I do apologise!' she blurted.

'No trouble,' he said gruffly in an English accent. He pulled the high collar of his coat tighter about his neck and strode off. She didn't think it was cold enough to be so wrapped up but then perhaps her daydream of Samuel was keeping her warm against the true temperature of the evening.

The rest of her walk home was uneventful and she climbed the steps of Acorn House in the twilight, yawning and anticipating the oblivion of sleep. When she opened the door, however, she found the front room full of bodies, bright with candlelight and noisy with chatter. Disorientated, she stepped inside.

'Welcome home!' her mother exclaimed, rushing forwards and enveloping her in a hug. 'And congratulations on your first day of employment. Most importantly, a very happy birthday to you!'

More birthday wishes echoed throughout the room and Emily realised that her family was accompanied by her two aunties, Uncle Charlie and all the Careys.

'Are you all here for me?' she said rather stupidly.

'Of course!' said her mother, drawing her further into the room so everyone else could greet her too. She bent down to let Gus smack a big kiss on her cheek, and even Auntie Tess gave her a quick embrace, but Rory just offered her a stiff nod from where he stood by the fireplace. Apart from his discomfited countenance, the atmosphere was jolly and she felt greatly cheered, even more so when the gifts were presented. A set of watercolour cakes from her parents brought delight, while the package Auntie Derval handed her generated confusion.

She held up the tiny dress fashioned out of what looked like the woollen fabric of a man's trouser leg and said, 'Is this...for Mabel?'

Auntie Derval's expression turned apologetic. ''Tis from Mr Lorenzo. I told him we were coming here to celebrate your birthday so he asked me to give you this. He's getting on a bit now. I reckon he's forgotten how much you've grown up.'

Emily's heart squeezed with fondness and not a little sorrow. 'Bless him, the poor dear. Please pass on my warmest thanks.'

Jack and Gus's contribution to the gift-giving was a piece of paper upon which Jack had carefully inscribed a promise that they would take care of Delilah, Jemimah and Beulah as long as Emily worked as a maid.

'I would trust no one else to do it,' she told them with grave gratitude.

'There's one last present,' said her father, digging his hand into his pocket. He produced a key and held it out to Emily. 'Those under this roof earning wages also earn privileges.'

Astonished, she glanced from the key to the front door and then to her father's face. He winked at her and she took the key from him, beaming.

With all the excitement of the gifts, her exhaustion fell away and, when her mother pressed her to tell them about her first day at Marlowe House, she said dramatically, 'Well, I had better begin with the pigeon...'

***

The fire popped and Cormac threw a wary glance at it as Bridget asked the room in general, 'Would anyone like the last slice of tart?'

'God Almighty,' said Orlaith, groaning as she leaned back on the sofa. 'I don't think I'll eat again until next week.'

'Same here,' said Charlie beside her. 'Thanks for a fine feast, Bridget.' An official member of the family at last, he had finally started using their first names.

'I'm glad you enjoyed it,' she replied. 'I wish I'd thought to give the last slice to Rory before the Careys left—he only took a very small piece earlier.'

Throughout the supper, Rory had eaten little and spoken less, and he had seemed quite relieved when the time had come to leave. Cormac wondered whether he could reveal the truth he had learned about Mabel's real kidnapper but decided that Rory had not given explicit permission for it to be divulged. At least Emily had been civil towards him during the supper, if not warm – she might naturally forgive him over time, even if he was not the one who required her forgiveness.

She had seemed in decent spirits following the end of her first day in service, which was a reassuring sign, but her liveliness had faded as the evening wore on and she had dragged herself up to bed almost as soon as Derval and her four children had departed. Jack and Gus had already given in to their weariness half an hour before that, so the five adults who remained had now gathered around the hearth, its warmth welcome on this cool May evening. Soon they would have no further need of it once the summer arrived. Cormac remembered how his mother used to keep the turf fire lit in their cottage all year round and, with a pang, he buried the memory.

Orlaith and Charlie occupied the sofa, surreptitiously brushing a hand or a knee against each other when they thought no one else was looking. Cormac had brought three kitchen chairs in and assembled two on one side of the fireplace for himself and Bridget, with the third on the opposite side for Tess. She sat up straight, a certain uneasiness in her demeanour as she toed the edge of the hearthrug in front of the grate.

'Well, I think the surprise party went off without a hitch,' Bridget continued in a conversational tone, but Cormac noticed that her attention had once more snagged on the two letters resting on top of the mantelpiece.

He sighed; there was no point putting it off any longer. He got to his feet and reached for them. 'I've had some news,' he announced to the room, displaying the letters to everyone.

'And most of it isn't good.' He unfolded one. 'This is the first response I've received from the initial queries I sent to New York. Similar to Boston, I started with boarding houses known for accommodating Irish immigrants.'

Mr and Mrs Rosemount, who had ordered the sideboard, had kindly loaned him a city directory of New York which they had in their possession because Mr Rosemount's cousin also ran a boarding house there. Among countless other advertisements, the directory listed a variety of housing establishments, many of which helpfully stated the type of clientele they were willing to accept.

'And?' said Orlaith.

'Another dead end,' he said heavily. 'I included one of Bronagh's portraits, as well as a written description of the other three in her company based on Mr Todd's account, but the landlord couldn't identify any of them as having stayed at his lodgings in the past.'

Orlaith's shoulders slumped. 'I suppose such a long time has passed that the trail's long gone cold.'

Charlie grasped her hand in a consoling gesture and said tentatively, 'Add to that the sheer size of New York City in comparison to Boston...'

'The landlord said as much,' agreed Cormac. 'He seemed to deem it an impossible task, although he did suggest putting a notice in one of the city's Catholic newspapers, like we did with *The Pilot*, so I will certainly try that as well.' Cormac folded over the letter. 'I know it's early days yet and this is only the first reply. However, I'm already expecting that I'll have to go to New York and search for Bronagh in person.'

Bridget's dark brown eyes were troubled but she just nodded and said, 'And the second letter?'

He glanced down at the grubby page and its untidy scrawl. 'Mrs O'Hara,' he said and dropped into his seat again. 'Henrietta ran away.'

Tess snorted. 'The little brat.'

He couldn't echo the sentiment. What disturbed him so much was not Henrietta's act of running away but the question of what, or who, she was running from. Had she simply become an ungovernable child, or was this evidence that Mrs O'Hara had been treating her grandniece cruelly? Guilt raked through him. He was the one who had placed Henrietta in Mrs O'Hara's care, therefore he was responsible for whatever abuse she might have suffered since.

At least the letter contained one positive detail. 'She eventually came back. Mrs O'Hara was in the middle of writing to me begging for assistance when Henrietta returned to the lodgings of her own volition. Rather than waste paper or time, Mrs O'Hara just included that information and followed it up with a request for more money instead.'

'Good God, the woman has no sense of morality,' spluttered Bridget.

'Are you going to send it to her?' asked Orlaith.

'I can't,' he replied, spreading his arms in an expression of helplessness. 'Emily is relying on us to help fund her place at Brubaker Art Academy. We need to save every spare penny we can.' He knew they had to put their daughter first, but he couldn't help feeling like he was forsaking Henrietta in the process.

'I wonder what the old crone thought you could do to help when the girl was missing,' said Tess derisively. 'Did she expect you to sail across the Atlantic and personally look for her?'

'I have no idea,' he said. 'But searching for one person is already more than enough.'

Silence billowed, broken only by the crackling fire. Dispirited, he tucked the two letters into his pocket as Bridget reached out to touch his arm, her gaze full of sympathy. Tess leaned back in her chair and yawned. Orlaith shared a glance with Charlie and a message seemed to pass between them with a raised eyebrow and a subtle nod. She cleared her throat.

'Seeing as it's an occasion for telling things,' she began, and Bridget straightened with eagerness, her eyes now focused upon Orlaith's midriff. Cormac concentrated very hard on not imagining what Charlie had to do to his youngest sister to bring about this happy news, but then Orlaith continued, 'There's something serious we'd like to discuss with yous. We've been considering it for a little while, although nothing's decided yet.'

Bridget deflated ever so slightly.

'You can talk to us about anything,' Cormac said, his tone encouraging.

'I know,' said Orlaith. 'That's partly what's making this decision so hard.'

Frowning, he said, 'What do you mean?'

Her teeth grazed her bottom lip.

'Do you want me to say it?' Charlie said quietly.

'No, I can do it.' She raised her chin as though steeling herself. 'As yous are aware, Charlie became a Catholic just before we married.'

Yes, Cormac remembered it well – he and Charlie had had several discussions on matters of theology and the practices of the churches to which each of them belonged. While Orlaith had in no way stipulated that Charlie's conversion had to be a condition of their marriage, he himself had acknowledged that their union would be less complicated if they did not have to request a dispensation from the bishop to marry and if they could raise their future children in one faith. He had acquainted himself with the traditions of the Roman Catholic

Church, determined that he was amenable to its teachings, and resolved to convert before they wed. If anyone had retained even a grain of doubt about Charlie's devotion to Orlaith, it had been entirely eradicated by this expression of his deepest commitment to her.

'I never asked him to,' Orlaith said, 'but I do adore him for it.' She gave her husband a shy smile and he returned it, his face glowing. Her smile fell away as she went on sombrely, 'Unfortunately, Charlie's parents were awfully unhappy about what he did. We thought they'd get used to the idea, but they're still refusing to accept it, even months later.'

Recalling the conspicuous absence of Mr and Mrs Adams from the small wedding ceremony, Cormac thought Orlaith and Charlie had been naive to hope that they would eventually relent.

'What about Mrs Adams at least?' said Bridget. 'She was fond of you in the beginning. Has she not come round?'

'No,' said Orlaith, the corners of her mouth turning downwards. Despite her earlier assertion, she couldn't seem to find the words to explain further.

Charlie stepped in. 'My father wore my mother down,' he said. 'And changing my religion was her breaking point. She's a very devout woman. They both did their best to dissuade me from it beforehand. I ignored them, needless to say.'

'So they remain adamant in their opposition to your conversion?' asked Cormac.

Charlie twisted his mouth. 'And to my marriage. Last week, my father stated in no uncertain terms that it's past time for me to recognise the error of my ways.'

'In what manner does he suggest you do that?'

'Separation,' said Charlie grimly. 'The scandal of that appears to be a lesser evil to them than having a Catholic for a daughter-in-law. And my mother wants me to convert back to Protestantism.'

Cormac swallowed. He eyed Orlaith, whose chin had drooped against her chest. 'I'm very sorry to hear this,' he said. 'It must be difficult for you both to bear.'

'It is,' said Charlie. 'My mother said that Orlaith will never again be welcome in their home. In my eyes, that is unforgiveable.' Those same eyes flashed with anger. 'I won't tolerate that kind of contempt for her, not when I know she is the most extraordinary and most selfless woman I have ever met.'

Orlaith's cheeks flamed. Tess poked her with her foot.

'No need to get all embarrassed,' she said. 'It's just the truth.'

The colour crept up Orlaith's forehead and down her neck. Charlie put his arm around her and she buried her face in his shoulder. She mumbled something which nobody could hear but he murmured, 'Love you too,' against her ear.

Cormac found himself feeling remarkably grateful to the instigators of the riot on Broad Street who had brought this man into his sister's life. 'Can you see any path to resolving this dilemma?' he asked.

Charlie averted his gaze. 'It's hard to picture anything beyond the way things are right now, with the parties immovable on both sides. We reside in the same city as my parents, whom I still cherish despite their flaws, and yet we face the distressing prospect of conducting our lives entirely separate from them, as though we have become strangers. What if we bump into my mother and father by accident on the street? Who will be the one to turn and pretend they didn't see the other? It would be unbearable.' He took a gulp of air. 'Which makes us wonder whether it might not be better for all concerned if we go away.'

'Away?' Cormac repeated. 'You mean…leave Boston?'

Orlaith lifted her head from Charlie's shoulder. 'Yes,' she said.

For the merest instant, he embarked upon a flight of fancy where the whole family relocated to New York, which seemed to address several of their issues all at once. But then he perceived the anguish in Orlaith's round eyes.

'Where to?' he asked. Did she wish to return to Ireland?

She hesitated. 'We thought we might go west.'

His mind reeled. As he tried to absorb the impact of her words, the fire in the hearth snapped and popped again and an ember leapt from the grate, landing on the rug. He froze, staring at the glowing piece of coal as it smouldered, a ribbon of smoke curling upwards from it. Then a small flame kindled and the rug began to burn.

He couldn't move. Glued to his seat, he could only recall the heat of a roaring blaze and the pain of blistering fingers and the suffocating lack of air. He thought of his three children asleep upstairs and willed his limbs to work but they refused to stir.

There was movement beside him. Bridget jumped up, darted towards the ember and stamped her foot upon it, extinguishing the tiny flame before it could spread. The coal crumbled into black fragments, revealing the singed spot on the hearthrug.

'All is well,' she said. Her voice echoed in his head, a blurry ricochet of sound. She stepped in front of him, cutting off his view of the scorched rug. Touching his cheek, she forced him to look up into her eyes. 'All is well,' she reiterated, her tone calm and confident.

He blinked, reading the reassurance in her gaze, and exhaled. He brushed his fingertips against her hip in a silent articulation of his gratitude. When he glanced at the other three, mortified at having revealed such vulnerability, he found no scorn or embarrassment in their countenances, only understanding and sympathy. None of them had been present at the burning of Oakleigh Manor, but at some point or another they had all heard what had happened that night. Tess, in particular, leaned forwards in her chair, radiating the impression that she sorely wished to soothe him herself.

He coughed. 'You're thinking of going west?' he prompted Orlaith and Charlie, folding his arms to hide the slight tremor in his hands.

Orlaith took the hint, accepting the spotlight again. 'It's something we've considered,' she said cautiously. 'But, like I said before, nothing's decided yet. It just seemed like one possible solution to the problem with Mr and Mrs Adams—we can't feel guilty about never seeing them if we live somewhere else altogether.'

'Do you have a destination in mind?' Bridget asked as she resumed her seat.

'We're not sure,' said Charlie. 'Although one of the fellows in my company told me that Chicago has become a thriving city. There would be plenty of opportunities for a fireman and a nurse and a washerwoman.'

Startled, Cormac said to Tess, 'You plan to go too?'

'Who would I stay behind for?' she said, giving him a pointed look. She added with a defensive bite in her voice, 'Orlaith was the one who suggested it. I didn't just invite myself along.'

'We want you to come with us,' Orlaith said earnestly. 'You're as close as a sister to me, you know that. And a fresh scene like Chicago might do you the world of good too.'

No one drew attention to the unspoken implication that this move would serve to put distance between Tess and her painfully unrequited love.

Orlaith directed her gaze towards Cormac and Bridget, her expression turning sorrowful. 'But yous are our family as well. And the hardest part of all this is imagining leaving yous after everything we've been through together.' She sighed. 'I also feel as though I'd be giving up on Bronagh, like going away would mean admitting I think she's never going to be found.' A tiny gleam of adventure sparked in her eyes. 'But there's something so very tempting about the west...'

Cormac's heart cracked a little at the idea of their family splitting apart when it had taken so much effort to find one another and overcome the agony of the past. And yet the last thing he wished was to stand in the way. Orlaith, Charlie and Tess had their own aspirations and they were entitled to lead their lives in whatever manner they saw fit.

He concealed his regret behind a faint grin. 'Very tempting indeed. It would be quite a courageous undertaking. If that is what you all choose to do, you have our full support.'

Orlaith gave him a grateful smile. 'We haven't settled on going for definite. We just wanted to let yous know we were thinking about it.'

The three of them departed Acorn House shortly after that. Before they left, Bridget wrapped the last slice of tart in a cloth and pressed it into Charlie's hands. 'You'll be hungry by the time you get back to Broad Street,' she said and, winking, he didn't contradict her.

After she and Cormac had tidied up the remains of the supper, they wearily climbed the stairs to bed, taking care to step over Barnabas so as not to wake any of the children. In their bedroom, Cormac shut the door quietly while Bridget set the oil lamp down on the bedside table next to the wooden carving of their family, caressing it fondly as she always did every night. Without speaking, they undressed in the soft glow of the lamp.

Cormac slid beneath the covers and winced when he leaned on his arm in an awkward way, causing his old wound from Cunningham's pistol to twinge. Bridget turned down the lamp and blew it out before joining him. She wriggled about, trying to find a comfortable position, and ended up nestling her back into his front. Draping his arm over her, he kissed her shoulder.

'Can you believe it?' he said, pitching his voice low.

'I certainly wasn't expecting it,' she replied. 'And yet it's not surprising at all. Mr and Mrs Adams might be the ostensible reason that could push them out of Boston, but I'd wager Chicago is calling out to them just as strongly. This kind of independent endeavour is so like Orlaith.'

'It does match her self-sufficient nature, doesn't it? At least Charlie would be there to keep her safe, and Tess too.'

Bridget snorted, her back rocking against his chest. 'Woe betide you if you ever express such a statement in her presence. I will not come to your aid.'

'A fair point. I didn't intend the misogynistic insinuation, only that she wouldn't be alone. Still, I'll guard my tongue against any such comments in the future.'

She chuckled. Silence fell between them but he drew up the courage to speak again before she dropped into slumber.

'I'm sorry about earlier,' he said. He felt her head rise in a questioning manner. 'The way I froze,' he clarified.

'Don't be,' she whispered, brushing her lips against the arm he had wrapped around her. 'It was perfectly understandable.'

'I feel like less of a man.' He was ashamed to admit it.

'You're not. Misogyny would make you less of a man. Fear makes you human.'

He took a breath to argue further but she cut him off by rubbing her backside provocatively against him. His body responded at once.

'Seems like you're a whole man to me,' she said.

'You saucy thing,' he murmured.

She did it again and he emitted a deep groan. He tightened his arm across her and felt the shape of her breasts through her nightdress. When she did it a third time, he buried his face in her neck, hungrily breathing in her scent. Reaching down beneath the bedcovers, he pulled at the hem of her nightdress, tugging the fabric up her legs. His hand glided underneath it and he discovered that she had shed her drawers for sleeping. Perfect. He laid his full palm on one glorious buttock and squeezed gently. She squirmed once more, but this time he was sure it had been an involuntary movement. His hand slid between her thighs and she parted them slightly, an exhalation slipping from her throat in anticipation.

Then the bedroom door creaked open.

'Ma? Da?'

Cormac snatched his hand back.

A loud sniff. 'I woke up and can't get back to sleep.'

As Bridget hastily pushed down her nightdress, Cormac rolled over and peered into the gloom. 'Did your brother wake too, *a mhic ó*?'

'No, just me,' said Gus plaintively. 'Can I come into your bed?' he added on a more hopeful note.

With any luck, he couldn't detect his parents' disappointed pause before Bridget said, 'Very well, little miracle, just this once.'

Even in the darkness, Gus bounded up onto the bed with unerring spatial awareness and burrowed beneath the covers, his plump form snuggling between them both. Cormac lay on his back as the excitement in his body subsided.

'I amn't a miracle,' mumbled Gus, his voice already growing drowsy.

'On the contrary, you have a miraculous sense of timing,' said Bridget, her words shaking with suppressed laughter. 'Let's all go to sleep.'

CHAPTER 38

'Gather around, and no talking!' Mrs Coleman barked.

Maids and footmen piled into the servants' hall at Marlowe House, buzzing with curiosity about the reason for the impromptu assembly before breakfast. At the housekeeper's order, the hum of chatter died away at once.

Emily found herself standing between Tilly and a footman who was so tall he seemed to tower above her. Only three days into her employment, she still did not know the names of most of the other servants and, feeling shy and insignificant, she kept her gaze trained upon Mrs Coleman and the formidable butler who loomed next to her.

'There is a new member of the household arriving today,' announced Mrs Coleman. 'The mistress's niece, Miss Amelia Knight, will be staying at Marlowe House for two months. This will signify several additional tasks in your daily routines—an extra place setting at mealtimes, another bedchamber to tidy, more laundry, and so on. However, Miss Knight is bringing her own lady's maid to attend to her personal needs which means those duties shall be covered.'

Emily tried to picture having a servant always at hand to dress her and do up her hair; she conjectured that it would engender both a splendid sense of leisure and a deplorable inclination for indolence. Her mother had retained the services of a lady's maid back at the townhouse in London but Emily couldn't recall her name.

Mrs Coleman carried on, 'Furthermore, as Miss Knight has travelled all the way from Philadelphia, the mistress wishes to introduce her to Boston society. She therefore intends to host a private ball in her niece's honour a week hence.'

'A ball!' Tilly echoed in a whisper as a ripple of excitement spread through the female servants. The tall footman next to Emily raised his eyes to the ceiling.

With a quelling glare, the butler waited for silence before picking up where Mrs Coleman had left off. He outlined the preparations that the whole staff would have to undertake for the ball, both in the run-up to the occasion and on the day itself, and Emily baulked as she listened to the dizzying list of chores that would fall to the housemaids. By the time he had finished, the female servants looked far less enthused about the prospect of the ball.

The butler and the housekeeper dismissed everyone from the servants' hall with a concluding warning about expectations of the highest standards in cleanliness and proficiency. Emily and Tilly conferred together as soon as they emerged into the corridor.

'We're gonna need to divide up some of the tasks to complete them all before the week's through,' said Tilly briskly. 'Let's do the bedchambers as usual and then you dust the stairs while I polish the reading tables in the library.'

As soon as the opportunity came later that morning to tackle the stairs, Emily slipped into the entrance hall with her broom, dustpan and cloths. It was her first time to set foot on the main staircase in the house and her stomach sank when she beheld it. It soared in front of her, a striking flight of stairs which split at a half-landing with the two divided parts rising symmetrically to the next floor. The treads were wooden but the handrail and the banisters were made of wrought iron, intricately designed with spirals and curves and flower shapes – all of which had countless surfaces where dust could accumulate. Steeling herself, she began.

She started at the top of each branching set of stairs, brushing down the steps just like she used to do at Broad Street. She dug her broom into the corners, seeking out every minute speck of dirt. Halting on the half-landing, she paused for an instant to envision herself coming up the staircase as a guest to the ball, the hem of her beautiful gown sweeping along each step rather than the bristles of her broom. She shook the image out of her head and continued with her work.

She had finished brushing the steps and was laboriously dusting the banisters on the right branch of the divided staircase when footfalls sounded on the landing above, immobilising her where she crouched. Might it be a member of the family? Servants were not supposed to be seen if it could be helped. Should she snatch up her cleaning things and dash out of sight? Or stay as still as a statue to avoid drawing any attention to her presence?

The footfalls neared before she could decide what to do and then their owner appeared at the top of the left branch of the staircase. It was Samuel. She relaxed, positive that he would not mind her being there. She had not seen him since the incident with the pigeon and delight filled her at this unexpected encounter.

As he descended the stairs, she straightened out of her crouch and offered him a fleeting curtsey. Once again, she found herself staggered by his handsome, flawless features. Without a pigeon flying about their heads, she was able to observe the lighter tones in his silken, bronze waves, although she still could not bring herself to look directly into his eyes. She focused on the cleft in his strong chin as she gave him a smile.

He did not return it. In fact, he hardly seemed to register her presence as he reached the half-landing and continued down the main flight to the entrance hall. She gaped at his back, unable to reconcile such indifference with the charming young man in the bedchamber. It was as though his gaze had travelled over her and moved on, finding her indistinguishable from the wrought-iron banisters.

Then it occurred to her: he had been raised in a wealthy home where servants were just an accepted part of the scenery. She was essentially a piece of furniture, as functional as a chair that bore his weight or a rug he trod on. Only for the pigeon's antics, he would have had no reason to notice her at all.

The first twinge of resentment stirred in her gut.

***

Bridget knelt on the floor of Madame Roche's establishment on Summer Street, checked that the hem of the gown was at the correct length, and fastened the final pin.

'That's perfect, Miss Halliwell,' she said to the slender girl standing patiently on the plinth. 'You may come down now.'

She rose and held out her hand to assist Miss Halliwell in stepping off the plinth. The girl's hair was a rich auburn colour; when she had first entered the dressmaker's shop, Bridget had been struck by the similarity in shade to that of her old friend Madeleine's ringlets. Eight years had passed since she had last seen Madeleine in Dublin, where her once dearest acquaintance had denounced her for running away with Cormac and declared that the ridiculous notion of love did not exist for any woman. How wrong Madeleine had been, but Bridget hoped she was not too unhappy in her circumstances. As for herself, she knew that if she was presented again with the choice of running away with Cormac or remaining with Garrett, she would make the same decision a hundred times over.

Once Miss Halliwell had taken off the pinned gown, Bridget wrapped it carefully to bring it home to Acorn House. She felt gratified that Madame Roche had entrusted her with such an important commission; Miss Halliwell's mother was a frequent and wealthy customer. If Bridget were to become the daughter's designated seamstress, that would be a triumph indeed.

That evening at home, she spread the gown across her sewing desk, ensuring that all of the pins were still in place. Made of blue silk, it had sloping shoulders, a pointed waist and a bell-shaped skirt. Once she added a lace flounce collar and sewed the hem, it would be ready for Miss Halliwell to wear.

She was still poring over it when the front door opened and Emily trudged in. The corners of her mouth were turned downwards but she made an effort to smile as she shut the door behind her.

'Good evening, Mother,' she said, crossing to the desk and kissing Bridget's cheek.

'Welcome home, gooseberry,' Bridget replied brightly, but she faltered at Emily's obvious wince. 'H-how was your day?'

Another wince. 'Fine,' Emily mumbled. She glanced down at the blue silk gown and uttered a small gasp. 'Oh, this is exquisite! Is it from Madame Roche's shop?'

'Yes,' said Bridget proudly. 'It's for Mrs Halliwell's daughter. I'm almost finished it—she will return for her final fitting in two weeks.'

Emily stretched out a hesitant hand over the skirt. 'May I touch it?'

Bridget nodded and Emily stroked her fingers along the silk, her expression almost greedy with delight. As she traced the shape of the waist, the glow faded from her face and she abruptly took her hand away.

'I'm very tired so I shall go to bed now,' she said.

Surprised, Bridget said, 'But you haven't had your supper yet, gooseberry.'

'I think I've grown a bit old for that pet name,' said Emily, her tone on the verge of mournful. 'And thank you for supper but I'm not hungry. Goodnight, Mother.'

She turned and climbed the stairs. Barnabas gave a doleful squeak and then her plodding feet disappeared from Bridget's view.

Thoughts swirling uneasily, Bridget was in the process of hanging the gown with care in the cupboard space under the stairs when Cormac came home. The boys abandoned their supper in the kitchen to charge towards him and she let them have their horseplay as she closed the cupboard door and they told him about their day ('I did a sum in my head at school,' reported Jack while Gus bellowed, 'Auntie Derval minded me and Brian taught me a swear!'). After doling out the appropriate praise and admonition, Cormac sent them back to their supper and greeted Bridget with a kiss.

'Is Emily home yet?' he asked.

'She's already gone up to bed.' Bridget told him about their brief conversation and added with concern, 'She seemed in low spirits. It was quite unlike her.'

Cormac hummed low in his throat. 'It could be that the reality of her situation is just hitting her now. Working in service is not an easy path to tread.' He grinned ruefully. 'It's hard watching our little girl mature into an adult, isn't it?'

Bridget couldn't return the grin. 'Sometimes I wonder if she is quite there yet. I was in her bedroom the other day and I'm almost positive that Mabel was lying in a different position in the cupboard, as though Emily had taken her out for a clandestine hug. She is trying to be more grown up by calling us "Mother" and "Father" but those are only the trappings of adulthood.'

He grimaced. 'I do find myself longing for the days of "Mama" and "Papa". I don't think she would manage "Da" as there's a bit too much English in her from her early childhood but "Father" doesn't sit too well with me either—it's like she's addressing a priest.'

This time, Bridget mustered a chuckle.

He took her hand. 'Her spirits will improve when she reminds herself why she chose this path in the first place. She has the resilience to persevere through these present challenges.'

CHAPTER 39

It happened again.

Emily and Tilly entered the empty breakfast room, seizing the opportunity to do a thorough scour of the whole space after the family had finished their meal and the footmen had cleared the dishes. They intended to move the various pieces of furniture into the centre of the room and cover them with dust sheets, enabling them to sweep and scrub all the elusive corners which couldn't be reached during their regular cleaning routine.

They had barely begun to shove at the solid cabinet that contained the linen napkins when the door opened and two figures came in. Emily's insides somersaulted at the sight of Samuel, his face alight as he spoke animatedly with his companion. His cousin, Miss Knight, was a pretty girl with blonde hair, paler even than Emily's own golden curls hidden beneath her maid's cap.

'Perhaps I left it in here,' Samuel was saying. 'I don't recall bringing it down to breakfast but it's worth checking just in case.'

He halted inside the door and scanned the breakfast table, which was completely bare; the footmen had not even left the tablecloth behind.

'It's not here,' he said and swivelled to exit the room. Just like on the stairs, he showed no sign that he had seen Emily, even though she and Tilly still hovered by the cabinet.

'Why don't you ask them?' Miss Knight suggested with a wave of her hand.

'Who?' he said, looking around. He smiled, and there at last was the recognition Emily had so badly craved. 'Ah! The pigeon liberators. Has your comrade made a reappearance since?'

Tilly giggled. 'No, Master Samuel, it hasn't, thank the Lord.'

'Tell me, have either of you seen a book of poetry with a red cover? I seem to have misplaced it.'

Emily found herself too tongue-tied to respond so Tilly said, 'We haven't but we'll keep a sharp eye out for it.'

'Much obliged,' he said, twinkling at them. 'Come, Amelia.'

The two cousins left the breakfast room. Tilly nudged Emily. 'I thought you were in love with him. You didn't say a word!'

Emily flushed. 'I was too dazzled.'

Laughing, Tilly said, 'You really haven't a hope. Come on, let's move this.'

Mortified, Emily joined Tilly in putting her weight behind the cabinet and they both heaved. As it scraped along the floor, she considered the fact that she had now met Samuel on three occasions and had only spoken three words to him across all those encounters. She wasn't sure if crying 'Shut the door!' even counted when she had not actually known who he was at the time. Tilly was right; she didn't have a hope, certainly not without the aid of an uncooperative pigeon. And not when she blended dully into the background as a maid either.

Idly, she wondered how Samuel would react if she was dressed differently, if she wore a ravishing gown and released her curls from the confines of her cap. Perhaps she was not as pretty as Miss Knight, but might she be appealing enough to attract his notice?

She hiccupped as a wild notion rushed into her head. Could she possibly...? No, it would be utter madness. She pushed the idea away, concentrating on tossing a dust sheet over the cabinet, but it returned almost at once, insisting that she give it her attention. Pulse racing, she considered the practicalities of such a madcap endeavour and the daydream swiftly turned into a plan. It was doable but she would need help for it to succeed.

Furtively, she eyed Tilly, who had started sliding the chairs out from under the breakfast table to line them up side by side. Could she trust her with this?

'Tilly,' she said, doing her best to sound offhand. 'Are you able to keep a secret?'

'Yes,' Tilly replied matter-of-factly. She dragged out another chair. 'I've been here long enough to see other servants steal from the kitchens or kiss in the hallways. It's their own business and I'm not a snitch.'

'Not even to Mrs Coleman?'

Tilly puffed out her chest. 'Not even to her. I'm already in her good graces—I've no reason to butter her up any more.' She squinted. 'Why are you asking?'

Emily swallowed. 'Because I've got a secret and I want to share it with you.'

'You already *told* me you're in love with Master Samuel.'

'That's not it,' said Emily, shaking her head. 'It's something else. Something I'm going to do.'

Tilly's ears perked up. 'What're you gonna do?'

Inhaling a deep breath, Emily declared, 'I'm going to pretend I'm a wealthy guest and attend Miss Knight's ball.'

Tilly gawked at her, mouth open wide and eyes bulging. Then she snapped her jaw shut to demand, 'Have you lost your senses?'

'I know it sounds like lunacy.' Emily, too, hauled out a chair and towed it over to the rest. 'But I'm confident I can manage it without getting caught.'

'*How*?'

Emily perched on the chair she had just moved and smoothed out her apron. 'My mother is a seamstress and she is currently working on a beautiful gown that would be just perfect for this ball. All I need to do is figure out how to sneak it out of the house and then get it back before she discovers that it's missing.'

Tilly frowned. 'Would the gown fit you?'

'From what I can remember, it's near enough to my size. And I can pin it in discreetly if needs be.' Emily could not smother the thrill in her veins; she had never contemplated such a daring venture in her life.

'What about everything else?' asked Tilly.

'Everything else?'

'Gloves and shoes and jewellery and fancy hair. All the bits that would make you look like a lady and not a maid!'

Emily bit her lip. 'That is where I need your assistance. My hair shouldn't be an issue because I have natural curls that will present nicely even in a simple style. But those additional items like gloves...' She tilted her head with a hopeful glance. 'Didn't you mention before that you once found a chest of such articles in the attic?'

Tilly's cheekbones stood out prominently as she grinned. 'By golly, I did. Aren't you the smart one?'

'Would it be feasible to...borrow from that chest for one evening?'

'I'd say it would. No one ever goes up there. I reckon the mistress only held onto those things in case she bore a girl, which she never did.' Tilly's eyes sparkled with adventure. 'You're right, this could actually be possible.' She tapped a meditative finger on her chin. 'What excuse would you give Mrs Coleman?'

Startled, Emily said, 'Will she expect the housemaids to work at that hour of the night?'

'Maybe not cleaning, but she might order us to lend a hand in the kitchens. I heard they're inviting at least sixty people. The staff will be run off their feet with so many guests.'

'Gracious, I hadn't thought of that. What shall I do?'

'I've got it! You could say you're unwell because of your courses. Mine have left me flattened some days so it wouldn't be too big a lie. Do you get bad cramps with yours?'

'Y-yes,' Emily stuttered. 'Good idea. I could say that.'

Tilly's mind had already barrelled on to the next obstacle. 'I know you can talk posh but can you dance?'

'I don't need to dance,' said Emily. 'I just want to have a conversation with him as his equal.'

'Him?' Understanding dawned. 'You're doing this so you can get friendly with Master Samuel?'

'I'd like to ascertain what he thinks of me when I am not a maid. When I am not invisible to him.' Her heart thrummed at the image she could so readily conjure of her and Samuel delighting in each other's company at the ball.

'But...' said Tilly, her brows bunching together. 'You *are* a maid. What's the point of all this?'

A maid she might be, but she was also an heiress, if an impoverished one. However, she deemed it prudent to emulate her parents' longstanding reticence on the matter. 'I have a reason but I'm afraid I can't explain it to you. Are you still willing to help me though?'

'I definitely am. This is the most exciting thing to happen all year, and that includes the day the climbing boy got stuck up the chimney!'

***

Bridget was sewing the lace flounce on the blue silk gown when Emily came home. She looked up cautiously, wondering what mood her daughter might be in this evening, and was pleased when Emily greeted her with a bright smile.

'You're working late, Mother. Do you always work up to this hour?'

Bridget laid her needle and thread on the sewing desk. 'I suppose it is a little later than usual. But I should like to complete this gown sooner than the allotted time frame if I can.'

She thought Emily might head on towards the kitchen, from where Jack and Gus's playful bickering drifted out, but instead she approached the desk with an air of interest.

'You said yesterday that Miss Halliwell's final fitting would be in two weeks' time. When do you expect to return it to her then? Within the week?'

'Maybe not quite that quickly as I have several other pieces to work on too. Ten days, perhaps.'

Emily nodded. 'It is such a splendid gown. I assume you're keeping it well out of the way of the boys' grubby hands.' She raised her eyebrows in an eloquent expression that only a long-suffering older sister could truly accomplish.

'Indeed,' said Bridget, amused. 'It shall stay safe under the stairs. Jack and Gus have been well warned that the cupboard is out of bounds to them.'

Satisfied, Emily gazed down at the blue gown. 'Mother, may I ask you something?'

Perceiving her serious tone, Bridget turned sober again. 'You can ask me anything.'

Emily's hand hovered over the silk skirt. 'There is a ball taking place at Marlowe House and Mrs Coleman has informed the maids of the extra duties required of us. She anticipates that the day itself will be long and tiring. May I have your permission to stay in the servants' quarters that night? I fear I shall be too exhausted to come home.'

Guilt pricked at Bridget. 'Of course, goose—Emily. That will be perfectly fine.'

'And may I borrow your valise to bring my nightdress and a change of underclothes with me?'

While Bridget thought the valise was a little excessive to hold the items necessary for a single night away, she said, 'By all means.'

Emily looked like she was about to speak further but then a smash sounded from the kitchen.

'Not my fault!' bawled Gus at once.

Bridget leapt up from her seat at the sewing desk and stalked through the kitchen door to find Gus's supper plate in smithereens on the floor. He swung his arm towards his brother.

'He knocked it off the table!'

Jack's wide-eyed, injured expression was enough to convey the truth. After sweeping up the shattered plate and crumbs, Bridget called Gus to her side and spanked him on his rump.

'That's not for breaking the plate but for trying to put the blame on your brother,' she said sternly. 'You must always own up to your mistakes.'

His lower lip trembled. 'Sorry, Ma. C-can I have some more cheese?'

She kissed his curls. 'No more for you tonight. Let Jack finish his and then it will be bedtime for the pair of you.'

Gus climbed morosely back onto his chair at the table and Bridget re-entered the front room to find Emily holding up the blue silk gown against herself, pressing it along the length of her body. She jumped and returned it hastily to the sewing desk.

'I was just taking another look. I promise I didn't knock out any of your pins.'

'Just be careful,' said Bridget, going back over to the desk and touching a protective palm on one sloping shoulder of the gown. 'It's an expensive fabric.'

Emily lowered her gaze, chastened. Bridget chucked her under her chin.

'I'm not cross,' she assured her.

'In that case,' said Emily tentatively, 'may I ask one more question?'

'Go ahead.'

'Why haven't I got my courses yet?'

Bridget blinked at the unforeseen change of subject. 'Well, it happens at a different age for every girl. I was eleven when I got them first but there was still a long gap before they came more regularly. You haven't noticed any blood at all so far?'

Emily's forehead creased with worry. 'No, and I'm four years older than you were.'

'You've scarcely turned fifteen,' said Bridget in a soothing tone. 'There's nothing to fret about. They will eventually come.'

Some of the tension left her daughter's face. 'Really?'

'Really,' she said and added wryly, 'And, to be honest, then you'll likely find yourself wishing they had stayed away a bit longer.'

CHAPTER 40

Emily clutched her stomach and doubled over. 'Oh, I do feel so dreadful, Mrs Coleman,' she said with a convincing whimper.

Tilly patted a consoling hand on her back. 'I bet it's you know what,' she said, giving the housekeeper a meaningful look.

Mrs Coleman's thick eyebrows drew together, appraising Emily. 'Hmm. I suppose you're at an age for it. Is it especially bad?'

Emily uttered a small moan in response.

Mrs Coleman clicked her tongue. 'You'll be of no use to anyone this evening.'

'I can take her upstairs,' said Tilly angelically, 'and check on her later, if you think that would be best, Mrs Coleman?'

The housekeeper nodded her grudging consent and Tilly led Emily away to the end of the corridor and up the servants' stairs. Neither of them spoke until they had closed the door on the poky room at the top of the house that contained two narrow beds and a washstand.

'It's a good thing you're sharing with me,' said Tilly, flopping down on one of the beds. 'Nobody will report you missing from your quarters.'

Emily's valise rested on the thin mattress of the other bed. She opened it and withdrew the few garments she had packed, leaving it empty. Snapping it shut, she said, 'Thank you for being such a good sport about this. I'm sure I wouldn't be able to manage it without you.'

'No, you wouldn't!' said Tilly frankly, bouncing back up off the bed. 'Are you ready?'

Insides fluttering with nervous excitement, Emily said, 'Yes.'

They descended the servants' stairs again, Tilly preceding her and keeping a wary eye out. Emily's steps faltered as last-minute doubts crowded her mind – what on earth was she thinking to behave so rashly? She had no business lying to Mrs Coleman and deceiving her mother and thieving a gown she didn't have any right to wear. But the ball was already in full swing in the main part of the house...and she wanted to have a taste of what that life was like, even if it was just for a few hours. She rekindled her resolve and tightened her grip on the valise.

When they reached the bottom of the stairs, Tilly stuck her head into the corridor, looked left and right, and beckoned quickly. Emily hastened up behind her and, at Tilly's signal, darted into the corridor which was at that moment devoid of servants. She flew down it to the door at the end and emerged, pulse pounding in her ears, into the paved courtyard beyond.

June had brought with it the expected hot temperatures of summer and, even now after sundown, the city air was warm. She slipped out of the courtyard, followed the lane at the back of the grand terraced dwellings where Marlowe House nestled, and headed for home, walking swiftly. She told herself she wasn't frightened to be out on the streets so late but she remembered the sensation of being watched on the Common on the evening of her birthday and hurried all the same.

By the time she reached Acorn House, she was sweating and panting. She halted on the path before the house and noted the lamplight in the downstairs front room. It was well past her brothers' bedtime but her parents were evidently still up. She had anticipated this and was prepared to wait as long as was necessary.

Then the door of the neighbouring boarding house opened and she panicked. Scurrying back along the path, she darted into Mr and Mrs Hill's garden and crouched in the shadows of their sycamore tree, the valise at her knees. A pair of male voices floated down the steps of the boarding house's porch and grew fainter as their owners headed off along the other side of the street.

When she glanced back at Acorn House, the lamplight had vanished and the lower floor was in darkness. A few moments later, the light reappeared in the front room on the upper storey; her parents had gone up to their bedroom. Another minute or two passed before the light was extinguished.

Still she waited. They might not fall asleep immediately and she wanted to be as certain as possible that her entrance wouldn't be detected.

She counted a full fifteen minutes before her stiffened knees begged her to move position. Rising awkwardly out of her crouch, she grasped the valise and left Mr and Mrs Hill's garden on silent feet. She flitted along the path and approached the front steps of Acorn House. Holding her breath, she climbed them gingerly one at a time, afraid to draw a creak from their aging wood right below her parents' window.

She paused on the top step to let out her breath, then inhaled again as she reached for the front door. It was locked. Remaining calm, she delved into her pocket, extracted the key her father had given to her on her birthday and inserted it into the lock, twisting gently. She eased the door open, thanking God that it did not squeak, and sidled inside, leaving it ajar behind her.

When her eyesight adjusted to the gloom within, all she could make out was the vague shape of the newel post at the bottom of the stairs but that was enough. She edged across the room, trailing her free hand along the lower banisters to guide her until she found the frame of the cupboard door. She opened it carefully and thrust a blind hand inside. Her fingers found silk almost at once.

Allowing herself a tiny sigh of relief – imagine if her mother had returned the gown to Madame Roche's shop sooner than she had planned – Emily felt about and ascertained that it had been hung across two pegs with precise care. She manoeuvred it off the pegs and withdrew it from the cupboard. Kneeling on the floor, she was folding it loosely into the valise, doing her best not to create creases, when—

'Emmy?'

Her heart seized. She looked up wildly and discerned Gus's curly-haired head peering down at her from behind the upper banisters.

He was standing on the step right above Barnabas.

'Don't move!' she whispered as urgently as she dared. 'Just stay where you are.'

'What're you doing?' he asked sleepily. 'Ma said you wasn't coming home tonight.'

'I had to collect something I forgot, that's all. Listen to me—don't come down any further. You should go back to bed.' She gulped as the cracks appeared in her perfect plan. 'And you mustn't tell anyone you saw me.'

He frowned. 'Not even Ma and Da?'

'Especially not them. I'll' – she cast about frantically for inspiration – 'bring you a treat if you keep this a secret between us.'

Even in the dark, she saw his face light up. 'What kind of treat?'

'It will be a surprise, but I know you'll enjoy it. Do you promise?'

He nodded eagerly. 'Promise!'

'Shh, you must be very quiet. Off to bed now. And remember, it's our special secret.'

Beaming, his curly head disappeared and she heard his bare feet padding back up the stairs. Her shoulders sagged. She hurried to tuck the rest of the gown into the valise and closed it with painful slowness to avoid making any noise. Then she got to her feet and tiptoed towards the door, slithering through the gap and locking it behind her.

Not until she had descended the front steps and scuttled all the way down the street to the corner did she stop to heave a proper mouthful of air into her lungs. There was scarcely a square inch on her body that did not drip with sweat: nose, chin, armpits, palms, back – all were damp and disgusting. But it had been worth it. She clutched the valise and strode back in the direction of Beacon Hill, anticipation mounting until she was almost running.

Re-entering Marlowe House would be the next tricky stage of her scheme. She dashed along the lane at the rear of the terraced houses, throat and legs burning, and slowed at last to creep into the paved courtyard. Fishing a pencil stub out of her pocket, she bent down by the back door and rolled it through the chink between its base and the sill. All she could do after that was wait, huddled in the corner of the courtyard with the valise pressed against her chest.

Tilly answered her prayers a short while later when the door cracked open and the maid's head materialised around the jamb. 'Corridor's clear,' she confirmed in an undertone.

Emily wasted no time; she darted forwards, slipped through the doorway and sprinted down the corridor to the servants' stairs. She had barely climbed four steps, however, when Mrs Coleman's voice rang out.

'Tilly!'

Emily froze and listened in dread.

'Yes, Mrs Coleman?' came Tilly's merry response.

'One of the maids just told me you sent her back into the kitchens to fetch the tray I instructed *you* to bring above stairs.'

'That's right, Mrs Coleman. I hope it wasn't too bold but I realised I hadn't gone up to check on Em for ages and I got worried all of a sudden.' A hitched breath. 'Oh no, it was very cheeky of me, wasn't it? I'm so sorry.' Her voice was full of contrition.

The housekeeper really did have a bias for Tilly because her own voice softened as she said, 'Hmm. I'll overlook it just this once. Go on up but make sure you hurry back.'

'I will, Mrs Coleman,' Tilly trilled and seconds later she appeared below Emily on the stairs. She winked and they sped up the steps.

When they had reached the safety of their room, Tilly blew out her breath with a nervous laugh. 'That was a close one.' She handed the pencil stub back to Emily. 'You were gone for so long. I had a crick in my neck from the amount of times I checked the corridor waiting for this!'

'I went as fast as I could,' said Emily, pocketing the pencil stub and setting the valise on the floor. She opened it and pulled out the gown, pushing aside her discarded possessions to lay it flat on the bed.

'It's pretty,' said Tilly admiringly.

Emily stroked a loving hand along the completed lace flounce before she turned the gown over and choked. 'She hasn't finished it!'

Her mother had sewn the hem the whole way around the bottom of the skirt except for two or three inches at the back. A couple of pins still jutted from the fabric.

Pragmatic as ever, Tilly said, 'It's not a disaster. You'll just have to keep your backside to the wall. Definitely no dancing for you.'

'You're right, it isn't a critical blow,' Emily allowed. She glanced around the room. 'Is there a towel or cloth I could use? My clothes are stuck to me with sweat. I need to dry off before I put this on.'

Tilly retrieved a small towel from the washstand and Emily took it gratefully. She stripped down to her shift and wiped the moisture from her skin, while Tilly eyed the blue silk gown.

'I think it might be too big for you,' she said.

'Yes, a little,' agreed Emily. 'We shall have to be creative.'

A short time later, she stood before Tilly, bouncing anxiously on her toes. Over her shift, she had donned the skirt she had already been wearing, along with another which she had packed early that morning in her valise, as well as a third which she borrowed from Tilly. The multiple layers were necessary to fill out the bell shape of the gown but they would not be visible because the silk skirt was longer than them – so long, in fact, that Emily would have to walk on the balls of her feet throughout the night to prevent it from dragging on the floor.

To her embarrassment, her bosom was not large enough to fill the bodice and Tilly had been obliged to pin it in at the back to make it a snugger fit. She would have to be careful not to make any jerky movements or she would risk dislodging the pins.

Tilly had proven to be the most indispensable and resourceful co-conspirator she could have hoped for. With a flourish, she had produced from beneath her bed a pair of cream satin slippers and a set of white elbow-length gloves ('It doesn't matter that the colours don't match seeing as no one will see your feet anyways...'). The slippers were too big, making it necessary for Tilly to tie the ribbons extra tightly around Emily's ankles. While the gloves were not as loose, they still had a tendency to slide down her forearms. She wished she wasn't so undersized in every part of her body.

She would have been fearful that she looked too young to attend the ball had it not been for her one saving grace: her hair. When she had tugged off her maid's cap to reveal her golden curls, Tilly had actually gasped. Together, they had arranged it in a fetching style, pinning it up simply at the back and letting her curls dangle in ropes on either side of her face. Even without a mirror, she knew she appeared more mature and sophisticated.

There had been no jewellery in the chest but Tilly said she would get by without it.

'Honestly, Em, I wouldn't even recognise you,' she declared, staring in awe.

Emily bubbled with exhilaration. They had succeeded in transforming her from a nondescript maid into an elegant young lady and she couldn't wait for Samuel Marlowe to lay his eyes upon her. And this time she would be worthy enough to look back into them.

A wistful expression flickered across Tilly's face as she continued to gaze at Emily. 'I'd never be able to do this.'

'On the contrary, I think you would be far braver than me,' Emily replied, truly believing it. She marvelled at Tilly's unremitting self-assurance; panicked pigeons seemed to be her only weak spot.

Tilly snorted. 'I'd definitely have the guts. But I'd still never be able to do it.' She held up her hands, displaying her skin. 'I think I'd stick out a bit, don't you?'

Emily gulped, mortified at her blunder. Tilly was regrettably correct; for all her talents, she would not be capable of blending in among the white guests.

'Ah...' she said weakly.

Tilly gave her a sad smile. 'Let's get you downstairs to that ball before everyone leaves already.' She shunted Emily towards

384

the door of their room. 'They'll all be dancing right now but remember that supper will be served from midnight.'

They made their way down the servants' stairs until they reached the door they accessed each morning to clean the family bedchambers, where a candle flickered in an alcove in the wall. There was no question of Emily showing up at Marlowe House's front entrance as her name could not be announced to the hostess. She would instead steal down to the ball from within the house and mingle casually among the guests as though she had arrived earlier in the night.

'Good luck!' said Tilly with only the barest trace of envy. She ushered Emily over the threshold and closed the door firmly behind her.

CHAPTER 41

Heart banging against her ribs, Emily moved along the landing to the top of the staircase, trying to keep her balance on the balls of her feet as she endeavoured to accustom herself to wearing a skirt that extended past her ankles. She was a storey above the main stairs with its pair of branching flights – the staircase in front of her was just a single set of steps flowing down to the next level, although its handrail and banisters were also made of wrought iron (with not a speck of dust upon them, she observed proudly). Music and conversation rose up from the floor below. Gliding her fingertips along the rail, she descended the stairs, treading cautiously.

The noise of the ball grew louder, stringed instruments accompanying tapping feet and gay chatter. She hesitated as she reached the bottom of the stairs and her legs almost began to retreat of their own accord. No, her courage could not fail her now after she had come this far. She took that final, decisive step and followed the sounds along the landing, stopping just short of an open pair of double doors.

The drawing room and morning room had undergone a transformation equal to her own. With their furniture removed, their carpets rolled up and the folding doors between the two rooms pulled wide, a large space had been created that was suitable for a ball. Guests danced in the centre of the pinewood floor or socialised around its edges, candlelight glowing upon them from the crystal chandeliers above. At the furthest end of the room, animated exclamations rose from a card table, the players obscured by so many engrossed spectators congregated around them. Emily peered through the doors, drinking it all in: the gentlemen and ladies clad in dazzling finery, the stirring melody emanating from the musicians, the laughter and heat and perfume of this upper class world that was so near she could practically taste it.

A burgeoning sense of dismay replaced her elation as she began to recognise a number of glaring errors on her part. The blue silk gown matched the opulence of the scene before her but the rest of her appearance was gravely lacking. Her hairstyle was too simple for she had not decorated it with feathers or jewels or ribbons. The absence of pearls or other gemstones at her ears and throat was in stark contrast to the glinting ornaments worn by every other female, young or old, within her view. Moreover, the ladies held fans and dance cards while her own hands were empty. Her inadequacy filled her with consternation and humiliation. She had to abandon this foolish plan before she was noticed and accused of being the imposter she was.

Whirling, she lurched away from the doors and walked headlong into a towering figure. She gaped upwards in alarm; it was the tall footman who had stood beside her in the servants' hall when they had first learned about the impending ball. His eyes widened. Wretched, she readied herself to be exposed and shamed. Would he reveal her deception to all and sundry or drag her away to bring her before the butler or Mrs Coleman? She would at least protect Tilly and refuse to divulge the identity of her accomplice in this sorry affair. Good God, how terribly disappointed her parents would be in her.

'Please accept my apologies, miss,' said the footman, his gaze dropping to his polished shoes. 'I was not paying attention.'

'I—' she stammered. 'I-it's fine.'

He bowed to her with a grateful glance and carried on into the room.

She backed up against the wall beside the doorway, trying to gather herself. He hadn't recognised her as his fellow servant and neither had he exhibited even a hint of suspicion that she did not belong there. Perhaps her masquerade was more convincing than she had believed.

Buoyed by this, she resolved not to flee just yet. Tugging her drooping gloves back up to her elbows, she approached the double doors once more and, this time, proceeded through them.

She hugged the edges of the room, angling herself so that the pins at the back of her bodice and on the hem of her skirt remained out of sight. No one paid her any heed. She kept a sharp eye out for Mistress Marlowe – she was probably the only person in the whole assembly who would be on familiar terms with everyone on the invitation list and who would therefore perceive Emily as an interloper rather than simply an unknown acquaintance of another guest.

It occurred to Emily far too belatedly that she did not have any clear understanding of the accepted etiquette at a ball. As she scanned the room and noted that virtually every young lady not engaged in dancing was in the company of an older woman, she realised that it must be inappropriate for unmarried females to be unchaperoned. Had she grown up with a governess, she might have had the opportunity to learn the correct codes of behaviour, the knowledge of which would have now aided her in avoiding impropriety. As matters stood, she was adrift in a sea of refined manners, with no notion as to what unintentional act on her part might constitute a gross breach of decorum in this assembly's eyes.

Trying not to feel bitter about the life she had missed out on, she contented herself with staying inconspicuous by the wall and observing the lively dance taking place in the centre of the room. As her gaze roamed over the participants, she caught a glimpse of Samuel himself among them. He was partnered with his cousin – Miss Knight looked radiant in a pink gown with pearls in her hair and at her neck. She had a becoming blush on her cheeks which did not surprise Emily in the slightest for she was dancing with the most handsome young man in the company. The candlelight shone on Samuel's bronze hair and he looked more resplendent than she had ever seen him in his dark tail coat and white cravat. Captivated, she stared at him, avidly following his progress around the pinewood floor.

He glanced over Miss Knight's shoulder and his gaze fell upon her watching him. Snapping her attention to an adjacent dancing couple, she surveyed them with detached interest for several bars of music before stealing another peek at him. Once again, he caught her looking. She reddened, but this time some audacious urge within pressed her to hold his stare. A surprised smile touched his lips until he was obliged to break the connection, circling towards the other side of the room with his partner.

She suppressed a shiver of delight. As she continued to absorb the sights and sounds around her, she resolved to savour every moment of this snatched night of freedom and sample the privileges that had once been her birthright. She might not be able to risk dancing but she could still relish the pleasure that came from relinquishing her menial duties in order to wear a pretty gown and partake of the delicious supper which she had witnessed the kitchen staff preparing earlier.

As though he had heard her thoughts, the tall footman rang a bell as the dance ended and announced to the assembly that the supper room was now open. The guests began to meander through the double doors and down the landing where Emily knew the breakfast room had been set up to provide the refreshments for the occasion. She spotted Samuel escorting Miss Knight and wondered if there was some protocol which prohibited ladies from attending the supper unaccompanied. She gnawed on her lower lip and lingered by the wall as much of the crowd dispersed. Fortunately, the musicians struck up their next tune so she could pretend she had remained behind to admire the fresh set of dancers who had taken to the floor.

However, with fewer people filling the room she came to realise that she was now more visible to roving eyes and she worried that Mistress Marlowe might sweep in at any instant. Perhaps it would be wiser to drift into the thronging supper room where she could more easily blend in. To prevent any semblance of improper conduct, she could hover near an older woman and act as though the lady were her chaperone. Not to mention, she might get another opportunity to feast her eyes upon the fine vision of Samuel Marlowe.

She departed casually from the room, keeping her poise even on the balls of her feet and feeling more and more like she belonged here. As she moved down the landing in the direction of the supper room, a figure emerged from it. Her stomach tumbled but she maintained an unhurried pace, glancing idly at a painting on the wall. Samuel drew nearer, his own momentum slowing when he noticed her. She thought he might pass her by but he paused, compelling her to halt too.

'Are—are you enjoying the ball?' he asked.

She raised her gaze to his. His dark eyelashes framed a pair of honey brown irises.

'Yes, I am,' she replied with a genuine smile.

'I'm aware that this is very forward of me as we haven't been formally introduced,' he said bashfully, 'but I'm Samuel Marlowe.'

'It is very nice to make your acquaintance, Mr Marlowe,' she said, conscious of the fact that neglecting to offer her own name verged on discourteous. Still, Miss McGovern did not sound aristocratic enough and she couldn't very well say Miss Lambourne, could she? It shocked her that that name had even entered her head. She hadn't answered to it since she was six years old.

Although his forehead creased, he did not call attention to her omission. After all, according to him, his own approach had been presumptuous in the first instance. 'I haven't seen you dancing yet,' he said. 'Do you choose not to? I can hardly suppose it is from a lack of willing partners.' He twinkled at her.

She blushed. 'I'm...not very confident in the steps,' she said with absolute honesty, given that she had never learned them at all. 'Dancing isn't a talent of mine. I am far more likely to trip over my own feet and land on my—'

She cut herself off. How could she be so vulgar? He would surely turn away from her in distaste.

But no, he chuckled heartily. 'I understand. Do I infer therefore that your talents lie in a different direction?'

'Yes, in art,' she responded. It was a simple admission of the truth and she had declared it without conceit, but she immediately wondered if she ought to have been more coy.

Intrigued, he said, 'Indeed? Watercolours?'

She nodded. 'And pencil drawings too. I have yet to try oils but I dearly wish to someday.' With luck, that wish would become a reality at Brubaker.

'And are you very good?'

She arched an eyebrow. Was he flirting with her? She sought to emulate her mother's most elevated mode of language as she

391

replied, 'You seem to be doing your best to provoke my vanity, sir.'

He grinned. 'I am merely curious. I swear I shall not consider you vain if you reply in the affirmative.'

'Then, yes, I believe I am very good.'

He looked impressed. 'Landscapes?'

'Sometimes. I do enjoy sketching scenes from nature. But I favour portraits most of all.'

'In that case, you have my admiration,' he said with an earnest bow. 'Portraiture is by no means an easy skill to master.'

'Thank you,' she said, very pleased by his compliment. 'Do you draw or paint, sir?'

He put a hand on his chest in mock regret. 'Not in the slightest. My artistic gifts are akin to your aptitude in dance.'

'I see.' The corners of her mouth twitched. 'Then do your own talents perhaps lie in a different direction?'

He beamed delightedly at her echo of his earlier words. A gentleman and two ladies came out of the supper room and passed them by but he hardly paid heed to them as he confessed to her, 'I write poetry.'

'How fascinating.' Of course, having expected this, she had her next question already prepared. 'What kind of subject matter do you explore in your poems?'

His expression became serious. 'That is a question of a highly personal nature. I don't believe we are sufficiently well acquainted for me to answer it.'

She withered under the weight of her mortification.

Those honey brown eyes glinted with mischief. 'I was only teasing,' he said, amused.

She nearly slumped to the flats of her feet before remembering to keep herself erect. 'How very unkind of you,' she said, her voice as lofty as her stance. 'I was quite enjoying our conversation up until that point.'

She made as if to move past him but he put out an urgent hand to catch her gloved wrist. 'No, please wait,' he said and she detected both the repentance in his tone and the yearning in his grip. Recollecting himself, he quickly let go but did not step back.

'Forgive me,' he said. 'That was indeed uncouth behaviour. Is our enjoyable conversation utterly irretrievable?'

'It is not,' she said, 'for I, too, was only teasing.'

His mouth dropped. After an astonished moment, he laughed. 'I am very glad to hear it. And I am happy to reveal that my tastes in verse are not dissimilar to your own in art—while I take pleasure in paying tribute to the bucolic, my preferences lie in the portrayal of people, their lives and dreams, their greatest passions and deepest losses.'

Her skin tingled. It was almost as though he were speaking poetry to her with his use of such lyrical language.

'How I should like to read your poems,' she said, the words spilling from her lips before she could stop them. She put her gloved palms to her cheeks. 'Oh, I do apologise. Now it is I who am being too forward.'

'On the contrary,' he said. 'I find our mutual honesty refreshing. Don't you?' His honey brown gaze seemed wholly sincere.

'Yes,' she breathed.

He held out his elbow. 'May I accompany you into the supper room? It would be my honour to do so.'

She thought her heart might burst from her chest when she took his arm but she attempted to maintain a calm facade as he led her along the landing. They entered the supper room, where chattering ladies gathered around cloth-covered tables and attentive gentlemen lingered at their elbows. The tables were laden with glasses of champagne and lemonade, slices of meats and fowl, and sweet dishes of all kinds, including jellies, cakes, ices and bonbons. Emily's stomach grumbled in anticipation.

A quick scan of the room informed her that Mistress Marlowe was not present among the guests so she allowed Samuel to guide her to the nearest table where he handed her a glass of champagne. She had never tried it before and took her first sip with excitement, but it required all her effort not to grimace. She forced herself to swallow, terribly disappointed, and set her glass back on the table, feigning a nonchalant manner. Desiring to eradicate the taste from her tongue, she reached towards a plate stacked with slivers of sponge cake and popped one into her mouth. The tangy flavour of lemon purged the champagne at once.

'Oh,' she said with a sigh. 'That is delicious.'

Samuel smiled broadly. 'Try the bonbons too. They're my personal favourites.'

He picked up a napkin, placed several chocolate bonbons onto it and pressed them into her palm. As she selected one to sample, a slender girl with auburn hair approached them.

'What a splendid supper, Mr Marlowe,' she said, batting her eyelashes at him. She acknowledged Emily's presence with a cordial nod before turning back to Samuel. 'I trust you have not forgotten that you engaged me for the next waltz?'

He eyed the dance card which hung on a ribbon at her wrist and Emily could tell by his faint wince that he had in fact forgotten that prior commitment.

However, he said gallantly, 'Indeed, I have not. Allow me to escort you to the dance floor forthwith.'

As he extended his arm to the girl, he offered Emily a look of apology. Leaning in, he murmured, 'Thank you for your most entertaining company. May I claim the dance after this, despite your earlier assertion of ineptitude? I promise I am a skilful partner and will not let you land on your...' He cleared his throat.

She flushed. Knowing she ought to refuse, she dipped her head in gracious acceptance. He looked very pleased.

'I shall come seek you after this waltz.' He turned to the auburn-haired girl. 'Come, Miss Halliwell.'

Emily went as still as a statue. Even as she recognised the girl's name, she also realised that she had neglected to keep her back to the wall – the pins on her bodice and hem would be visible to anyone who cared to glance at her. She sidestepped around the corner of the table, twisting her body away from a cluster of guests nearby and praying that the action appeared casual. She hoped fervidly that Samuel and Miss Halliwell would depart without delay but Miss Halliwell was observing her with a small furrow between her eyebrows.

'What a charming gown,' she said. 'I have one that is remarkably similar, although it is with my seamstress at present.'

'Oh, th-thank you,' Emily stuttered. 'I mean, h-how lovely.'

Miss Halliwell continued to stare at her with some puzzlement, but Samuel said, 'I believe we shall be tardy for the waltz if we do not make haste,' and he offered Emily a final bow before leading Miss Halliwell towards the door. She did not resist and they disappeared out onto the landing, her voice floating in their wake, 'I have been watching your mother preside over the card table—she is quite the fearsome competitor...'

Emily's fist clenched around the napkin of bonbons as nausea roiled in her belly. It had never occurred to her that she might come face to face with the owner of the blue silk gown. How could she have put her mother's livelihood and reputation at such risk? She stumbled away from the supper table and out the door.

On the landing, she heard the spirited commencement of the waltz but she did not follow its tempting summons – there would be no dancing with Samuel Marlowe tonight, even though she knew the musicians would play on until at least five in the morning. Instead, she sought the staircase that led upwards to the next floor and hurried up the steps, almost tripping on the gown in her rush. The arms of her gloves slipped all the way down to her wrists but she paid them no mind. All she could think of was fleeing as quickly as possible.

She gained the upper level and dashed for the door to the servants' stairs. She would run straight up to her and Tilly's room and take off this abominable gown before she wreaked irrevocable damage. Perhaps it was already too late – if Miss Halliwell's puzzlement turned to suspicion, she might bring her accusations to Madame Roche the very next day. Bile rose in Emily's throat and the residual taste of lemon was like acid on her tongue.

Flinging open the servants' door, she darted through but came to a sudden halt with a gasp. Two figures stood on the steps, lit by the candle in the alcove which guttered at the draught she had created. Tilly spun towards her, the candlelight gleaming on her cheekbones, and promptly dropped her hand away from where it had been resting...on the broad chest of a male stranger. Emily gawked at him – she didn't recognise him as a member of Marlowe House's staff, although he wore liveried clothing which indicated that he had to be somebody's servant.

He had big lips which twisted as he looked her up and down with a searing gaze, and she recollected that she was dressed far too elegantly to be using a servants' access door.

Tilly, thankfully, saved her. 'Are you lost, miss?' she enquired. 'Were you looking for the commode?'

'Y-yes,' stammered Emily. 'I seem to have taken a wrong turn.'

'I'll show you the way,' said Tilly cheerily. She pushed the stranger's shoulder. 'Go on back down to the kitchens.'

He said nothing, only pivoted on his heel and descended the stairs into the gloom below.

'It's this way, miss,' Tilly said in a raised voice and tapped her feet on the steps. She waited, then cocked an ear and listened to the silence. 'We're safe enough now, I reckon.'

'Who was that?' Emily hissed.

Tilly shrugged. 'I don't know his name. No need to look at me like that! Come on, let's go upstairs and you can tell me why you're back so soon.'

In the safety of their room, Emily dropped onto the soles of her aching feet with a moan of relief. She put the napkin of chocolate bonbons on her bed. They had started to melt in her sweating fist but she passed one to Tilly. 'Here you go. I have to save the rest as a bribe for my younger brother.'

Tilly accepted the bonbon eagerly and stuck it into her mouth with a moan that conveyed as much satisfaction as Emily's had. 'So, what happened?' she demanded, her words indistinct as her teeth cracked into the chocolate shell.

A plethora of emotions warred within Emily. On the one hand, she felt miserable about her unexpected encounter with Miss Halliwell and its potential ramifications. But on the other...

'Oh, it was wonderful. *He* was wonderful. Life is wonderful!' She couldn't contain her jubilation. There had been an almost instant connection between her and Samuel and it had felt extraordinary.

As Tilly removed the pins from the back of the bodice and helped her undress, she described all the marvellous details that were now emblazoned upon her mind: the way he had flouted etiquette to speak to her without an introduction, the rich colour of his eyes, the clasp of his fingers on her wrist, the intimate disclosure about his poetry. By the time she had donned her own drab clothing, her worries about Miss Halliwell had been entirely extinguished by her deep conviction that Samuel Marlowe was capable of – and was perhaps already – falling in love with her too.

'Then why did you leave before the end of the ball?' asked Tilly, running her tongue along her teeth to savour every last remnant of the bonbon.

Emily divulged her apprehension about meeting the owner of the blue silk gown. 'But she did not look at it too closely,' she reasoned, 'so I doubt I should worry overmuch.' She knelt to open her valise. 'Now, your turn. Who was that man?'

Tilly lay back on her bed, cushioning her head with her hands. 'One of the coachmen for the guests attending the ball. A few of them had gathered down in the kitchens to pass the time and get a cup of tea. That one started talking to me and he was very nice so I gave him a wink and he followed me up the stairs.' She cut her gaze to Emily. 'I know what you're going to say. I'm not stupid—I might've let him steal a kiss but that would've been it.' She heaved a sigh. 'I just wanted to have a bit of fun tonight too.'

'Where was Mrs Coleman?' asked Emily, careful to keep her tone non-judgemental.

'Scolding one of the footmen for not noticing a tiny stain on his shirt and scolding one of the kitchen maids for dropping a plate of sliced ham and then arguing with the butler and the cook over who should be doing the scolding.' Tilly chortled. 'And in the morning, they'll all agree that the whole night was an astounding success.'

Emily finished tucking the gown inside the valise. 'I had better bring this back. Will you help me again?'

Tilly sat up. 'I will, even though I'd rather be daydreaming about my coachman and his divine English accent!'

They repeated their earlier actions of the evening, Emily hiding out of sight near the bottom of the stairs until Tilly could ensure that the corridor was clear. Matters were complicated by the continuing altercation between the housekeeper, butler and cook, but at last all three vacated the corridor with apologetic grumbles to each other and Emily could make a dash for the paved courtyard.

The air was a little cooler this late into the night so she didn't sweat quite so much on her second trek to Acorn House, where she hoped she might slip in and out this time without mishap. Unfortunately, although on this occasion Gus did not wake to expose her subterfuge, she very nearly managed to do so herself. Leaning inside the cupboard, she had replaced the blue silk gown on its two pegs and was feeling victorious when, withdrawing, she banged the back of her head on the lintel and let out a stifled yelp. She went immobile with dread, expecting her parents to emerge from their bedroom immediately to investigate the noise. However, after many seconds ticked by and no one appeared, she eased the cupboard door shut and, eyes still watering, made good her escape.

Now all that was left to do was to return to Marlowe House and perform her pencil trick one more time. As the predawn light tinted the sky above the city, she felt triumphant that, barring the unforeseen complication of Miss Halliwell, her adventure that night had proven to be a success. She sorely wished she could have danced with Samuel, but the touch of his fingers at her wrist was still worth every risk she had taken.

CHAPTER 42

'What has got you so giddy this morning?' Bridget demanded in exasperation as Gus scampered in circles around the kitchen table.

'Nothing!' he piped back and giggled.

Shaking her head, she handed him a plate of vegetable scraps. 'Go and feed the hens, please.'

He ran out to the back yard, still buzzing with energy. She savoured the brief respite from his antics for she herself was feeling rather weary. She recollected having a restless night's sleep, particularly after a strange dream during which she thought she heard Emily's voice cry out in pain. It was no doubt in reaction to the fact that her not-so-little girl had been spending her first night away from home. Bridget was very glad she would return this evening.

Entering the front room, she went to the cupboard under the stairs to retrieve the blue silk gown. Her creation was nearly complete and she had only a few inches of the hem left to finish. She hoped that Madame Roche, along with Mrs Halliwell and her daughter, would be highly pleased with her handiwork.

She laid the gown out on her sewing desk with its front facing downwards so that she could access the back of the skirt. Her glance fell upon the bodice and she noticed a stray pin sticking out of it. How odd, she couldn't remember leaving it there. With a shrug, she slid it out and bent over the skirt to resume working on the hem.

There was a sharp rap on the door. First arranging the gown to ensure it would not slide off the desk in her absence, she went to answer it. No one was there. She frowned; could it be local ragamuffins making mischief in the neighbourhood? If so, she pitied the children should Mr and Mrs Hill catch them in their prank.

She was turning to close the door when she looked down and spotted a letter sitting on the doorstep. She stooped to pick it up. To her surprise, it was addressed to Emily. Jutting her head back out through the doorway, she peered up and down the street but she couldn't see anyone. Mystified, she returned inside, the letter clutched in her hand.

She stared at it, powerfully curious. Who could it be from? She did not recognise the handwriting. If it was correspondence from Brubaker Art Academy, then surely it would have come via Charlie and he would not have left it anonymously on the step. Did Emily have a secret beau? Bridget could imagine what Cormac might have to say about that.

Quite at a loss, she left the letter on top of the mantelpiece and went back to the blue silk gown.

***

Emily yawned widely and then coughed as a cloud of dust drifted towards her mouth. She was in the library of Marlowe House, where Mrs Coleman had assigned the task of removing the books from the bookcases one shelf at a time and dusting thoroughly before replacing them. Exhaustion made her limbs heavy but elation kept her spirits uplifted, as her thoughts continued to obsess over the ball the previous night.

What did Samuel think of the nameless girl he had met? Would he try to seek her out? If he asked his mother for the list of guests, he would remain none the wiser. Would that disappointment consume him?

As she absent-mindedly swept her feather brush along the bookshelf, she pictured him from head to toe, lingering over every attractive detail. She was so glad that she had plucked up the courage to gaze into his honey brown eyes. She wished she had not been wearing gloves so that his beseeching hand would have grazed the actual skin on her wrist. She yearned to rake her fingers through his lustrous, wavy hair. She remembered his teasing grin and wanted to press her lips to his smiling mouth.

Her brush faltered. That last thought had triggered an unusual sensation inside her, a burst of molten excitement deep in her core. Experimentally, she tried again to envision herself kissing Samuel and experienced the same hot surge, her whole body seeming to tighten and tingle. Recalling the passionate kiss she had witnessed between Auntie Orlaith and Uncle Charlie several years ago on Independence Day, she conjured up the image of Samuel once more and this time she imagined him touching his tongue to her lips, running it lightly over them, encouraging her to part them and, when she did, slipping it between them to caress her own tongue.

Blood rushed to her cheeks and to other parts of her body too; she had never been so physically conscious of herself before. She was still trying to come to terms with this new sense of awareness when the door to the library opened. She expected it to be Tilly but, to her shock, Samuel Marlowe walked in.

She almost gasped out loud, alarmed that he might be able to perceive the bodily reactions that her mental picture of him had provoked, but she managed to rein in her exclamation and dropped into a curtsey as he crossed the room towards a bookcase on the far side. He didn't seem to notice her and stopped with his back to her, perusing the spines with an air of appraisal.

If he looked at her properly, would he recognise her as the girl he had spoken to at the ball? That was what she desired, even if it meant revealing her deception. Surely it would be possible for him to see past her trifling ruse and remember their intense connection, dismissing everything else as unimportant. She was prepared to throw caution to the wind to find out.

He selected a book from the shelf, tucked it under his arm and turned to go back to the door. She stepped forwards.

'Good day, Master Samuel,' she said. She curtseyed again but kept her head raised, every particle of her burning with anticipation.

He offered her a civil nod. 'Good day,' he said and left the library.

All of the air rushed out of her, like she had received a punch to the stomach. Had her masquerade at the ball been so consummate that he could not distinguish her now in maid's clothing? How could he not glimpse the real her underneath?

Tears sprang to her eyes. What a simpleton she was. He only saw a maid because that's all there was to see. A maid and an artist and a fool. Why had she exposed herself to that upper class world? Now that she had tasted it, she wanted it a hundred times more. And, thanks to her mother and father, she could not have it. Despair rose in her, eradicating that scorching arousal and leaving cold rejection in its place.

And yet, still she clung to a desperate sort of hope. Could Samuel save her from her inferior status? Should she run after him, haul off her maid's cap and blurt out the truth? Was it too much to believe that her future inheritance of Oakleigh, even with its monetary limitations, might be enough to outweigh the lower class taint of her current situation?

The library door opened again and she inhaled a gulp of air to tell him everything, but it was Tilly who entered, puncturing her breath.

'It's done,' Tilly announced. 'The gloves and slippers are back in the chest and no one spotted me going up to the attic. We got away with the whole thing!' She stared at Emily, taken aback. 'What's wrong?'

'Nothing,' Emily replied, even as her chin trembled.

Tilly regarded her with a sceptical expression as she came over and picked up her own abandoned feather brush.

'Samuel was just here,' Emily murmured, 'and he didn't recognise me at all.'

'I'm not surprised,' said Tilly. 'You look so different with your curls down around your face.' She frowned. 'You don't *want* him to recognise you, do you? We'd be in so much trouble if you were found out.'

'No, you're right,' said Emily, discreetly dashing away a tear. 'I was just having a silly daydream, that's all.'

Tilly nodded understandingly. 'We all have those now and then.'

Curious, Emily asked, 'What do you daydream about?'

Tilly resumed dusting the bookshelf next to Emily's. She shrugged. 'This and that.'

'Do you have a dream that you long for more than any other?'

The corner of Tilly's mouth lifted. 'Yes.'

'I'm happy to listen, if you're willing to share,' said Emily. 'I promise not to tell anyone.' After all, Tilly had been an outstanding confidante to her.

Tilly turned to face her. 'It's just as silly as yours,' she confessed. 'I wish I was important enough to be called by my proper name.'

'Your proper name?' Emily repeated. 'What is it?'

'Matilda,' said Tilly. 'A bit too grand for a humble black maid, don't you think?' She gave an embarrassed grimace.

'Not at all,' said Emily bracingly. 'It suits you very well because it's just as splendid as you are.'

Tilly blinked and peeked down at her feet. It was the first time Emily had ever seen her so self-conscious.

'If you'd like,' said Emily, 'I shall call you Matilda from now on.'

Her companion glanced up and Emily smiled warmly to convey her genuine intention.

'I'd definitely like that,' said Matilda, beaming.

***

As Cormac approached the steps of Acorn House, he glanced towards Mr and Mrs Hill's garden to see the couple stooped beneath their sycamore tree, scrutinising the ground under it.

'Damn troublemaking delinquents,' Mr Hill griped as he poked his toe into the disturbed soil.

Cormac waved to them and called, 'Good evening.'

Mrs Hill grumbled a noncommittal response, like she didn't want to admit that there could be anything good about the evening. He saluted again with a tolerant smile and continued on into the house.

Emily arrived home not long after him, carrying the valise. He could scarcely admit, even to himself, how much her night away at Marlowe House had affected him – after eight years living under the same roof as his daughter, a certain portion of which they had even shared the same room, he had suffered a poignant sense of loss at her absence. Filled with gladness to see her coming through the front door, he gave her a tight hug.

'Welcome home, *a stór*. We missed you.'

She seemed a little rigid within his arms and he reflected that she had probably viewed the previous night as an opportunity for freedom, even if she had been required to work for it. He supposed grown-up children didn't need their parents as much as parents needed their grown-up children and he released her a little sadly.

'Come on into the kitchen and tell us about yesterday,' he said, trying not to sound too eager. 'Did Mrs Coleman work you to the bone?'

'She did,' Emily began with a wince but, right at that moment, Gus charged down the stairs, bellowing, 'Emmy!' over Barnabas's trumpeting screech.

Emily shooed Cormac away. 'I'll follow you into the kitchen in a second.'

As he went through the doorway, he glanced back and caught sight of her opening the valise and passing a bulging napkin to Gus. He jumped up and down with glee. Some sort of covert communication passed between them which culminated in Emily wagging an authoritative finger at her brother. Cormac put it down to sibling secrets and carried on through to the kitchen where Bridget had supper waiting.

At the kitchen table, Emily's account of the servants' activities for the ball was somewhat stilted and she hurried through her supper, asking to be excused as soon as she was finished.

'I'm worn out,' she said and, in truth, she did look pale and fatigued. 'I'll go up to bed now. I think I could almost sleep standing up.'

'Bedtime for the pair of you too,' Cormac said to Jack and Gus. Gus whined but they both got up from the table as well.

All four of them had gone into the front room when Bridget hastened after them. 'Goose—Emily, I nearly forgot! There's a letter for you.'

Emily paused with her foot on the bottom step of the stairs. 'For me?' she said, her brow furrowed.

Bridget plucked it off the mantelpiece and held it out. 'Are you expecting a message from Brubaker?'

'No.' Emily crossed the room and took the letter, peering at her name in bemusement.

Oblivious, Jack and Gus raced each other to the top of the stairs. Gus whooped in triumph when he reached the summit first.

'I'll follow you up,' Cormac called after them. He, too, was intrigued by the mysterious note.

Emily broke the plain seal, unfolded the letter which included two sheets, and began to read. Colour flooded her wan cheeks and her mouth fell open in a silent 'Oh!' of astonishment. Cormac watched as her blue eyes reached the end of the first page, raced down the second and then darted back to the beginning, scanning the whole lot again. An expression of hunger filled her face.

'Who is it from?' he asked, unable to restrain himself.

She didn't answer at once. Gripping the pages tightly, she swallowed and glanced from him to her mother. 'It's from...Garrett.'

'What?' said Bridget, bewildered. 'But he doesn't know our address. And that wasn't his writing on the outside.' She stole a glimpse over Emily's shoulder, gaping. 'Gracious, the letter is undoubtedly composed by his hand though.'

A frisson of misgiving ran down Cormac's spine. 'What possible reason could he have to contact Emily?'

Although Bridget did not attempt to peruse the letter, Emily still angled it away from her in a possessive gesture. Bridget stepped back and motioned for Emily to divulge its contents herself. Emily skimmed the sheets again, as though she didn't quite believe that she had accurately read what was penned there the first two times.

At last, she said, 'He is inviting me to London. He wishes to leave his inheritance to me.' Her voice was filled with dumbfounded wonder.

Cormac's misgiving erupted into loathing and alarm. Why did that fiend want to spin such lies to Emily? Bridget inhaled a sharp breath; she looked utterly shocked.

Cormac extended his hand to Emily. 'May I see the letter?'

She hesitated but, with a grudging nod, passed it to him. Just as she had done, he read it and reread it, trying to absorb its grave implications.

My darling Emily,

You may well be surprised to hear from me after so many years but please do not consider my silence as indicative of any deficiency in my affection for you. Rather, I was so ashamed of my past actions that I deemed you far happier without my influence in your life. My imperfect conduct as a father and a husband drove you and your mother away and I have no one to blame for that but myself.

And now I must confess that my innate failings have come to the fore yet again for I am acting out of pure selfishness by writing to you. As an affluent gentleman in his forties, I should be experiencing the satisfaction that such prosperity brings. However, I cannot find pleasure in amassing wealth when there is no purpose to it. For whom do I hoard it all?

I have always believed that children are the greatest joy of mankind. It is how we continue to live on even after we die. The birth of your brother, James, was truly the most exultant moment of my existence. Sadly, his death was the most harrowing. I pray that you never suffer such grief. And here, once more, I must acknowledge my own critical faults. For in mourning the son I had lost, I forgot the daughter I still had.

I shall not claim blindness to the truth of your parentage. And yet none can deny that it is my lawful marriage to your mother which gives legitimacy to your status in society. I am legally your father. And I desire to at long last fulfil those duties which I have until now so unforgivably neglected.

I deeply regret the manner in which we parted all those years ago and I ache to reform the bond that was broken. This I vow: if you can find it in your heart to forgive me, you shall want for nothing while I live and, upon my passing, you shall inherit everything I possess.

To that end, I invite you to visit me in London. Wyndham House on Berkeley Square remains your home and you will always be welcome here. Given your age, I would be delighted to make arrangements for your coming out in society. Every girl should experience the London social season at least once. Every daughter deserves the very best her father can offer her.

There shall be no subterfuge in my proposal. I insist that you do not keep this letter a secret as I wish for the relevant parties to be informed that I mean you no harm. They will likely seek an ulterior motive in my words but I assure you that there is none. I am merely a lonely man who yearns to have his child by his side, to nurture an heir, to cherish a reason to live.

I beg you to pardon the errors of my past but, above all, give thought to your own future.

Your loving father,
Wyndham

Cormac's stomach churned. His hand shook as he passed the letter wordlessly to Bridget. Her gaze flew down the pages, her eyes widening with growing revulsion. When she had finished reading, she glared up at him, her jaw clenched.

'That unprincipled charlatan,' she managed to get out through gritted teeth.

'I couldn't agree more,' he growled.

She turned the letter over to scrutinise the writing on the front. 'He must have solicited someone else to address it so that we would not identify his handwriting. Perhaps he suspected that we might not deliver it if we knew he was the author of it.'

Emily crossed her arms. 'Would you really have done that?' she demanded. 'Kept my correspondence from me?'

Her accusatory tone disturbed Cormac. 'No,' he reassured her. 'Of course we would have given it to you. But we can't stress enough that you must categorically disregard its contents.'

Her face fell. 'You think he is lying?'

'We are certain of it,' said Bridget. 'He is doing this for some devious personal gain.'

'So you don't believe he is just lonely?' said Emily, her voice pathetically small.

Her distinct note of longing pierced Cormac like a knife; she really wanted Garrett's proposal to be genuine. He supposed she saw it as a faster path to accepting her place at Brubaker, but perhaps it had not occurred to her that by going to London she would be acknowledging Garrett as her father while denying the same of Cormac. He had not missed the pointed remark in the letter: 'Every daughter deserves the very best her father can offer her.' And Garrett could offer Emily so much more than Cormac ever could. How he detested that bastard.

'Loneliness is suffered by those who place value in the companionship of others,' he said to Emily. 'Garrett cares for nobody but himself.'

'Are you quite sure?' she appealed. 'It has been so many years since any of us last saw him. Perhaps he has changed...'

Fear gripped Cormac that Garrett's insidious words could have snaked so easily inside his daughter's mind. 'I say this with absolute sincerity: he cannot be trusted.'

'Please believe us,' Bridget entreated, brandishing the pages. 'Garrett wields his pen like a weapon. He used it in the past to manipulate me into sending your father away from Oakleigh—I thought I was giving Cormac a note with an address for a manservant's position in Dublin, but it was only a threat from Garrett that your father must never contact me again.'

'And shortly after that,' said Cormac, 'he wrote to countless estates within Carlow and beyond warning them not to hire me as a stable hand. I was left with no means to make a living and found myself in poverty because of it. Because of *him*.'

Emily's features became full of chagrin. 'I-I understand.' She shook her head, tears trembling on her eyelids. 'How vile. I cannot fathom his despicable behaviour.'

Relieved, Cormac said, 'I'm glad you can see the truth of the situation. The best thing to do is to throw the letter away.'

He didn't pause for her consent before he seized it from Bridget's unresisting hand. He spun around and strode back to the kitchen where he pulled open the door of the stove.

'Wait!' Emily cried from behind him.

He tossed the two pages onto the glowing embers. They shrivelled and burned at once. When he looked back at Emily, her face was eloquent with disappointment.

'I wanted to do it myself,' she said.

'Either way, it's done now.' He closed the stove door on the letter's blackened remains. Putting out a tentative hand, he cupped her chin. 'It's gone.'

Her lips pressed together in a thin smile. 'Thank you, Father.'

CHAPTER 43

Emily walked to Marlowe House the next morning with her wits in total disarray. The sun was already climbing the sky for these were some of the shortest nights of the year, and yet the previous night had felt like an eternity as she had twisted restlessly in her bed, fixated upon that letter and the capricious man who had written it.

What chaos Garrett had managed to wreak with nothing but ink – she marvelled at how he could so thoroughly discompose her from all the way across the ocean. She had read the letter just three times which had left her with the essence of its message but not the particulars. If only her father had not burned it, she would have been able to examine it more closely for clues as to Garrett's underhand intentions. That was clearly how her parents had interpreted it, but she could not recall any sinister insinuation in his words; rather, she had found him humble and remorseful in admitting his flaws and sincere in his desire for reconciliation.

And how neatly that desire dovetailed with her own. The timing was remarkably fortuitous but, she supposed, no more coincidental than the flailing entrance of the pigeon that had brought her and Samuel Marlowe together. Garrett had presented her with the perfect solution to her predicament.

If he was prepared to acknowledge her as the heiress to his estate, then she would inherit the title of viscountess, which was in fact a rank above the title of baroness that she would gain whenever Oakleigh eventually passed to her. Moreover, he had said she would want for nothing while he lived, indicating that she would have liberal access to the kinds of funds Oakleigh was unable to provide. That meant she could obtain the money to immediately accept her place at Brubaker Art Academy. She would also undeniably become an eligible match for Samuel; neither he nor his parents could have any objection to her based on status or means if society recognised her as a wealthy viscount's daughter.

Still, all of that was beside the point because her parents had forbidden her to give any credence to Garrett's offer. But in whose interests had they issued that command? Garrett's past offences had been committed against them, not her, and they continued to bear ill will towards him, even when he was now making an overt effort to atone for his mistakes. Maybe it was easier for them to be persuaded that he harboured a wicked motive beneath it all, instead of acknowledging that he was actually in a position to improve her life in a way that they could not. Perhaps it made them feel less inadequate if they judged that they retained moral superiority over him. If that was the case, they were thinking of themselves, not of her.

As they had done all along.

She knew she was being unfair to them. They had fallen deeply in love all those years ago and the only way they could be together was to flee from London in a cloud of scandal. She had always regarded it as marvellously romantic, back when she was young and naive enough not to realise its ramifications. Now she wondered if they had even given a moment's consideration at the time as to how that fateful decision would ultimately affect *her*?

Granted, their choices had brought her to this country where she believed she had found her own love of her life. But it was also where she had been exposed to Mr Miller and his biting leather strap, to the frightening riot on Broad Street, to menial chores at home and a role of servitude as a maid. Had she remained in London, she would have had servants to wait upon her, beautiful dresses, parasols, gloves that fit her properly, a governess who would not have struck her, and the chance to be presented as a debutante in the most fashionable city in the world. Who could say whether she might not even have been the jewel of the season with all the gentlemen vying for her hand?

Indeed, that opportunity had not yet passed her by. She was only fifteen. There was still time to have her coming out as Garrett had promised. Except that her mother and father had claimed that his promises were lies. What if *they* were the ones telling falsehoods?

Her guts cramped uneasily, which felt like a fitting retribution after having feigned her complaint on the night of the ball. How could she have such spiteful thoughts about her parents? They were good people. It just seemed like they had lost sight of what was best for her. She dragged her feet through the Common and reached Marlowe House in a state of misery.

By the time she and Matilda, whose grin almost split her face when Emily greeted her thus, had proceeded above stairs to attend to the bedchambers, she was ready to burst with the conflicting emotions fighting for dominance inside her. Matilda had hardly shut Mistress Marlowe's bedchamber door before Emily exclaimed, 'I have another secret to tell!'

Matilda rubbed her hands together in delight. 'Excellent! You have the best secrets.'

'Just wait until you hear this one,' Emily said dismally.

As they progressed from one chamber to the next, dressing the beds and emptying the slops, she told Matilda everything,

415

from the truth about her upper class beginnings to the impropriety of her parents' love affair, from her birthright associated with Oakleigh to the tantalising contents of Garrett's letter. Matilda interjected on several occasions with loud gasps of 'By golly!' and 'You don't say!' and 'Well, I never!' and 'You *don't* say!', while her eyes nearly bulged out of her head.

Emily concluded her tale with the burning of the letter just as they finished arranging the pillows on Miss Knight's bed. She fell quiet and Matilda offered another 'By golly!' into the silence.

After needlessly twitching a pillow one more time, Emily said, 'I feel wretched. The commandments say to "Honour thy father and thy mother" but I have thought some dreadful things about them since last night.'

Matilda gave her a sympathetic look. 'That's because you don't think they're right, do you?'

Emily hesitated, then admitted, 'I don't.'

'You want to go to London?'

'I do.' It came out in a whisper.

'Do you trust the gentleman who wrote to you—this Garrett fellow?'

Emily cringed. 'I'm not sure. I think so. I can't imagine why he would take the trouble to deceive me. I wish I could read his letter again to be certain, but from what I recall it did seem very heartfelt.' She paused. 'What would you do?'

Matilda arched an eyebrow. 'Somehow I doubt that a viscount would ever be likely to invite me to London for the social season.' She winked. 'But if it were me, I'd jump at the chance not to be a maid anymore.'

Something clicked into place inside Emily. She nodded slowly. While she abhorred the idea of disobeying her mother and father, this opportunity was too great to pass up. Perhaps she could go to England for six months or a year and return to America thereafter. If Garrett stated his preference for her to remain there with him, she would have to explain that both Samuel and Brubaker were in this country so she could not stay away indefinitely. Surely she could make arrangements to travel back and forth in moderation when the cost of it would be no object.

This wasn't her choosing one father over another – it was a choice she was making for herself, and her artistic prospects, and her romantic hopes.

'I'm of the same opinion as you,' she said to Matilda, and that was her decision made.

True to form, Matilda raced on to the practicalities straight away. 'You'll have to check the shipping schedules. Is there a direct route from Boston to London?'

'I have no notion,' said Emily as she felt a tiny spark of excitement flicker into life inside her.

'Did Mr Garrett send any money with his letter?'

She gulped. 'No.'

'Do you plan to keep this all a secret?'

Sighing, she said, 'I'll have to. My parents would never give me permission.'

'So you won't be able to borrow money from them for your ticket anyways.' Matilda wrinkled her nose. 'Wait a minute, who will you travel with?'

'What do you mean?'

'You can't go alone. It wouldn't be safe. There could be brigands or pirates, and you're only a girl.'

'I'm a woman,' Emily corrected. 'And I don't need a travelling companion.' A thought struck her and she said hopefully, 'Unless you should like to come?' It would be a fine adventure if the pair of them went sailing across the ocean together. In just a few short weeks, she felt that Matilda had become more of a friend to her than Emmeline had been during her entire time at Hawes.

Although Matilda's longing was palpable, she shook her head. 'You won't need a job when you come back, but I will. I can't walk away from Marlowe House just like that.'

'I understand,' said Emily, quelling her disappointment. 'And besides, I shall be perfectly fine taking the journey on my own.'

'No, you need someone to go along with you,' Matilda insisted. 'Preferably a man who can protect you. You'll be travelling for weeks on end and I bet there'll be any amount of criminals out there looking to pounce on a girl who's by herself.'

'Woman,' said Emily again. 'Let's put that aside for now and figure out how I shall actually accomplish this...'

***

'We could put the bedside table on the left and the rocking chair next to it maybe. What d'you think, Mr McGovern? Mr McGovern?'

Cormac blinked. Rory was staring at him with some concern, waiting for a response. 'Sorry, Rory. Yes, you're right. That's a good suggestion.'

He returned his concentration to the display they were assembling in the front window of the workshop. They changed the exhibited pieces every so often with the aim of catching the fresh attention of passersby and enticing them inside. While some made a swift exit once they learned that the proprietor was Irish, many were impressed by the quality of the workmanship and willing to give him their custom.

He heaved the bedside table onto the dais they had erected below the window. As Rory manoeuvred the rocking chair into place beside it, Cormac's thoughts drifted back once again to Garrett and the pestilential letter he had managed to sneak into the hands of his innocent, precious daughter. How had he discovered their address? Who had delivered the note? Could Garrett possibly be in Boston himself? What was his intent with regard to Emily? There was no doubt that he had not contacted her solely for the sake of her welfare. Some nefarious scheme was in motion and Cormac was both ignorant of it and fearful of its repercussions.

'Mr McGovern? Sir?'

He grimaced. 'Sorry, Rory,' he said again. 'I'm a bit distracted today.'

In fact, his head pounded from the endless questions running through it and his jaw ached; Bridget had told him that morning that he had been heavily grinding his teeth during the night. Since the appearance of the letter from Garrett, his every waking moment had been consumed by it, and so had his dreams as well, it seemed.

If only he was in a position to give Emily everything she wanted so that she would have no need to fall for Garrett's silver-tongued enticements, which dangled with as-yet-undisclosed conditions. He was already exploring ways to increase the output of the workshop and bring in more income; with Rory's own skills developing all the time, they might now be able to undertake larger projects together. If he could attain the wherewithal that would enable Emily to begin her studies at Brubaker sooner than projected, then Garrett's proposal would no longer present such a temptation.

How quickly might Emily lose patience though? What if she wrote back to Garrett without Cormac and Bridget's knowledge? After all, she had already proved herself capable of concealing correspondence prior to this. He would have to check with Charlie in due course if she had asked him to post any more letters on her behalf. In the next instant, he berated himself for thinking that. How could he suspect his little girl of having the capacity for artifice of that magnitude? This was a far different situation to submitting a hopeful application to an art academy.

With a vigorous shake of his head, he endeavoured to focus upon Rory. 'My apologies. What did you say?'

But instead of repeating whatever he had said, Rory asked, 'Is something amiss, sir?'

Cormac gave a helpless shrug. 'There is, I suppose.' At Rory's alarmed glance towards the display in the window, he hastened to add, 'It's nothing to do with the workshop. I've got a troubling personal matter.'

Rory nodded soberly. 'Anything I can do to help?'

Sometimes Cormac forgot that Rory was a grown man now – the lad had turned eighteen but Cormac still occasionally saw him as the young boy who thought he had failed his mother when he couldn't protect her from the rioters. However, a calm maturity bloomed now in those green eyes.

So, instead of concealing his qualms as he would from a child, Cormac said, 'I greatly appreciate that. While I wish I could confide the particulars, I regret that it concerns a part of my family's history which I cannot divulge. Suffice to say, an objectionable person from our past has re-entered our lives and I'm worried that he might become a threat to Emily.'

'Emily?' said Rory in surprise.

'She received a letter from this man in which he made her a vow that I am certain he does not intend to fulfil.' Cormac felt his anxiety rise again as he recalled the hunger in Emily's features as she read the letter. 'He has given her false hope. Bridget and I did our best to convince her of that but I fear the man's empty promise will fester with her, even though we burned the letter. And I do not believe that this will be his only attempt to contact her. When he does not get a response to his message, he will undoubtedly make his next move.'

'Can you guess what that next move might be?' Rory asked, remaining composed in the face of this unsettling news.

Cormac rubbed his jaw. 'Christ, I can't tell what he might do. I don't even know what he is plotting beyond his attempt to invite her to London. But he is a powerful man with no conscience and ample resources at his disposal. That is a dangerous combination.'

Rory had nothing to say to that and Cormac wondered if he had imparted too much.

Trying to make light of it, he said, 'Of course, the alternative scenario is that I am simply an overprotective father fretting needlessly. I just want Emily to be safe, that's all.' He swallowed. 'Happy and safe.'

CHAPTER 44

Bridget softly shut the door of the boys' bedroom. The lamb had drifted into slumber without protest but the miracle had insisted upon several renditions of every rhyme and lullaby she could think of before he, too, dozed off to sleep.

On the landing, her gaze fell upon the door to the box room which was ajar. Through the crack, she glimpsed Emily kneeling in front of her cupboard – she had extracted Mabel from its depths and was giving her a fond caress. Smiling to herself, Bridget went downstairs without alerting Emily to her presence.

Cormac sat at the kitchen table below, ledgers and designs spread out before him. He had informed her that from now on he would do this type of work in the evenings to afford him more time for carpentry at the workshop. To keep him company, she brought in her latest sewing task from her desk in the front room and joined him at the table. She had finished the blue silk gown and returned it to Madame Roche's – Mrs Halliwell had gushed upon the sight of it but Bridget's pride had been somewhat dampened by Miss Halliwell's faint frown. Still, they had taken it away from the shop without complaint and she had received her payment for the labour which, while still modest, had been greater than her usual humble earnings.

Emily came down to the kitchen shortly after that, betraying no sign of the companion she had been hugging upstairs. She sat at the table with some paper and a pencil and began tranquilly sketching. Bridget stole a glance at Cormac and she could tell from the curve of his mouth that he was enjoying the three of them sharing this interlude of quiet industry.

After a few minutes, he cleared his throat. 'I have some good news. Mr and Mrs Rosemount visited the workshop and are so happy with the sideboard that they have already commissioned additional pieces for their boarding house. Rory and I are going to be very busy.' He waited for Emily to look up and said with a wink, 'Several steps closer to Brubaker.'

She smiled back at him. 'That's wonderful to hear.' She resumed sketching and, as her pencil dashed across the page, she said casually, 'In fact, I might have the prospect of earning a little extra money as well. Mistress Marlowe's niece, Miss Knight, is inviting some of her friends from Philadelphia to stay. They are not bringing their own lady's maids so Mrs Coleman has asked if anyone on the staff feels competent enough to step up to the role while they are here. I volunteered and so did Matilda—by the by, that's what Tilly prefers to be called now.'

While Bridget thought it strange that the young ladies would travel so far without their own maids to accompany them, she said, 'That is a fine opportunity. A lady's maid is a prestigious position and it's very difficult to gain experience in it at your age.'

'Yes, Mrs Coleman said as much. We'll receive training beforehand and ought to learn many useful skills.' Emily reached for another sheet and started a fresh sketch. 'The only negative aspect is that I would be required to attend to the young lady when she is preparing for bed. As that could be quite late on any given evening, it means I shall probably have to stay in the servants' quarters again.'

'Oh,' said Bridget, disappointed. 'I suppose that does make sense with the longer days and more unpredictable hours. Do you know for what length of time Miss Knight's friends intend to stay?'

'Mrs Coleman didn't say. May I borrow the valise again?'

'You may, although I hope they shan't have a very extended visit. I couldn't bear for you to be away for too long!'

Bridget said it with a merry chuckle to conceal how much she really meant it but, for some reason, it seemed to make Emily rather teary. She sniffed and rose to give both of them especially tight hugs before saying, 'Goodnight, Mother. Goodnight, Father.'

She exited the kitchen, leaving her sketches behind her. Bridget looked at them – Emily had drawn a fresh batch of portraits of Bronagh.

***

The worms were back. They slithered around inside Emily, so numerous that they seemed to fill her from her gut to the back of her throat. She had told more lies in the past week than she had in the rest of her whole life.

Nevertheless, the final stage of her plan was in motion and she walked along Broad Street with the valise bumping against her thigh. She had packed into it the garments and items she would need for her journey, including her skirts with their hems let down enough to cover her ankles. She was not so talented as her mother with a needle but it was still a vital step she refused to skip. Her childhood had come to an end and the longer skirts marked her ascension to adulthood. She had been obliged to wear her maid's clothing upon her departure from Acorn House but she would change as soon as it was feasible to do so.

It had been so distressing to take her leave of her parents and brothers without any of them knowing how significant the separation would truly be. Her mother had once again expressed the hope that Miss Knight's acquaintances would not overstay their welcome and Emily had quailed to imagine the betrayal she would feel when she realised that her daughter had lied and would be gone for far longer than a few days. But it had to be done in this clandestine fashion or they would prevent her from going. And every fibre in her being told her that she *must* make this journey.

Having said that, it would be no easy feat for her either. She had been too preoccupied on the occasion of the ball to feel an ounce of wistfulness regarding her first night away from home, but after she had left Acorn House that morning, packed valise in her hand, the reality of what she was embarking upon had sunk in and homesickness had already begun to prick at her, even while she was still on American soil. But she straightened her shoulders resolutely; the end result would make it all worthwhile.

Still, it had felt important to acknowledge the sorrow of that severance and to say farewell to this chapter of her life in any way she could. Hence, she had taken time in recent days to murmur her goodbyes to Delilah, Jemimah and Beulah and had even unearthed Mabel to snatch a furtive hug for old times' sake. Strangely, she had noticed that Mabel was not lying in the same position in which she had left her and she wondered if her mother had moved her for some unknown reason. She couldn't think of anyone else who might have gone near Mabel; surely neither Jack nor Gus would have been interested in the doll at all. Enjoying one last cuddle before putting her back, Emily had sorely regretted the cowardice which had led her to consign Mabel to the darkness of the cupboard just so she could conform to the expectations of a friend who had never really been a friend, now that she knew what a friend could be.

At least Matilda was the one person from whom she could part with absolute openness about her travel plans. She had been an enormous support to Emily over the past week and she understood the role she would still have to play when the time came. Before Emily had left Marlowe House the previous evening, she had thanked Matilda with nothing but a tight embrace because she couldn't seem to form any words. Matilda had just grinned and said, 'I might be Mrs Coleman's favourite but you're definitely my favourite!' The mention of Mrs Coleman had reminded Emily of how furious the housekeeper would be when her newest housemaid did not turn up for work the next day and she had scuttled from the house before Mrs Coleman could sense that a conspiracy was afoot.

When she had reached the street, she had cast a final glance back at Marlowe House, hoping in vain to catch a glimpse of Samuel at one of the windows. 'Wait for me,' she had whispered. 'Soon I shall be good enough for you.'

Now she approached her old home on Broad Street, feeling nervous. The success of her scheme rested on this final crucial element and she had taken a gamble by delaying it until almost the last moment, for the *Integrity* was scheduled to leave port that afternoon. But she was determined to be on board.

She entered the building and climbed the stairs to the next floor, where she took a fortifying breath to calm her nerves before she knocked on the door to the rooms shared by Auntie Orlaith, Uncle Charlie and Auntie Tess. No one answered at first and she began to panic, but then she heard a shuffle on the other side of the door and it opened to reveal Auntie Tess clad in a robe, her red hair dishevelled and sleep crusting her pale eyelashes.

'Emily?' she said, confused. She looked around the landing as though expecting someone else to appear too.

'It's just me,' said Emily. 'Sorry for disturbing you. May I come in?'

Auntie Tess's forehead creased. 'Orlaith isn't here. Herself and Charlie both left early.'

Relieved to hear this, Emily said, 'That's fine. It's you I wanted to speak to.'

Even more baffled, Auntie Tess stepped back and let her in. Emily set her valise down by the door and took a seat on the sofa. Auntie Tess pulled over the stool from the table and sat on it opposite Emily, crossing her legs – the bare skin of her shins peeked out from the lower folds of her robe and it struck Emily how remarkably comfortable Auntie Tess was with her own body. Emily would faint if anyone glimpsed that much of her legs.

'I'm sorry again for waking you,' she said. 'I didn't realise you might still be in bed.'

'I'll be going to Tremont House in a while but they don't need us to wash the sheets until after the guests have left their rooms, so being a washerwoman for a hotel suits a slugabed like me.' Auntie Tess rubbed the sleep out of her eyelashes. 'Orlaith stuck her head in at the crack of dawn and said something about giving Derval a hand with a birth up the street. I'm the only lazy sod around here these days.' She squinted at Emily. 'So what's brought you here this morning?'

Emily fidgeted with the fabric of her skirt. 'I need some help.' She gulped a mouthful of air before plunging on. 'I'm aware that it's an enormous favour to ask but this is something that's very important to me, though I can't tell you exactly what it's for. And I would completely understand if you say no because you don't have it, or if you have it but don't want to give it. I

427

do wish I could explain it better and someday I hope I'll be in a position to—'

'Slow down,' said Auntie Tess. 'What's the favour?'

Emily hesitated. 'Could I please borrow some money from you?'

Auntie Tess's eyes widened. 'From me? Why not ask your ma and da?'

Emily bit her lip. 'I can't. Not for this.'

Auntie Tess shot her a suspicious look.

'I'll be able to pay you back,' said Emily quickly. 'Not right away but I'll return it all to you, Auntie Tess, I swear I will.' It was a good thing that substantial funds lay in wait at her destination.

Auntie Tess folded her arms. 'Then why me and not Orlaith, your actual aunt?'

'I already owe Uncle Charlie money for posting my correspondence to the art academy. I didn't want to add further to their burdens.' In truth, she had chosen Auntie Tess on the assumption that she would be the least likely to ask questions, although Emily appeared to have been mistaken on that score.

'What makes you think I have money to spare?'

Voice small, Emily said, 'I heard from my parents that you and Auntie Orlaith and Uncle Charlie are thinking of going west to Chicago. I imagine you must have some money set aside to be contemplating such a plan.'

Auntie Tess lifted one shoulder in a shrug. 'I suppose that would be the smart thing to do.' Her tongue darted out to lick her lips. 'How much do you need?'

Hardly daring to hope, Emily named a figure which would supplement the wages she had received to date at Marlowe House to help pay for her ticket on the *Integrity*. Auntie Tess considered before nodding grudgingly.

'I'm meant to be a Christian person nowadays. I guess I can manage that.'

She rose from her stool and disappeared into the back bedroom. Emily waited, her pulse thumping in her throat. She knew that Auntie Tess had spent a couple of years in a place that, according to her parents, was very like a convent. Although Auntie Tess, like Auntie Orlaith, had chosen not to become a nun in the end, Emily supposed that its religious surroundings had still made an impression upon her.

Auntie Tess returned with a coin purse clutched in her hand.

'I've been keeping this under the floorboard. Some of it is money I saved from before I was a washerwoman. D'you know what I used to do then?'

Emily knitted her brows. 'You healed injuries like Auntie Orlaith, isn't that right?'

Auntie Tess bared her teeth. 'Right.' She held out the coin purse. 'Here you are. There's a little bit more in there than what you asked for.'

Emily stretched out a shaky hand to take it, her heart soaring. 'Oh, I honestly can't thank you enough.'

'Mind you, I'll be expecting it all back, just like you swore.'

'Yes, I promise,' said Emily fervently. 'Thank you so much.'

She got up from the sofa and went to retrieve her valise. Tess eyed it dubiously as she held the door open for her and Emily stepped through to the landing.

'Just a final thought,' said Auntie Tess and Emily turned back to her. 'Your parents are decent people. If this money's for something you don't feel you can tell them about, then you should seriously question the wisdom of it.'

Guilt-ridden, Emily just said, 'I'm very grateful to you for helping me.'

With an arched eyebrow, Auntie Tess shut the door. Emily descended the stairs, valise in one hand, coin purse in the other, and exhilaration bursting within her. This was actually, finally, definitely happening.

She halted two steps from the bottom with a hiccup. Rory Carey stood in the hallway, his palm on the door to his family's rooms as though he had just closed it behind him.

'What're you doing here?' he asked.

'Visiting my aunties,' she said haughtily.

He gave her a hard stare, which came to rest upon her valise. 'Jesus,' he said. 'Your da was right to be worried.'

Alarmed, she said, 'I don't know what you mean.'

He pointed at her. 'You're accepting that man's invitation. You're going to London.'

She couldn't fathom why her father might have chosen to confide in Rory of all people about Garrett's letter but she continued to feign ignorance. 'I'm going to Marlowe House where I work. Excuse me, or I shall be late.'

She went down the last two steps and made to cross the hallway but he strode in front of her, blocking her way.

'Excuse me!' she repeated indignantly.

'Are you daft?' he demanded. 'I don't know the first thing about the fella who wrote to you but 'tis obvious from what your da said that he's bad news. Why would you trust him?'

She raised her chin, trying not to feel tiny in comparison to Rory's towering height. 'It's none of your business.'

He gave her a withering look. 'I have to tell Mr McGovern.'

'Don't you dare!' she hissed in panic. 'Just keep out of it!'

Implacable, he said, 'I was just on my way to the workshop now. Mr McGovern's almost always there ahead of me. How quickly d'you think he'd catch up to you? I bet he'd easily find you before your ship leaves.'

Rage surged up in her. 'It would only make me ten times more determined to go! If you or he thwart me today, then I shall just bide my time and run away the next chance I get.'

His expression turned shocked. 'Aren't you ashamed to think of the worry you'll put him and Mrs McGovern through? Are you really that selfish?'

That wounded her deeply so she lashed out, 'It's *their* actions that put me on this path. It's *their* fault I have to do this. This is the only prospect I have of attaining a better life for myself and I am getting on that ship no matter what you say.'

He regarded her in silence. Her chest rose and fell in angry pants. The distant sound of cheerful singing drifted down from Mr Lorenzo's rooms on the top floor.

At last, Rory said, 'Who're you travelling with?'

'No one.'

He gaped at her. 'Are you serious?'

'Yes,' she snapped. Matilda had tried to convince her all week that she needed a companion on her trip but she had resisted.

'You mean to sail across the ocean by yourself? Have you no sense?'

She glared at him in answer.

He raised his palms in an exasperated gesture. 'D'you think you'll be safe? What d'you plan to do if someone tries to rob you?'

'I shall scream and run away,' she declared.

Without any warning whatsoever, he seized her wrist, forcing her to drop the valise in surprise. It thumped to the floor as he pushed her towards the wall and clamped his other hand over her mouth. Stunned, she found herself pinned in place, his body pressed against hers and his palm sealing her mouth shut.

'Come on,' he murmured. 'Scream. Run away.'

She struggled against him but his grip on her was like iron. She tried to bite at his fingers but couldn't part her lips. He stared her down, waiting for her to give up. She strained to break free, not wanting to give him the satisfaction.

Eventually, she let her limbs go loose in defeat. He released her and stood back.

'Beastly creature,' she flung at him. Furious tears stung her eyes. 'You're spoiling everything!'

He ran his hands through his shaggy hair. 'I'm trying to protect you.'

'I don't need protection,' she retorted, in spite of the evidence that proved otherwise.

'Your da wants you to be safe.'

'Who cares what he wants?' she said petulantly, loathing her father and Rory Carey in equal measure. Between them both, they would ruin the marvellous future that she had dreamed might become a reality.

'I do,' was Rory's simple response. 'He deserves that respect and he should have it from you too.'

A tear spilled over and trickled down her cheek. She felt like such a horrid person, but she didn't know how to stop wanting that future. 'I have to go.'

Rory blew out his cheeks. 'Then I'll have to come with you.'

She couldn't help herself; she laughed.

Looking injured, he said, 'If you're determined to go, you can't go alone.' He actually seemed to mean it.

Perplexed, she said, 'You're the last person I'd want accompanying me for weeks on end. And I'm certain you'd say the same about me.'

He glowered. 'Maybe I would. But I'll put up with you anyway. What you're about to do is really going to hurt your parents but they might bear it a little easier if they know you went with someone they can trust.'

His argument made sense but she refused to yield. 'You can't abandon your mother on her own with the children.'

Pain and guilt filled his face. However, though his expression was torn, he said, 'The children are well able to take care of themselves now. Brian's ten—I was practically the man of our family at his age. And I'll leave some money behind for Ma.'

'And what if your mother needs help of some kind?'

'Charlie, Orlaith and Tess are right upstairs.' He had warmed to his idea and he wasn't letting go of it.

'What about your job at the workshop?' she pointed out, latching onto his tenacious loyalty to her father. 'Would you walk away from your employment just like that? As soon as you come back, my father will dismiss you for such dreadful conduct.'

Rory crossed his arms. 'I don't think so. I reckon if your da knew what my choices were, he'd prefer me to do whatever I could to keep you safe.'

'We can't travel together,' she said desperately, 'because we're two single people of opposite genders. It would be unseemly.'

That gave him pause. 'Then we'll make up a story about who we are.'

Against her will, she found herself pondering it. 'Perhaps you could pretend to be my servant?'

'Older brother,' he countered. 'And you're my younger sister who always does what I tell her.'

She uttered a cross 'Hmph!' but did not gainsay him. A brother-and-sister act could very well work. And, after he had demonstrated just how physically helpless she was, the suggestion of having a fellow traveller held a great deal more appeal to her now than it had before.

Still, she was nothing if not stubborn. 'I only have enough money for one ticket, and the *Integrity* departs this afternoon. I can't wait around for the next ship.'

His green eyes flashed. 'What did you say the ship is called?'

'The *Integrity*,' she replied and faltered at the blatant anger in his features. 'What's the matter?'

'Nothing,' he muttered. 'How much does a ticket cost?' When she told him, he winced. 'I've been saving my earnings from my apprenticeship. That and the money for my ma will clean me out but I might have enough.'

She showed him the coin purse still clutched in her fist. 'I borrowed some money from Auntie Tess to help cover my ticket and she gave me a bit extra. That might make up the difference.' How had she suddenly begun looking for solutions instead of obstacles?

'Grand,' he said. He still looked incensed as he said, 'We'd better head for the docks. I just need a minute to pack a bag.'

'Wait a second,' she said. This was all moving far too fast. 'I made careful arrangements so that I would be long gone before anyone realised I was missing. If you don't appear at the workshop this morning, that will immediately alert my father that there's something amiss. We need a more elaborate plan to get us both away without suspicion.'

'Fair point but I think I've got an answer for it.' He marched over to the door to his family's rooms, thrust it open and yelled, 'Una!'

A short time later, they departed from the building on Broad Street with no witnesses other than Rory's sister and old Mrs Kane who observed them with beady eyes as they hurried past her on the street.

They made it to the waterfront and encountered their first complication when the ticket seller in the booth asked for their surname.

'Mc—' Emily began.

'Car—' Rory said at the same time.

'McCarey,' Emily confirmed breezily.

They purchased their tickets without any further incident, although Auntie Tess's coin purse was now significantly lighter.

Suppressing her worry, Emily tucked it away in her valise. They would manage to scrape by.

'This ship sails to Liverpool,' she told Rory, who stood taciturn next to her in the queue of steerage passengers. 'We shall need to get a stagecoach from there to London.'

'Fine,' he said curtly. His gaze roamed over the *Integrity* sitting in the water by the dock, scrutinising the sailors as they scurried to and fro on the deck; it was almost as if he were seeking a familiar face.

She chewed her lip as her mind ran back over all the details of their plan. 'Are you quite convinced that Una will cooperate?'

'I am.'

'How are you so sure? We asked her to tell a downright lie.'

He scowled. 'Because I did the same for her once. She owes me one.'

Emily said no more about it, but she was already doubting her intellect for agreeing to this madcap notion. She and Rory would be travelling together for at least a month. How would she be able to endure his dour presence in the cramped quarters of a ship, followed by the even tighter space of a stagecoach? And then what on earth would she do with him when they reached London?

She scanned their surroundings – was there any way she could possibly give him the slip? He might forsake the venture altogether if he lost her in the crowds.

'Don't even think about it,' he said and she glanced at him, startled. 'I can tell you're looking for an escape. The only chance of that is if neither of us get on the ship.'

She reddened at having been so transparent.

'Listen,' he said, 'we can't carry on like this if we're going to make it to England without killing each other. Can we agree to a truce?'

He stuck out his hand. She wavered before shaking it.

'Very well,' she said. 'A truce it is.'

The line of passengers shambled onwards. At long last, she and Rory reached the top of the queue where the inspector checked their tickets and let them pass without question.

Emily stepped onto the gangway, excitement flooding through her veins. 'I feel like I'm heading to Tír na nÓg,' she said exultantly.

Rory snorted behind her. So much for their truce.

'What?' she said peevishly.

'You know that legend doesn't have a happy ending, right?'

She frowned, trying to recall what happened at the end of the tale. Had she always fallen asleep before her father had finished recounting it?

Timidly, she asked, 'What happens?'

'Oisín gets homesick for Ireland so Niamh lets him leave Tír na nÓg on the magical horse but warns him that he can't touch the ground. When he gets home, he realises three hundred years have passed and his family are long dead. He falls from the horse, ages instantly and dies.' Rory failed to keep the amusement out of his voice.

'Oh,' she said, crestfallen as all the charm of the romantic legend leaked away. She shook herself. 'Never mind. It's not Tír na nÓg we're heading towards. It's just a better future.'

And, buoyant, she kept walking up the gangway.

CHAPTER 45

Cormac had opened up the workshop and was measuring timber in the back room when he heard the bell on the door tinkle. Thinking that Rory was quite a bit later than usual, he was astonished when Una Carey appeared in the doorway.

'Rory's sick,' she announced. 'He can't come to the workshop today. Maybe not tomorrow either.'

Startled, he said, 'I'm sorry to hear that. Is he very poorly?'

'Yes, he's real bad,' she said with relish. Cormac's alarm must have shown on his countenance because she amended quickly, 'I mean, he'll be grand in a couple of days but he's pretty bad for today and probably tomorrow.'

Without further elaboration, she spun on her heel and made a hasty exit.

Cormac decided that this report was both worrying and confusing enough that, after he closed up the workshop at the end of the day, he proceeded to Broad Street to find out how Rory was faring. Una squeaked when he showed up at the Careys' door and retreated at once into the bedroom, while Sorcha and Brian sat eating supper at the table.

A dishevelled Derval welcomed Cormac in, saying, 'You'll have to excuse the state of me. I'm not long back from delivering a babby up the street—he took the whole day to make his appearance!'

'I won't stay long,' he assured her. 'I just wanted to enquire after Rory. Is he feeling any better?'

Her brow furrowed. 'Better? I don't know what you mean by that.'

'He didn't come to the workshop today. Una said he was unwell and that he likely wouldn't come tomorrow either. I thought I'd look in just to check that it wasn't anything too serious.'

'You have me rightly puzzled now,' said Derval. 'Una told me you'd asked Rory to fetch some carpentry supplies out of town and not to expect him back until tomorrow evening.'

Cormac tilted his head. 'Is that so?'

Derval browbeat her daughter to come out of the bedroom and she emerged, head hanging.

'Explain,' said Derval.

'I can't,' said Una. 'They didn't tell me anything. They just said ye'd find the note.'

Cormac and Derval exchanged mystified glances.

'Did anyone see a note?' demanded Derval.

After a swift bout of searching, during which Derval discovered that most of Rory's clothes were missing, Sorcha found the note tucked underneath the pillow on the bed, along with some coins. The note was just a narrow strip of paper that said 'Ask Matilda'. And it was written in Emily's handwriting.

Astounded, Cormac wasted no time in hastening to Beacon Hill, all sorts of wild ideas running through his head along the way. What connection could there possibly be between Rory and Emily? As far as he was aware, they hardly ever encountered each other anymore and, when they did, animosity smouldered between them. Had they made amends without anyone realising? Had they fallen in love and eloped? But, if so,

438

why would they feel the need to do that? While it would have come as a staggering surprise, neither of their families would have objected to them marrying – apart from the fact that Emily was too young for such a notion just yet.

He reached Marlowe House in a state of bewildered agitation. Striding across the paved courtyard at the rear of the house, he rapped on the door and met the housekeeper, Mrs Coleman.

'I need to see my daughter, Emily McGovern,' he said. 'It's a matter of urgency.'

Her thick eyebrows rose. 'Emily did not turn up this morning and there's been no sign of her all day. It's utterly unacceptable behaviour. I'm afraid to tell you that the security of her position is gravely in question.'

Recollecting the note, Cormac demanded, 'Matilda. I must speak to Matilda.'

'Who?' said Mrs Coleman.

'That's me, Mrs Coleman,' said a voice behind the housekeeper and O'Mali's daughter materialised. She took a letter from her pocket and held it out to Cormac. 'Here you go. We didn't think you'd show up so soon but I reckon she's left by now anyways.'

Cormac almost ripped the note in his rush to read it. It was short. Written in Emily's own hand, it communicated that she had boarded a ship for England so that she could go to visit Garrett. She reassured her parents that they must not worry, that this was what she dearly wanted, and that she hoped to see them again within the year.

A hand of ice gripped Cormac's heart. 'Oh, my sweet baby girl,' he breathed. 'What have you done?'

What's Next

Don't panic! I left you with several questions at the end of this book but the good news is that you don't need to wait to find out the answers. All is revealed in Book 5, A Class Reunited, which is available now.

If you're not already a member of the **Susie Murphy Readers' Club**, be sure to join on www.susiemurphywrites.com to stay up to date with all the latest news on A Matter of Class.

Please help other readers discover Bridget and Cormac's story by leaving an honest review about A Class Coveted on Amazon and/or Goodreads. A short review will make a huge difference in spreading the word about this series. Thank you so much!

Acknowledgements

It would be remiss of me not to begin my acknowledgements by thanking you, the person who has just read this book. I began working as a full-time author this year and such a reality would not have been possible without you. Thank you for reading my books, for telling your friends about them, for reviewing them online, and for spreading the word far enough that you have enabled me to do what I love for a living. You have given me an incredible gift and I promise I'll work as hard as I can to be worthy of it.

Thank you to my editor, Averill Buchanan, and my cover designer, Andrew Brown at Design for Writers. I know I can always trust them both to help produce the best version of my book, inside and out. Thanks also to my audiobook narrator, Gary Furlong, the newest member of my professional team. His terrific interpretation of this series in audio form is beyond anything I could have dreamed.

Heartfelt thanks to my first readers who offered such invaluable feedback on A Class Coveted: Bob Murphy, Miriam Bourke, Grace Noon, Miriam Lanigan, Noreen Uí Ghríofá, and Elizabeth Bell. Thanks especially to the two Miriams, whose eloquent reactions before I even started this book ensured that I didn't skip too far ahead in the story.

Virtual high fives to my advance reader team who read this book before it was released. I can't express how much I appreciated their enthusiasm!

I extend my unending gratitude to the reviewers and authors who have so generously brought my books to the attention of their followers and readers. Thank you especially to Claire Bridle, Lisa Redmond, Valerie Whitford, Ashley O'Melia, Anne Mendez, Stacie Tyson, Kelsey Gietl, Pam Lecky, and Michele

Quirke. Many thanks also to Yvonne Brewer and Emma Davis at Shop Irish Writers, and Noel Dundon at the Tipperary Star.

I am unutterably grateful to my wonderful circle of family and friends who continue to be so supportive of my writing dream.

Last but not least, thank you to my husband, Bob. When I told him I might be ready to go full time as an author, his response was an unequivocal 'Go for it'. I thank my lucky stars every day that he is in my life.

Get in Touch

www.susiemurphywrites.com
www.facebook.com/susiemurphywrites
www.twitter.com/susiemwrites
www.instagram.com/susiemurphywrites

Milton Keynes UK
Ingram Content Group UK Ltd.
UKHW012006131223
434291UK00004B/279